S0-ALD-460

SHUTTLE CHALLENGER

David Shayler

An Arco Aviation Classic
Prentice Hall Press · New York

A Salamander Book

Published in 1987 by Prentice Hall Press
A Division of Simon & Schuster, Inc.
Gulf+Western Building
One Gulf+Western Plaza
New York, NY 10023

PRENTICE HALL PRESS is a trademark
of Simon & Schuster, Inc.

An Arco Aviation Classic

Originally published in the United Kingdom
by Salamander Books Ltd.

This book may not be sold outside the United
States of America and Canada.

**Library of Congress
Cataloging-in-Publication Data**
Shayler, David.
Shuttle Challenger.

1. Challenger (Spacecraft) I. Title.
TL795.5.S484 1987 629.44'1 86-30228
ISBN 0-13-125147-3

10 9 8 7 6 5 4 3 2 1

First Prentice Hall Press Edition

Dedication
This book is dedicated to the men and women of the US space programme who designed and built *Challenger*; the men and women who prepared and controlled the 10 missions of the Space Shuttle OV-099; and, in particular, the 51 individuals who flew on her and especially to the memory of the seven members of the Shuttle 25 (51-L) *Challenger* 10 crew. The book is also dedicated to my grandfather, Arthur Shayler (1892-1971).

Credits

Project Manager: Philip de Ste. Croix

Editor: Anthony Hall

Designed by: Lim & Lim

Photographs: All the photographs in this book were supplied either by NASA or Rockwell International. The publishers and author offer their sincere thanks to both organisations.

Diagrams: TIGA © Salamander Books Ltd.

Jacket: Stephen Seymour

Large color profile: Terry Hadler, © Salamander Books Ltd.

Contents

Foreword 4
Challenger in the Programme 6
Building the Vehicle 14
The Missions 24
The Inquiry 50
The Astronauts 54
The Payloads 60
Flight Data 62
Glossary 64

Acknowledgements

In the compilation of this book I would like to extend my thanks to fellow researchers Tim Furniss, Rex Hall, Neville Kidger, Roger Collett, Harry Siepmann and Phil Clark in the UK; to Lee Saegesser of NASA HQ; Norma Kersman of NASA JSC; Lisa Vazquez and Diana Ormsbee of Media Services JSC Houston; Sue Cometa and Joyce Lincoln of Rockwell and Sharon Hanson of Martin Marietta; Gail Macnaughton of Spar Aerospace Ltd, Canada; Rocky Raab of Morton Thiokol; Dick Young of KSC and the PAO/Photo Dept. of JSC, as well as Curtis Peebles, Iva Scott and Mike Cassutt of the USA. Thanks also to everyone who has assisted at NASA HQ, JSC, MSFC, KSC, EAFB and other *Challenger* contractors. A thank you too to Gordon Fullerton for his Foreword.

I would also like to thank my wife Janet and my parents for their support, together with Lynn for her proof reading. To everyone a very large thank you.

Author

David Shayler has been writing and researching articles on the manned exploration of Space since 1968. In 1982 he set up Astro Info Services, a private organisation dedicated to researching and publishing data on manned space exploration, and has written and published biographical data books that provide exhaustive information on US astronauts and Soviet cosmonauts. He also publishes regular periodicals dealing with the Shuttle and Salyut programmes, and annual reports logging the Space Shuttle's flight operations.

Color cutaway drawings: Mike Badrocke

Filmset by SX Composing Ltd.

Color reproduction by Melbourne Graphics Ltd.

Printed in Belgium by Henri Proost et Cie.

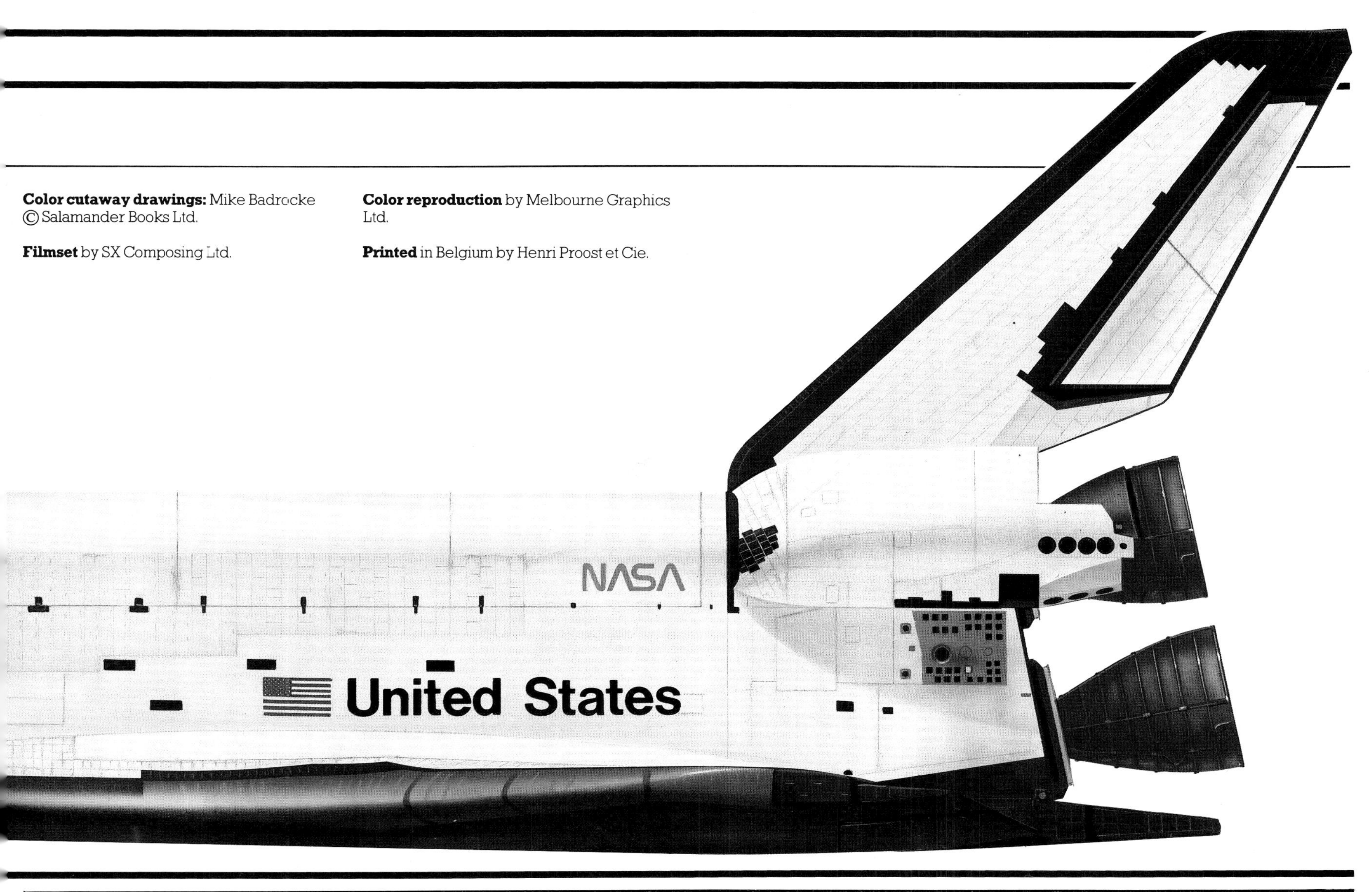

Introduction

Late in the afternoon of Tuesday January 28, 1986 I was at work thinking of the expected Shuttle 25 launch, and hoping that all had gone according to plan and that the vehicle was safely in orbit. Then I was asked if I had heard of the Shuttle accident, and told that the vehicle had 'blown up'. Guessing that the astronaut crew had been lost, I immediately phoned my parents to start recording TV coverage whilst I tried to review what could have happened, and on the way home I tuned in my car radio to hear the first news reports of the tragedy. All of this hit very hard and very deep. However, when I finally saw the recordings on TV later that night I was shocked by the sheer devastation and total destruction of the event: so instant, so vivid, so complete. The recorded picture of the instant loss of *Challenger* will remain in my memory for the rest of my life.

Almost at once I decided to push forward with a plan of a book which I had formulated over the previous three years. I felt that a book dedicated to the lost vehicle and crew, and to those who built and flew it, would be a fitting tribute to a colourful career.

Shuttle Challenger is a book about a space vehicle. In detailed text and official NASA photos, the complete story of OV-099 unfolds from its development through its construction, nine missions and 10 turnarounds to the ill-fated Shuttle 25 launch and subsequent inquiry and programme recovery. This book is the story of why *Challenger* succeeded and succeeded well, rather than just a book of why she and her crew of seven were lost.

To help readers find their way about, the book opens with two chapters that explain *Challenger*'s role in the overall Shuttle programme, and her construction history. The central section of the book consists of a detailed examination of each of her ten missions, including the disastrous 51-L. A final chapter looks at the findings of the Commission of Inquiry. In conclusion, appendices list all *Challenger*'s astronauts and payloads; tables of data and a glossary are also included.

When Shuttles return to space and a new orbiter joins the fleet, I hope that this book is recognized as a fitting tribute to a 'fine ship'.

Foreword

Gordon Fullerton, Commander *Challenger* 8, STS-51F
March 1987

Above: The red and blue shifts pictured in *Challenger's* mid-deck area during 51-F with their Mission Commander Gordon Fullerton in the striped shirt.

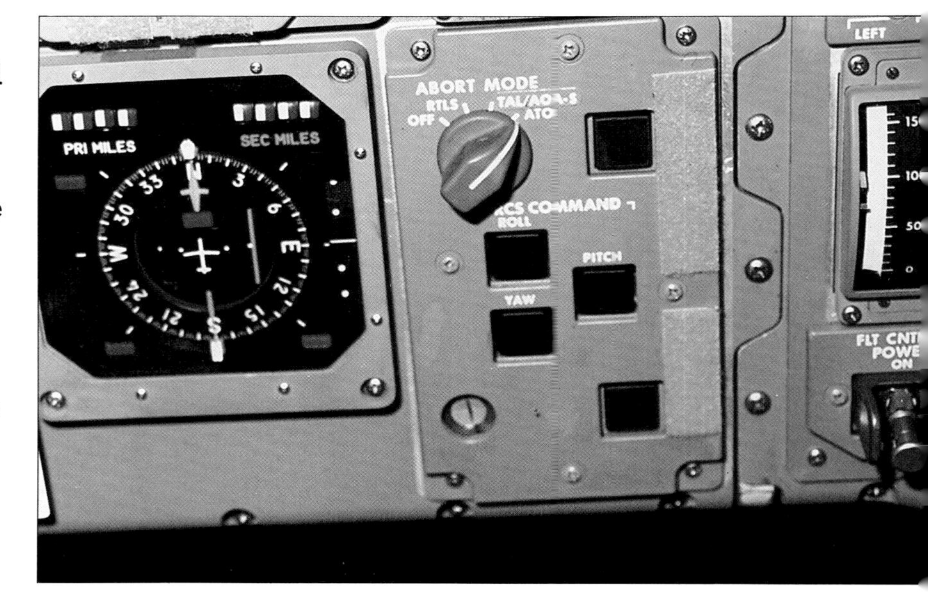

Below: A close-up of a flight deck console taken on July 29, 1985 during *Challenger's* 51-F mission. The Abort Mode switch is seen in the Abort to Orbit (ATO) position.

Above right: Gordon Fullerton's first Shuttle flight into space was aboard *Columbia* on STS-3, March 22-30 1982. Note that as this was one of the four test flights, he is wearing a pressurized flight suit.

Right: By contrast a shirt-sleeved Gordon Fullerton is seen checking a consumables chart on *Challenger* during 51-F. Careful husbandry of on-board resources was of critical importance on this mission.

To my knowledge no one ever took an 'orbiter popularity poll' but I have no doubt that if they had, the *Challenger* would have won hands down.

She was the favorite of the program managers because she was the most reliable, the one that was most quickly turned around for a subsequent flight. In her short three year lifetime she flew nine times, more than any other orbiter. She functioned nearly flawlessly up to the moment of her demise. The explosion was due not to a failure in the spacecraft but rather in the supporting solid rocket system.

With the largest payload capability of the four space-capable orbiters she was the mission planners' first choice also. Ironically, she was designated OV-099, built to be a ground structural test article, never to be outfitted, never to leave the factory. When it became apparent that excessive structural modifications would be needed to convert OV-101, the *Enterprise*, from an atmospheric test ship into a space-capable craft, OV-099 became the basis for the follow-on to the first orbital ship, the *Columbia. Columbia*'s airframe design was frozen early in the engineering process. The resulting conservatism and extensive instrumentation made it considerably heavier than the *Challenger*, which could carry nearly 7,000lb (3,175kg) more payload.

One would have expected the design of the later orbiters, *Discovery* and *Atlantis*, to have benefited from flight experience, but here the engineers out-foxed themselves. Material was pared from their wing structure since the early analysis and flight data showed less than anticipated airloads during launch. Actual flight measurements on high performance missions with *Challenger* showed higher bending loads, but the information came too late to incorporate in manufacture. So the lighter but weaker wings on the two newer spacecraft had to be restricted to a lower speed and less efficient launch trajectory. Paradoxically, the originally ground-bound OV-099 turned out to be the top performer of the fleet.

Those of us who flew both *Columbia* and *Challenger* liked the newer ship for more personal reasons. *Columbia* had ejection seats installed for the original test flights. Even after they were deactivated after flight four, the bulky seat rail structure remained, greatly encroaching on the available space and blocking visibility on the flight deck. By contrast, *Challenger*'s upper deck seemed like a living room. On the STS-51F mission we had at times all seven crew members on the flight deck at once. It was cosy but workable. In the *Columbia* it would have been impossible. Also the special flight test controls and instruments of *Columbia* were eliminated in *Challenger*, presenting a much cleaned-up cockpit.

Challenger lived up to her name on my final flight (STS-51F, July 29-August 6, 1985). Our first attempt at launch was aborted just three seconds before liftoff, after the main engines had started, because of a slow-responding valve. Problems plagued our second try two weeks later, keeping us on the pad strapped to our seats for nearly five hours. We finally got away only to have a main engine shutdown midway in the ascent. Fortunately we had gained just enough velocity to stagger into a lower but safe orbit on the two operating engines. A failure a few seconds sooner would have had us on our way to Zaragoza, Spain (undoubtedly setting a new trans-Atlantic crossing record).

The event began the real challenge for us and the scientists and planners in Mission Control. Our detailed flight plan became instantly useless due to our lower orbit and the missing 5,000lb (2,268kg) of maneuvering fuel that had been expended getting into orbit. But with a herculean effort on the ground and some very consumable-conscious operation on board, we eked out the planned duration, and even added an extra, eighth day.

Now, more than a year after the tragic loss of *Challenger*, the meaning of her name is more significant than ever. Recovery from the shock of the event, the loss of seven fine people, the painful discovery of serious technical and managerial flaws and the slow rebuilding of devastated morale are the greatest challenges the American space program has ever faced.

The challenge will be met. The legacy of that fine craft will be a strengthened resolve among all who built, controlled, and flew her to return to the space frontier.

C. Gordon Fullerton

NASA
LOUSMA

ORBIT OPS C/L

Challenger in the Programme

In 1972 the USA decided to press ahead with the development of the world's first reusable spacecraft: a vehicle that could climb into space with the aid of two refurbishable boosters, undertake its on-orbit tasks, and then return to Earth as a glider. As part of the USA's greater ambitions to create a permanent manned space platform, the object was right, but soon political and budgetary constraints interfered in the technical programme of which *Challenger* was first a test article and then an operational orbiter.

Above: A 1972 illustration shows one of the layouts considered by NASA for the Shuttle, with the orbiter and ET atop one vast recoverable booster.

On May 18, 1969 and from the same pad that the orbiter *Challenger* would use for its tenth and last mission almost 17 years later, NASA (National Aeronautics and Space Administration) launched its Apollo 10 mission to the Moon, a dress rehearsal for the historic Apollo 11 mission which would follow just eight weeks later to land the first men on the Moon. The vehicle used to put Apollo 10 on course for its lunar orbit mission was the gigantic Saturn V rocket. At a height of 363ft (110.6m), the Saturn V/Apollo combination was at the time the largest vehicle built by man to fly through the atmosphere, yet such was the pace of the programme that each mission required one such vehicle, as all that returned from the mission was the 12ft (3.66m) high Command Module carrying the three-man crew. It had been appreciated for several years that to sustain regular operations in space a much better and cheaper system of getting to and from orbit was needed, for not even the USA could afford to throw away so massively an expensive vehicle after only one launch! Thus pressure from political and public circles, the desire to avert attention from the Vietnam War and the need to see benefits from man's operations in space decided NASA to press for a Space Shuttle Transportation System (SSTS), in the form of a reusable manned vehicle capable of transporting payloads into orbit (providing a base for constructing space platforms) and returning payloads to Earth.

The idea of such a Shuttle was far from new: indeed, detailed plans had been studied before World War II. The studies continued after that war into the 1960s. At the same time developments of a series of rocket-propelled aircraft in the 1940s and 1950s provided important information on the control of a winged vehicle at high speeds and high altitudes. The famous X-series of experimental vehicles led to the X-15 programme, in which three aircraft completed 199 flights between 1959 and 1968, including 13 flights above the 50 mile (80km) recognized boundary between air and space, in short ballistic-type flight paths. The X-15 programme was a direct ancestor of today's Shuttle orbiter. Moreover, one of its 12 pilots, Joe Engle, later commanded two Shuttle missions.

Throughout the 1960s and early 1970s research teams and aerospace companies across the USA investigated the theoretical problems of designing a Shuttle vehicle, while NASA and the US Air Force performed further flight tests with the lifting-body series of vehicles. In 1962 the USAF announced plans to fly the X-20 Dyna-Soar vehicle on Shuttle-type flight profiles in the mid 1960s, but the programme was cancelled in 1963 before it reached the flight stage. By the early 1970s the Space Shuttle programme had received presidential approval and on January 7, 1972 President Richard Nixon gave the formal go-ahead for the programme. Over the previous few years several aerospace companies had put forward designs for Shuttle vehicles and systems, the most promising of these including a manned booster which would carry the Shuttle into the upper reaches of the atmosphere, where the two craft would separate to allow the booster to make a piloted return to a runway near the launch site, using air-breathing engines, while the Shuttle itself pressed on into orbit for the completion of its mission before it returned to a runway landing in a manner similar to that of the booster vehicle.

As is still the case with most aerospace projects, budget restrictions were foremost in the selection of a final design, which was that of the Rockwell International Corporation, builder of the X-15 and Apollo command modules.

The contract awarded on July 26, 1972 formalized a design that was a compromise of what had originally been planned. The Rockwell design envisaged a partially reusable system which retained the capacity to deploy commercial satellites and was able to sustain crews for a short period in orbit, providing them with a small 'space station' from which to conduct research until a larger permanent space platform was developed later in the USA's ambitious manned space programme. Economic restrictions resulted in an orbiter lifted by three main engines, fed with fuel and oxidizer from a huge External Tank (ET), and two Solid-Rocket Booster (SRB) units. The boosters would be separated after burnout and recovered from the ocean to be refurbished and re-used on later flights. The ET was designed to be wholly expendable, being destroyed during its ballistic re-entry after separation from the orbiter proper. Once the objectives of the flight had been met, the crew brought their orbiter back to a runway landing to be refurbished for its next mission.

In 1972 a fleet of five orbiters was planned for operations from two former Apollo launch pads at the Kennedy Space Center (KSC) in Florida and (later) from the military west coast launch site at Vandenberg Air Force Base (VAFB) in California, from the pad designed for the cancelled Manned Orbiting Laboratory programme. First flight was planned for 1977, building up to about 20 missions per year by 1980,

Left: Invaluable results were gained from the X-15 test programme, especially with regard to kinetic heating and the control of so massive an aircraft in the glide regime.

en route to a rate of 50 missions per year (or one per week) by the mid-1980s. In reality this was a gross overcalculation, and it was soon realized that the programme would never reach the 'mission per week' prediction, or even two per month.

The effects of adopting a partially reusable system over fully reusable components, budget restrictions which resulted in the fleet of only four orbiters instead of the planned five, and several production and technical problems through the years of development and subsequent first five years of operations placed serious doubts on the efficacy of the Shuttle as the sole launch capability for all US space business (again lending more support for unmanned boosters) or as a reliable carrier of important time-critical payloads such as planetary probes and spaceborne observation platforms destined for such limited events as Halley's Comet. What the Shuttle did prove is that given reliable equipment and relaxing of political and media pressure the programme could perform useful and important research in orbit, demonstrate the utility of a manned spacecraft for retrieving or repairing faulty satellites, and performing construction work in orbit.

Flight profile

The Shuttle mission profile during a normal year of flight operations really begins with the landing of the vehicle from its previous mission, and its transfer back to the launch site for the preparations leading to a new flight.

The preparations for the new mission take place at KSC on the Atlantic coast of Florida. (VAFB had yet to support a Shuttle launch before the loss of *Challenger*, and for a variety of reasons is not expected to do so for several years of flights. However, the preparations for a mission are similar at each site, despite different facilities.) Upon arrival at KSC the orbiter is transferred to the Orbiter Processing Facility (OPF), a building adjacent to the giant Vehicle Assembly Building (VAB) used to prepare the Saturn V/Apollo vehicles in the late 1960s and early 1970s. Inside the OPF the orbiter's payload bay doors are opened and any elements of the previous mission's payload (such as satellite support structures, experiments etc) are removed, and the orbiter undergoes a period of refurbishment from the effects of its last mission. Faulty components are replaced, and the Thermal Protection System (TPS) vital to a successful re-entry is checked and repaired as necessary. Once the orbiter has been thoroughly cleaned and checked, the new payload is loaded into the payload bay and the lockers within the habitable sections of the orbiter are replenished for the new crew. Once all preparations have been completed the orbiter is transferred from the OPF to the VAB for attachment to the ET and SRBs before the slow move to the launch pad.

The orbiter

Outwardly the orbiter resembles an aircraft, but it has three widely differing modes of operation: it is launched as a rocket, operates as a spacecraft, and lands as an aircraft. The orbiter has an empty weight of 150,000lb (69,039kg), is 122ft 0.2in (37.19m) long and 56ft 7in (17.25m) high with the landing gear lowered, and has a wing span of 78ft 0.68in (23.79m). The habitable part of the orbiter is a two-level section located in the forward section of the vehicle, and is called the crew compartment. The upper level or flight deck resembles the cockpit of a modern jet airliner, with the conventional two flight positions up front: the commander sits at the left station and the pilot at the right station looking forward. Around them are located the flight control instruments, three cathode ray tubes (CRTs) for the real-time display of pertinent data, and the controls for the orbiter's attitude in space and during the landing phase. Behind the flight crew sit one or two mission specialist astronauts, the third person acting as flight-engineer during launch and re-entry, assisting the flight crew during these phases in checklist readout and monitoring of flight instrumentation.

Behind the astronauts on the flight deck are the aft-facing controls and displays which are used for deploying payloads, operating the robot arm (Remote Manipulator System, or RMS) and controlling the orbiter's attitude when working with equipment related to payload bay operations. Two rear-facing windows provide the crew with adequate observation into the payload bay, and two overhead windows are also available for visual observations. One of these can double as an emergency escape hatch after landing.

Above: The launch of a Shuttle flight is a mightily impressive occasion as the whole assembly is accelerated by the three SSMEs and two boosters.

Orbiter Flight Profile

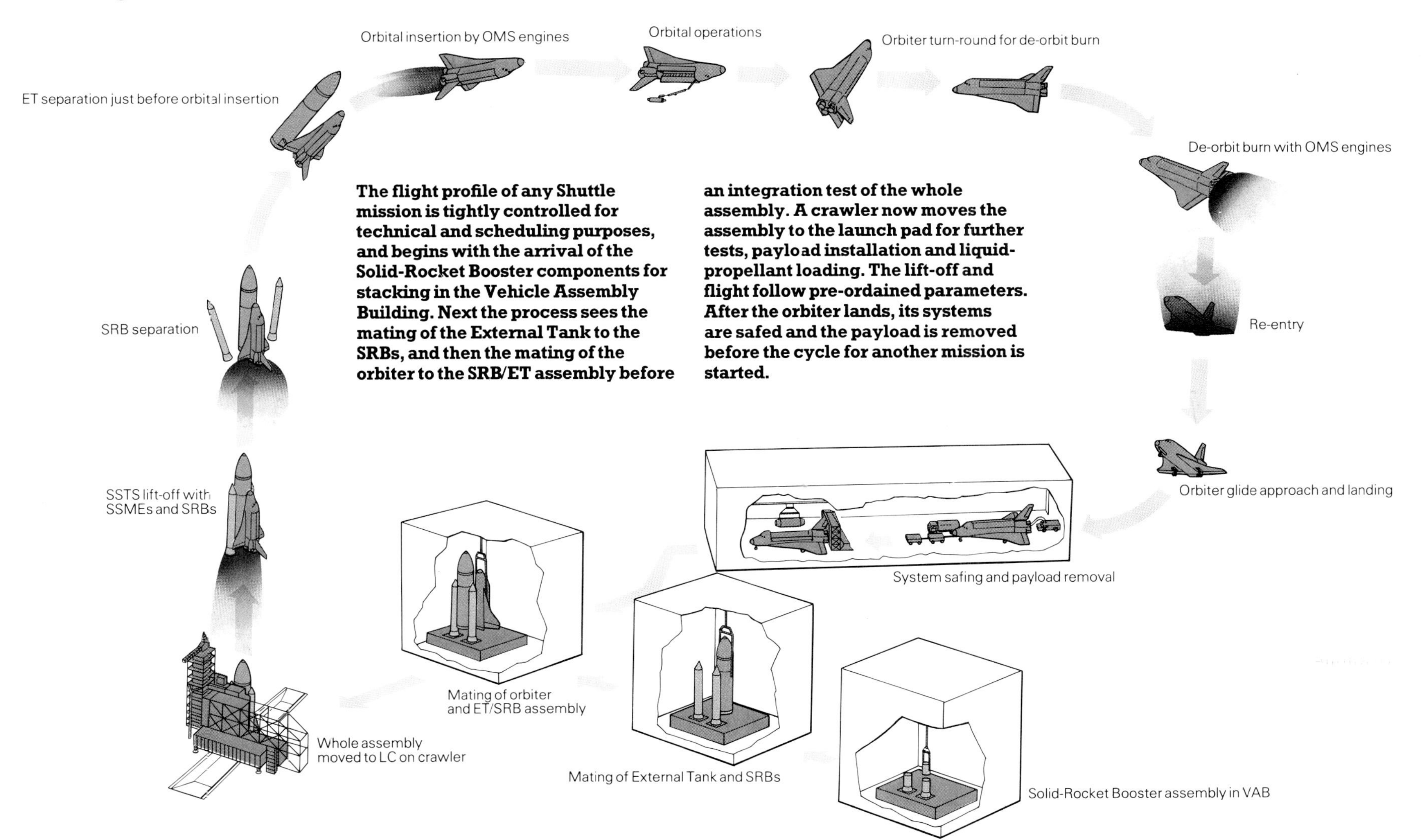

The flight profile of any Shuttle mission is tightly controlled for technical and scheduling purposes, and begins with the arrival of the Solid-Rocket Booster components for stacking in the Vehicle Assembly Building. Next the process sees the mating of the External Tank to the SRBs, and then the mating of the orbiter to the SRB/ET assembly before an integration test of the whole assembly. A crawler now moves the assembly to the launch pad for further tests, payload installation and liquid-propellant loading. The lift-off and flight follow pre-ordained parameters. After the orbiter lands, its systems are safed and the payload is removed before the cycle for another mission is started.

Under the flight deck is the orbiter's mid-deck, which is accessible through two hatchways in the floor of the flight deck; one ladder is provided for access to and egress from the flight deck position in a 1-g environment. Up to four passengers (the remaining mission specialists and payload specialists) sit in the mid-deck area for launch and landing, and have no responsibilities during the launch and re-entry phases. The only windows in this area are located in the launch/landing entry and exit hatch behind and to the left of the seats, and in the airlock which is generally mounted in the centre of the mid-deck aft bulkhead but can be located out in the forward section of the payload bay. The mid-deck includes the sleeping restraints, meal preparation area, personal hygiene facilities (for both male and female crew members) and a range of lockers holding everything from toothpaste and clothes to a vacuum cleaner and scientific equipment. The orbiter's configuration is normally for a seven-person crew, but eight people have flown on a single mission and the vehicle has the capacity for 10 in a rescue mode or for crew delivery to a space station.

In front of the crew compartment and below the mid-deck are the avionics bays, environmental control systems, storage, twin-wheel nose unit of the tricycle landing gear, and related subsystems.

Behind the crew compartment is located the payload bay of the vehicle, called the mid-fuselage. This is the primary cargo-carrying area of the orbiter vehicle, measuring 60ft (18.29m) in length and 17ft (5.18m) in width. Here all satellites and deployable payloads are restrained, as too are non-deployable payloads such as the European-built Spacelab modules, pallets and flight support structures. The RMS is located down one of the payload bay hinge lines, and the area is covered during launch, certain orbital periods and re-entry by four payload bay doors, which also carry radiators on their inner surfaces for thermal control in orbit.

The aft fuselage, measuring 18ft (5.48m) in length, 22ft (6.70m) in width and 20ft (6.09m) in height, is attached behind the payload bay to form the rear of the vehicle. This area locates the Orbital Maneuvering System/Reaction Control System (OMS/RCS) pods, the vertical stabilizer, the three main engines and their associated plumbing, and the body flap used for thermal protection and aerodynamic trimming during re-entry and landing.

The vehicle is completed by the two halves of the double-delta wing, each with a root chord of 60ft (18.29m). This 2,690sq ft (249.9m^2) structure also houses the main landing gear units (each having twin wheels) and aerodynamic control surfaces for use during glide and landing.

The orbiter is hoisted vertically in the VAB and attached mechanically and electrically to the ET, which is already mated to the twin SRBs atop the Mobile Launcher Platform (MLP) adapted from the Apollo programme.

Below: *Challenger* hangs in the lifting sling within the VAB's High Bay 3 before being mated with the ET/SRB assembly on November 23, 1982.

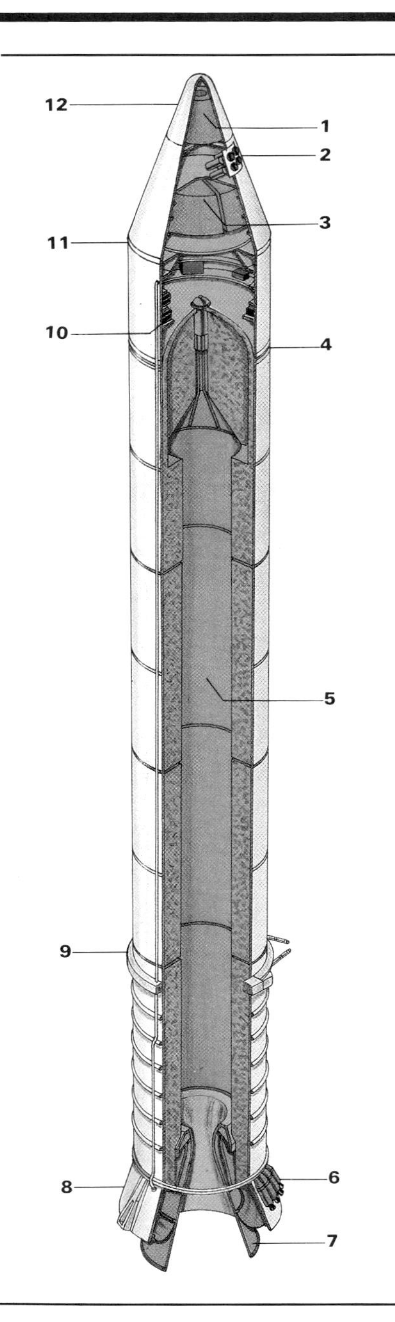

Shuttle External Appendages

External Tank (right)

1 LO_2 tank vent valve and fairing.
2 LO_2 tank.
3 LO_2 slosh baffles.
4 Inter-tank structure.
5 Orbiter forward attachment.
6 LH_2 tank.
7 Propellant feed, pressurization and electrical umbilicals.
8 Internal stringers.
9 Inter-tank umbilical plate.
10 SRB forward attachment.

The External Tank holds the propellants for the Space Shuttle Main Engines in two large pressurized tanks. Spray-on foam insulation is applied over the forward portion of the liquid oxygen tank, the inter-tank structure and the sides of the liquid hydrogen tank. This insulation serves the double purpose of hindering ice accretion on the pad and of hampering heat leaks into the tanks which cause the propellants to boil. All external projections are protected by an ablative coating.

Solid-Rocket Booster (left)

1 Drogue parachute.
2 Four 21,680lb (9,834kg) forward separation motors.
3 Main parachute pack.
4 SRB/ET thrust attachment.
5 Segmented motor, its propellant comprising aluminium perchlorate powder (oxidizer), aluminium powder (fuel), iron oxide (catalyst), and a polymer (a mixture binder that also serves as fuel).
6 Four 22,000lb (9,979kg) aft separation motors.
7 Nozzle and thrust-vector control system.
8 Aft skirt and launch support.
9 SRB/ET attachment ring, aft avionics, tank thrust attachment and sway braces.
10 Separation avionics, operational flight instrumentation, recovery avionics and range safety system.
11 Forward skirt with tapered frustum above.
12 Nose fairing.

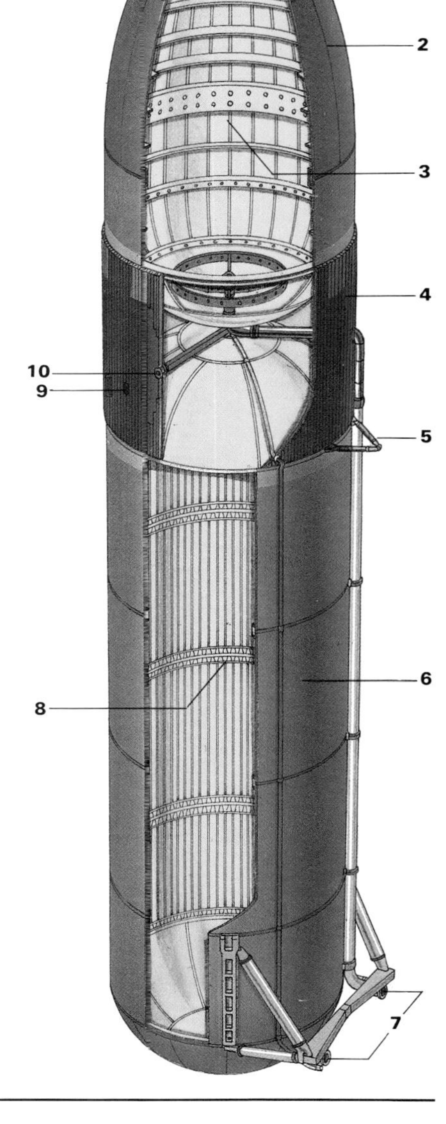

Solid-Rocket Boosters

Stacking of a Shuttle mission combination begins with the SRBs mounted on the MLP. The SRBs are constructed of 11 individual weld-free steel segments each having a wall approximately 0.5in (12.7mm) thick. With each segment heat-treated, hardened and machined exactly to the required dimensions, the high-strength steel hoops are held together by 177 high-strength steel pins at each case segment joint. The clevis-type joints are wrapped with reinforced fibreglass tape and each sealed with a rubber seal band (called an O-ring) bonded to the case with adhesives. These O-rings were the major area of investigation following the *Challenger* accident, for it was thought that the failure of an O-ring was the major factor contributing to the explosion of the vehicle during ascent.

In its assembled form each booster towers to a height of 149ft 1.8in (45.46m) and measures 12ft 1.66in (3.70m) in diameter. Each booster was designed to be reused following recovery in the ocean after a descent under three parachutes. The spent boosters are towed back to the launch site, refurbished, restacked, refilled and used on other missions, though no two adjoining segments make a second flight in the same booster.

The construction of the SRBs begins with the nozzle for the solid-propellant rocket engine, which is surrounded by the aft skirt section. Above this is attached the aft centre segment, the forward centre segment, the forward segment, the forward skirt and the frustum, the stack being topped off with the nose cap. The SRB is the largest solid-propellant motor ever developed for spaceflight and the first to be used on a manned programme. Larger solid-propellant systems had been developed, but none had gone ahead to the flight stage. The USAF Manned Orbiting Laboratory (MOL, pronounced mole) programme in the 1960s was to have used solid boosters with the Titan launcher, but this never reached flight configuration with a manned launch. The SRBs each weigh about 1,259,001lb (571,073kg) at launch, with 85% of this weight comprising the solid propellant composed of ammonium perchlorate oxidizer (69.93% by weight), aluminium fuel (16%), iron oxide catalyst (0.07%), a polymer binder (12.04%) and an epoxy curing agent (1.96%). The thrust of these elements has reached 3,239,001lb (1,469,184kg).

External tank

Once the refurbished SRBs have been mounted and secured on the MLP, the ET is lifted for attachment to the twin motor casings. The ET is designed to carry the fuel and oxidizer for the three Space Shuttle Main Engines (SSMEs), and its design provides the structural backbone of the Shuttle launch configuration. Designed to absorb the full thrust of the SSMEs, each rated at a nominal 375,000lb (170,100kg), as well as the power of the SRBs, the ET consists of three main components: the liquid oxygen tank, the liquid hydrogen tank and a collar-like intertank structure which connects the two propellant tanks and houses the instrumentation and processing equipment. The ET is 154ft 2.4in (47.00m) long and 27ft 6in (8.38m) in diameter, with an empty weight of 73,861lb (33,503kg). The walls of the ET vary in thickness from 0.069 to 2.06in (1.75 to 52.3mm).

The liquid oxygen tank, located in the forward position, contains 143,060 US gal (541,539 litres) of oxidizer at −297°F (−183°C) and has a length of 53ft 6in (16.31m). When empty this tank tips the scales at a mere 12,555lb (5,695kg), whilst fully fuelled it weighs 1,371,697lb (622,191kg). The tank is constructed of preformed fusion-welded aluminium alloy gores, panels, machined fittings and ring chords, all machined or chemically milled. Because the tank is the forward part of the assembly (and indeed of the whole Shuttle combination) its nose section curves to a pointed arch shape designed to reduce aerodynamic drag during powered flight.

The liquid hydrogen tank is the largest component of the ET and holds 383,066 US gal (1,450,058 litres) of liquid hydrogen at a temperature of −423°F (−253°C). The tank is again an aluminium alloy structure, this time 97ft (29.57m) long, and is comprised of a series of barrel sections, ellipsoidal domes and ring frames. Unfuelled weight is 31,750lb (14,402kg), whilst fully fuelled the tank weighs 257,987lb (117,021kg). The hydrogen tank assembly also provides a mounting platform for the orbiter and SRBs.

The inter-tank structure is not a tank assembly, but rather a mechanical connection between the forward oxygen tank and the aft hydrogen tank, thus providing a structural continuity between the tanks and also giving safe accommodation for instrumentation. The assembly also features attachment points for the forward section of the SRBs. It measures 22ft 6in (6.86m) in length, and has the same diameter as the fuel tanks.

Launch phase

Once the orbiter has been mechanically attached to the SRB/ET combination and successfully completed a series of fit and function tests, the whole stack is rolled out to the launch pad. Travelling the 3.5 miles (5.6km) from the VAB along the crawlerway to the Pad 39 launch complex at the Cape, the stack is carried by the veteran Crawler Transporter (CT), which has a top speed of 1.5mph (2.4km/h) and is a former carrier of the giant Apollo/Saturn family of vehicles.

Ground turnaround continues at the pad area, where in some cases payloads are inserted or even removed during the days up to launch. Again adopting modified Apollo launch pads, the Shuttle sits on its tail, nose pointing skywards, as final preparations continue around it. Like nearly all the orbiters, *Challenger* experienced several difficulties in the OPF and VAB, or on the pad. Engine problems plagued the first launch, and damage to the system of protective tiles delayed the seventh flight of the vehicle for several months. Weather can pose a problem at the Cape at certain times of the year, and this was clearly demonstrated by the 10th Challenger mission. Payload changes occurred during the first missions and between the 6th and 7th, and other minor problems plagued most of the *Challenger* launch preparations.

The typical launch countdown for a Shuttle mission begins about two days before the scheduled launch and includes a number of scheduled 'holds' to enable any delays to be overcome. During the final countdown the Shuttle combination is surrounded by the Rotating Service Structure (RSS), which also provides weather protection to the upper surfaces of the orbiter (the other side receiving a measure of protection from the ET/SRB combination) and allows certain payloads to be fitted in or taken out of the payload bay. The ET is fuelled on the pad and topped up constantly, while the orbiter receives its final checks and (in some cases) last-minute additions to the cargo: the Challenger 7 mission, carrying the life science experiments on Spacelab 3 in 1985, received its monkey payload only hours before the launch, and secret military payloads are often installed late in the countdown.

Delays in the launch while the vehicle was on the pad were encountered on the Challenger 1, 8 and 10 missions as a result of hardware difficulties and severe weather conditions. As the clock counts down towards zero the day of launch approaches and after breakfast (or dinner depending on the planned launch time) the flight crew are taken to the launch site and enter the vehicle through the side hatch some two hours before launch. By now the RSS has been removed and the ET filled, and the ground support crew soon departs to a safe area for launch.

As the crew prepare for launch, strapped into their seats, the countdown reaches T–9 minutes and its last planned hold period of 10 minutes. (Two other short periods are available if required.) Following the resumption of countdown the crew access arm is retracted, the orbiter's auxiliary power units (APUs) are powered up and verified, the vehicle is switched to internal power, and the three SSME nozzles at the base of the vehicle are gimballed to check their ability to move in flight and thus control the direction of thrust as the vehicle climbs away from the pad. During the final moments before launch the ET is pressurized to flight pressure, the SRB hydraulic power units (HPUs) are activated, and the engines' nozzle profile is completed.

At T−6.46 to 6.22 seconds the three SSMEs ignite in sequence. At T−3 these main engines reach 90% thrust, and 2.64 seconds later the SRBs ignite. The hold-down bolts are released at T–0 seconds, as are the eight hold-down posts supporting the vehicle on the MLP, and the vehicle lifts off, passing close to the launch tower which it clears at T+3.5 seconds. All the while, the water deluge system continues to pour thousands of gallons of water across the pad, cooling it after its fiery blast. The Shuttle, now clear of the launch tower, starts to perform its roll programme and pitchover (involving a 120° roll to the right) at T+7 seconds as the vehicle climbs through the dense layers of the lower atmosphere, and the engines are throttled down from 104% shortly after launch (at T+60 seconds) as the vehicle passes through the area of maximum aerodynamic pressure (Max Q). Shortly after this the engines are again throttled up to the required power and the combination streaks for space. Max Q is reached at T+69 seconds, and it was immediately after this event that *Challenger* was lost on its 10th launch.

As the combination climbs higher, the SRBs continue their 120-second burn. Unlike the SSMEs, the engines of the SRBs cannot be shut down, and even if the SSMEs fail the crew have to endure an SRB ride to 28-mile (45-km) altitude before separation and a quick return to Earth. The separation occurs at 2 minutes 4 seconds after ignition, the SRBs being released by explosive bolts and then powered outward and away from the Shuttle vehicle by their Booster Separation Motors (BSMs). After a free coast of a further 75 seconds the SRBs start a programmed descent, controlled by parachutes for final impact with the ocean 141 miles (227km) down-range from the Cape after a flight of 281 seconds and a maximum altitude of 220,000ft (67,055m). The boosters are later recovered and returned to the launch site where they are taken apart, cleaned, dried and prepared for a further launch. It is this process that was another major area of investigation for the Shuttle 25 (51-L) investigation committee.

Meanwhile the Shuttle continues upward, its engines being fed by the enormous ET at a rate of 19,017 US gal (71,987 litres) of liquid oxygen per minute and 48,724 US gal (184,440 litres) of liquid hydrogen per minute. The cut-off of the SSMEs occurs at 8 minutes 38 seconds into the flight, and is followed 12 seconds later by the separation of the ET, again by explosive bolts which sever all connections with the Shuttle. The ET too curves away, but is destroyed during re-entry and subsequent ocean impact. The

Above: The 20-second Flight Readiness Firing of *Challenger's* three SSMEs on December 18, 1982 validated the engines' capability for Shuttle 6.

SRB Descent, Splash-down and Recovery

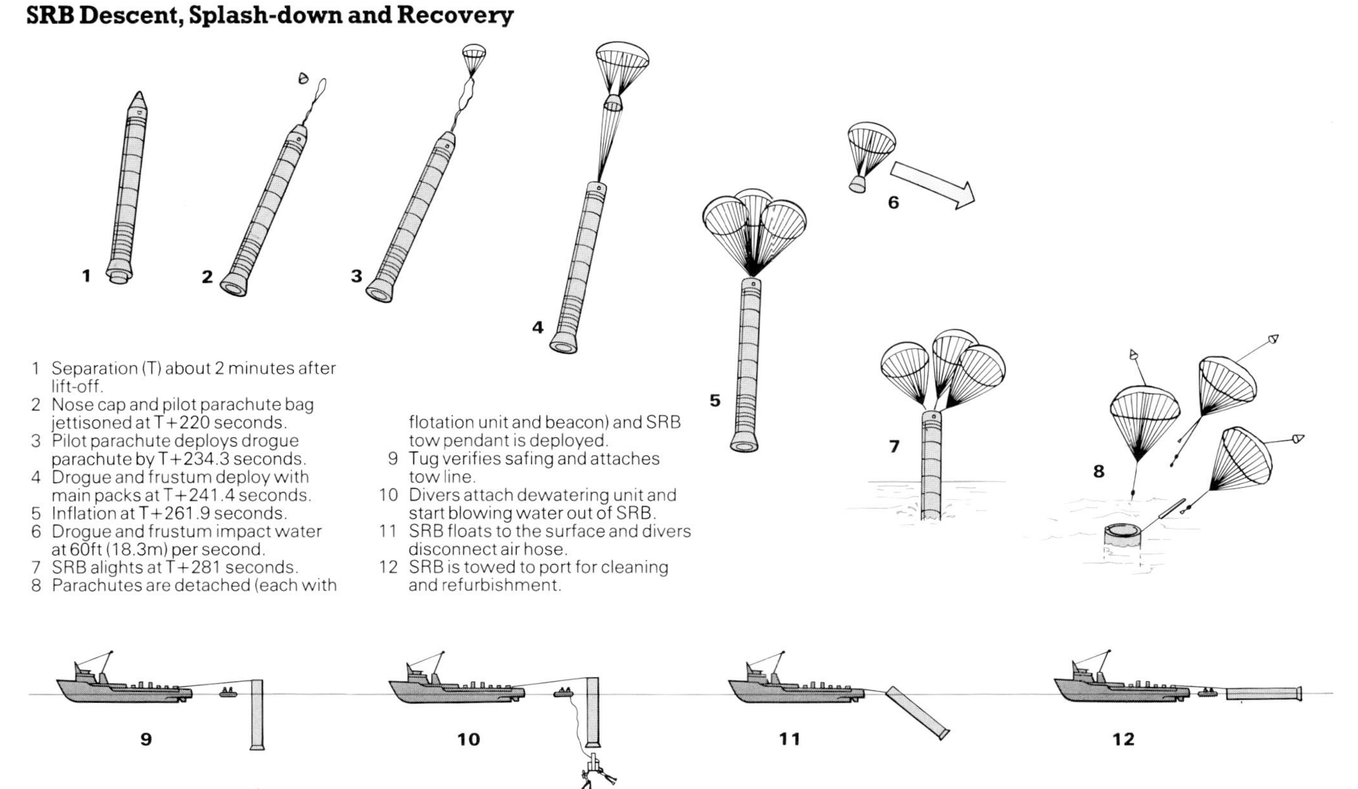

Above: A major safety feature is the automatic abort selector unit with four options, seen here in the Abort-To-Orbit position.

remnants of the tank impact the ocean some 58 minutes after launch, almost half way around the globe after the ET has completed its suborbital flight.

Now on its own, the orbiter coasts under the momentum of its powered flight into low Earth orbit, and at 10 minutes 39 seconds the twin OMS pods fire for almost 2 minutes to kick the vehicle into Earth orbit, travelling at 25,405ft (7743m) per second. If required, another burn is initiated at Ground Elapsed Time (GET) 43 minutes 58 seconds, and with its cut-off the Shuttle orbiter is in Earth orbit.

Unlike *Columbia, Challenger* was never fitted with ejection seats during its early missions. (*Columbia* had these disconnected after its fourth flight and removed after its fifth.) Up to T–30 seconds the crew can escape from the pad by means of a 1,200ft (366m) slide wire in a basket-type box which leads to an underground launch safety bunker on the edge of the pad. SSME shut down before SRB ignition was experienced on *Discovery*'s first launch attempts in June 1984, and with Challenger 8 in July 1985. Once SRB ignition has been initiated the Shuttle is committed to launch. If a serious problem does occur during the launch phase several abort options are available to the crew, who can try to bring the orbiter back to a safe landing on a number of runways around the world or on the ocean surface.

The first inflight abort mode occurs following SRB separation at T+127 seconds, when an SSME failure would bring the Return-To-Launch-Site (RTLS) abort mode into effect. In this the crew jettison the SRBs (if not already separated), and use the remaining SSME(s) to burn off the remaining fuel until the load remaining equals that required for the reversing of the direction of flight. The crew pitches the orbiter around, jettisons the ET and then glides to an unpowered landing at the Shuttle landing facility at the launch site. Early in the test programme NASA pressed for flying one of the Orbital Flight Test (OFT) missions in the RTLS abort profile, and suggested such a flight to the astronauts then in training for the Orbital Flight Tests (OFTs). Total confidence in the abort mode was not forthcoming, however, and as no astronaut volunteered to try the system, the 'test flight' necessarily had to wait until the real thing occurred.

For KSC launches the second abort mode is the Transatlantic Abort Landing (TAL), posited on a double SSME failure before the vehicle attempts a landing at any one of several Western European or West African landing sites. Comparable facilities are available for aborted Vandenberg launches across the Pacific in French Polynesia or on Easter Island.

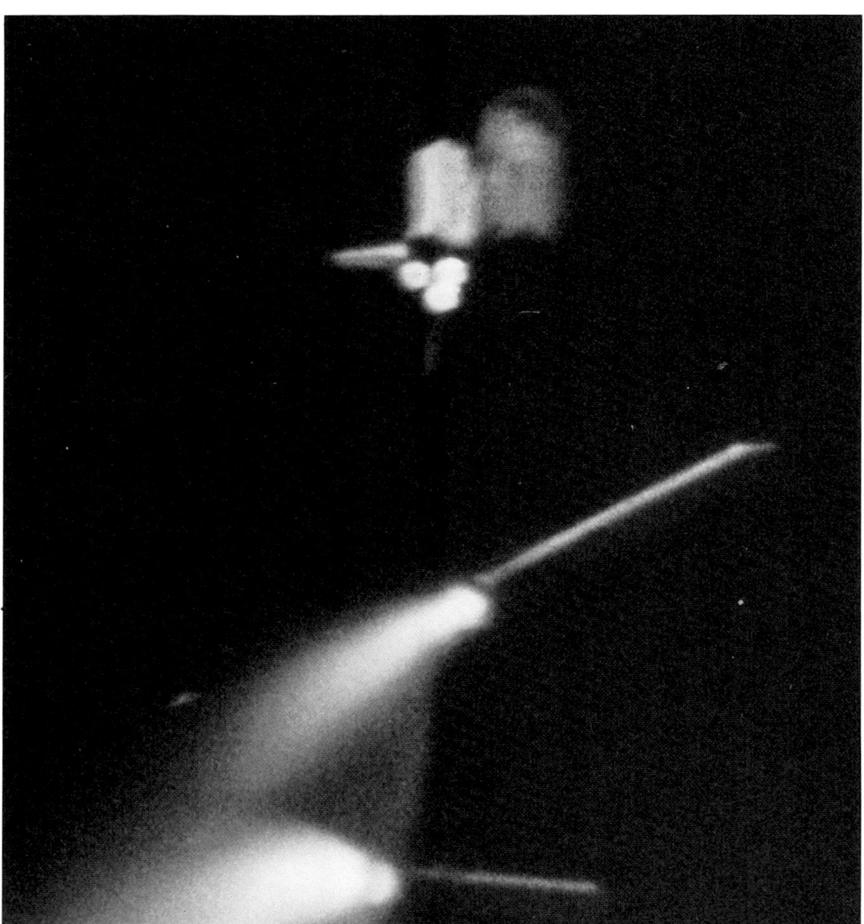

Right: Decisive in any flight is the correct separation of the SRBs, seen here on Shuttle 1. After separation the SRBs continue their climb to an apogee at T+70 seconds.

If an SSME failure occurs some two minutes after the separation of the SRBs (well past the RTLS and TAL capabilities), the next abort mode available to the crew is Abort-Once-Around (AOA), in which the vehicle is injected into low Earth orbit and makes a normal control landing after one orbit.

The final abort mode for the ascent phase is the Abort-To-Orbit (ATO) method, used when the vehicle is travelling fast enough to attain low Earth orbit on its OMS engines, so giving the crew time to assess the situation from the comparative safety of orbit before committing themselves either to the mission or early return at a number of landing sites. It was this abort mode that was first used by Challenger 8 in 1985.

It was believed early in the programme that a failure in the SRBs would result in a 'non-survivable' abort attempt. The SRBs, thought fully reliable in operation, placed this type of accident on the 'acceptable' list during Shuttle launches. In the 25th mission, however, the worst did happen and a failure in an SRB segment joint resulted in a catastrophic explosion and loss of seven astronauts in the *Challenger*. As the investigation into the disaster got under way, evidence surfaced that this was not the first time such an event could have resulted in an inflight explosion: the eighth mission (the third by *Challenger*) also suffered SRB problems, as did several other flights. Before the Shuttle flies again a complete overhaul of SRB and crew safety methods has been demanded, including the possible design of an escape system from the crew module, which would delay the next Shuttle launch several years instead of the months anticipated.

Orbital operations

With the orbiter safely in space, the crew settles down to a period of activity (usually lasting one week) in Earth orbit. First task on all missions is the complete checkout of vehicle and payload, and the opening of the payload bay doors which also carry the radiators needed to maintain even temperatures in the constant day/night cycle of Earth orbit.

On most (but not all) Shuttle flights the RMS arm is carried, and this has proved to be a valuable and versatile addition to the equipment list. Developed by Spar of Canada, it is 50ft 3in (15.32m) long and installed down one of the payload bay hinge lines for launch/re-entry and when not in use. Resembling the human arm in configuration, it has shoulder, elbow, and wrist joints, as well as a series of TV and video cameras which afford the operator a close-up view of what he is controlling the arm to do from inside the aft flight deck. With 62° field of view out of the aft windows and 80° field of view from the overhead windows, the operator is assisted by other payload bay cameras, the other crew members and the complex variety of arm movements which can enable the operator, for example, to place the mechanism underneath the orbiter belly to inspect tile damage and ensure closure of ET service doors etc. The 'hand' of the RMS is called the end effector, and this is the primary handling system for satellites and other equipment used with the RMS. In the open position, three wires are extended around the circumference of the tube-like end effector, and when the satellite grapple fixture is inserted into the effector the operator commands the wires to close around it, so locking the satellite in place.

The system is used for deploying satellites, retrieving them and assisting astronauts in Extra-Vehicular Activity (EVA) or space walking, as well as undertaking visual inspection of the orbiter surfaces and constituting an effective persuader with difficult equipment, as displayed during the famous 'ice-breaker' incident on Shuttle 12 (41-D) and *Challenger*'s sixth flight, Shuttle 13 (41-G), both in 1984. The arm was carried on eight of the 10 *Challenger* missions, those not using the system being Challenger 1 in 1983, and Challenger 7 in 1985. Although only one arm has so far been carried each time, it is possible to adopt a two-arm system for more complicated payloads, such as construction of the planned US space station in the 1990s.

Satellite deployment

One of the primary goals and promotional highlights of the Shuttle system before the loss of *Challenger* was the system's ability to deploy commercial satellites and free-flying scientific packages. From its early inception the Shuttle was billed as the launch system to replace all unmanned US launcher systems. As events turned out this was not to be, and the future of the Shuttle as a major satellite-deployment system seems in doubt as the investigations into the *Challenger* loss and repercussions in other areas of the programme continue. There is no doubt that satellites will be deployed from the Shuttle as several satellite types are made with only Shuttle-launch capability in their design, but the day of unmanned boosters is far from over.

The most widely used satellite deployment system employed by Shuttle is the McDonnell Douglas Payload Assist Module (PAM) D or D2 system. The shuttle has the capacity to carry four of the earlier PAM D version and three of the more powerful PAM-D2 version. The PAM D/D2 satellite payloads are loaded into the payload bay at right angles to the longitudinal centreline of the orbiter. Protected in space by folding sunshields, the PAM payloads are usually deployed on successive flight days, though a double PAM deployment was achieved on one flight day during Shuttle 20 in 1985. The deployment sequence begins with the crew opening the sunshield and releasing the restraint mechanisms. This is followed by the spinning of the satellite up to 50rpm (whilst it is still in the support cradle) as a means of spin-stabilizing the satellite after ejection. Once 50rpm has been achieved, the clamp band is released and four springs eject the PAM and its satellite payload up out of the Shuttle. Some 45 minutes after deployment from the Shuttle, and at a safe distance from the orbiter which turns its belly towards the deployed payload, the solid rocket motor ignites to push the satellite towards its geosynchronous orbit, which takes about two days to reach.

Challenger successfully deployed five satellites using PAM D upper stages (on the second, third and fourth missions). No PAM D2 systems were flown on *Challenger*.

Challenger was the first Shuttle to demonstrate the deployment of the larger Inertial Upper Stage (IUS) during the first mission of the vehicle, and following several delays to the IUS programme it carried the second civilian IUS on its 10th flight. On both flights deployment of the NASA Tracking and Data-Relay Satellite (TDRS) was planned, the object being improvement of Shuttle on-orbit coverage with longer periods of air-to-ground communications.

Deployment sequence for the IUS usually occurs on the first or second flight day, and begins with activation of the Airborne Support Equipment (ASE) used to secure the IUS to the payload bay during the launch phase. The ASE raises the IUS/satellite payload to an angle of 59°, and after a systems check the combination is spring-ejected from the cargo bay and over the flight deck roof of the orbiter. About 55 minutes after deployment, and again after the Shuttle has been manoeuvred away to a safe distance the aft (first) stage of the IUS ignites and burns its solid-propellant fuel for 2 minutes 26 seconds. After a predetermined period of free flight the stages separate and the forward (second) stage ignites to push the payload to its planned geosynchronous orbit. Measuring 16ft 4.5in (5.00m) in length and just under 10ft (3.05m) in diameter, and with a weight of 32,000lb (14,515kg) including a 21,400lb (9,707kg)

Spar Aerospace Remote Manipulator System

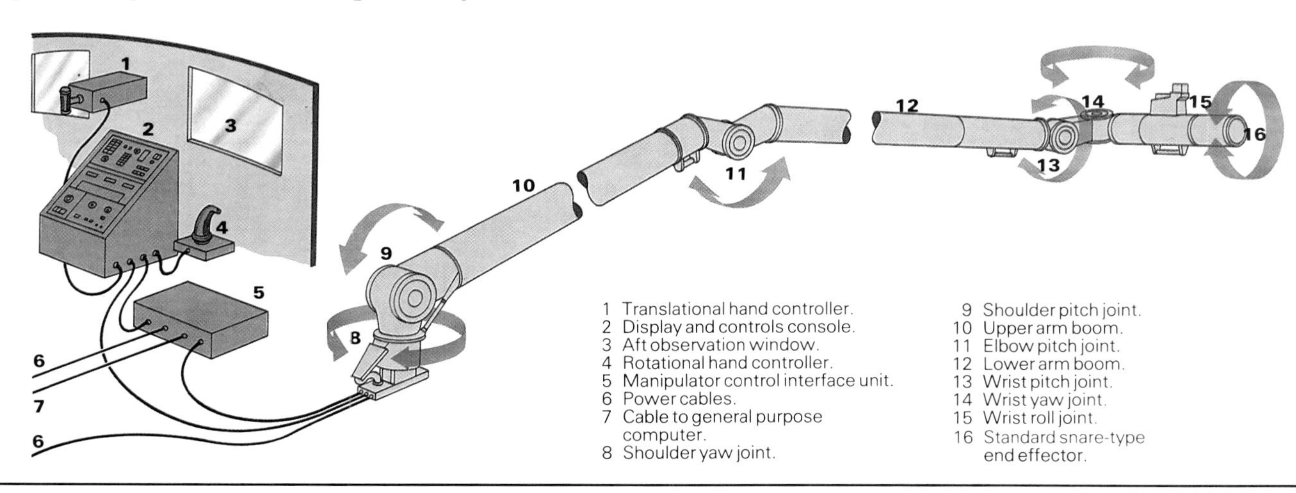

aft-stage motor and 6,000lb (2,722kg) forward-stage motor, the IUS is one of the largest payloads carried by Shuttle. With its payload mounted on top, the system lies horizontally in the bay, which it nearly fills though there remains the capacity to fit one PAM D launch satellite in front of the IUS system on some missions if required.

One of the other methods of satellite deployment successfully demonstrated by *Challenger* on several occasions is by 'deployable' means using the RMS arm, which can also capture satellites and lower them back into the bay, a feat ably demonstrated by *Challenger* in 1984. RMS-deployed satellites usually have no large onboard manoeuvring systems of their own and remain in the orbit in which they are deployed. *Challenger* deployed the Long Delay Exposure Facility (LDEF) and Earth Radiation Budget Experiment (ERBE) satellites in this way during its fifth and sixth missions in 1984. Other satellites deployed by the RMS during *Challenger* missions were classed as retrievable payloads, in that after a few hours of independent flight away from possible contaminations of onboard instruments by the orbiter's environment they were recaptured and secured in the bay for return to Earth for further use on later missions. *Challenger* deployed SPAS-01 and the Plasma Diagnostic Package (PDP) on its second and eighth missions, and was scheduled to deploy the Spartan-Halley observatory on its 10th mission.

Challenger also demonstrated small satellite launches by spring ejection on its fourth, seventh and ninth missions, these being a NASA rendezvous target (which subsequently exploded shortly after deployment) and two small scientific satellites.

The 'frisbee' method of launch was not accomplished on a *Challenger* flight.

The capture of faulty or serviceable satellites is another highly featured activity of Shuttle operations, and one that will have more emphasis as the flight programme resumes. Challenger 4 demonstrated this fully in the capture and repair of Solar Max, and later rescue efforts of *Discovery* flight crews (with Westar, Palapa and Leasat satellites in 1984 and 1985) clearly demonstrated the importance of man's presence in space and the capabilities of the Shuttle system in satellite servicing and repair operations.

EVA equipment

Unlike the individually tailored spacesuits of the Gemini and Apollo era, the Shuttle EVA suit comes in a standard size but with the capacity to be adjusted up or down the size scale to fit small women and men as well as astronauts with larger frames. Constructed from a selection of different-size parts, the suits fit together to allow the wearer freedom of movement but firm control during EVA activities. The suit, or more formally the Extravehicular Mobility Unit (EMU), is made of several components. First the wearer puts on (or dons as NASA likes to call it) a Liquid Cooling and Ventilation Garment (LCVG), a mesh one-piece suit constructed of spandex and zippered for entry from the front. Connected to the suit's primary life-support system, the cooling garment controls the metabolic rate of the wearer during periods wearing the suit and on EVA. With a dry weight of 6.6lb (3kg), the garment includes a urine-collection device and is worn with a 'Snoopy' communications headset and a 21oz (595g) in-suit drink bag of potable water for refreshment during long EVAs.

Wearing the above undergarments, the astronaut now dons the lower torso garment incorporating the legs and boots. The lower torso comes in various sizes, and the wearer slips on boot inserts to allow proper fit. The Hard Upper Torso (HUT) is donned from underneath, being put on like a jumper, and then attached to the lower torso by a matching hard waist ring which clips into place and seals the closed joint. All junctions are made with combinations of mechanical joints (sewn, clamped, screwed etc) and adhesive bonding, and all materials used in construction are designed to prevent fungus or bacteria growth. Produced for a 15-year operational life, each suit is cleaned and dried between missions. The upper torso comes in five sizes and connecting gloves in 15 sizes, but the helmet is available in only one size. The use of bearings in the shoulder and arm joints greatly increases the astronaut's ability to bend, lean and twist in relative ease while wearing the suit.

The suit is constructed of several bonded layers, beginning with a polyurethane-on-nylon pressure bladder, moving to several Kevlar layers with folded and tucked joints for mobility, and completed with a Kevlar, Teflon and Dacron anti-abrasion layer. The HUT has an aluminium shell. Total weight of the suit and associated garments is 85lb (38.6kg). The normal pressure within the suit is 4.0lb/sq in (0.276 bar) differential, with a top level of 10.6lb/sq in (0.73 bar).

A visor snaps onto the outer part of the helmet, providing protection from ultraviolet and infrared radiation from the Sun, micrometeoroids and solar glare. On the wearer's chest is the digital caution and warning facility for consumables, and the unit is completed by a comprehensive radio communications and biomedical instrumentation assembly, providing constant data to the astronaut and ground control, as well as real-time two-way communications between the two EVA astronauts, the crew on board the orbiter and ground control.

Below: EVA astronaut Bruce McCandless evaluates the combination of the RMS arm and attached Mobile Foot Restraint extension during the 41-B mission. The evaluation confirmed the system's great practical value.

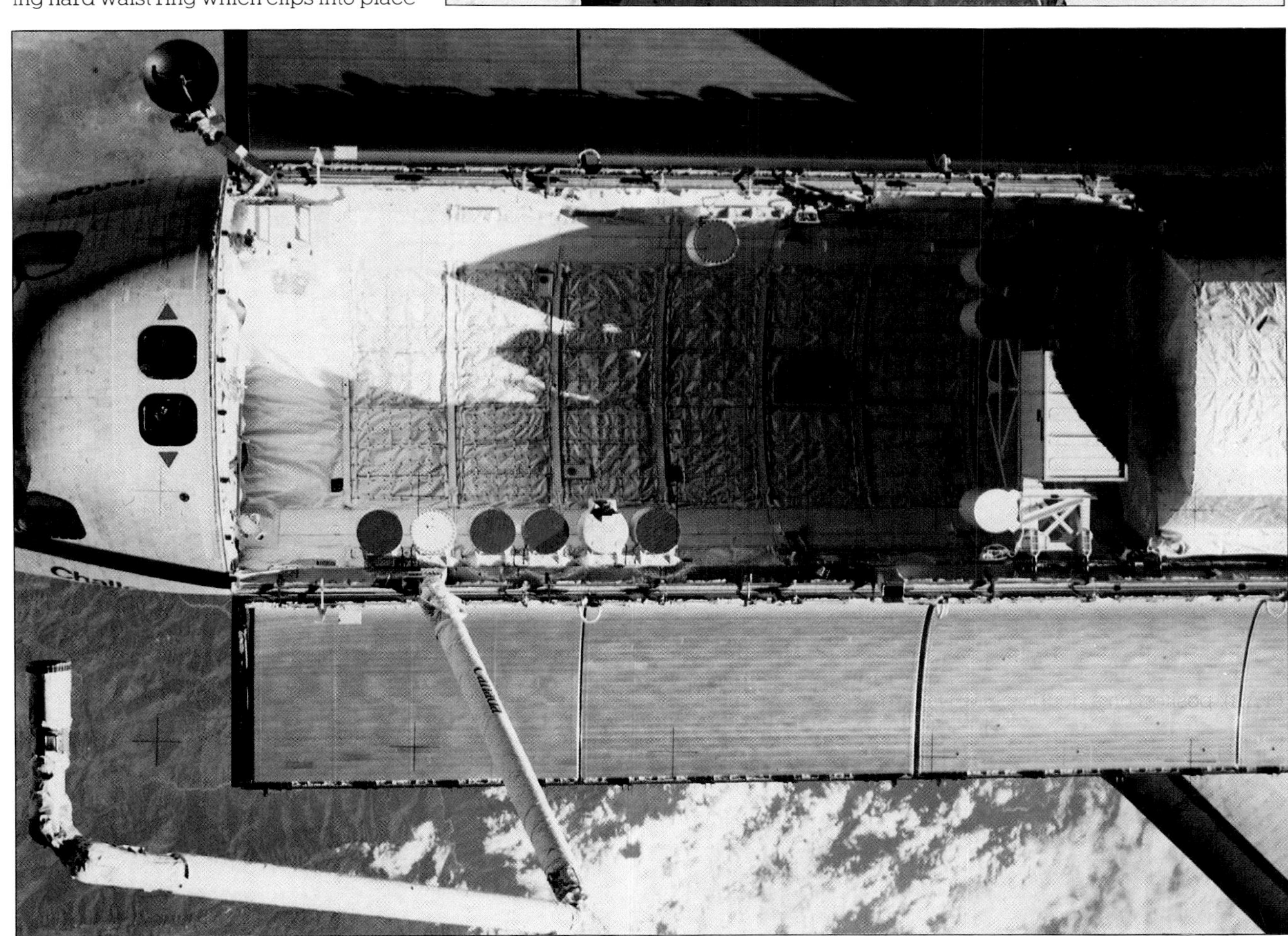

Right: A photograph by the free-flying SPAS-1 deployed by Shuttle 7 reveals details of *Challenger*'s payload bay with GAS canisters along its sills, and the RMS arm.

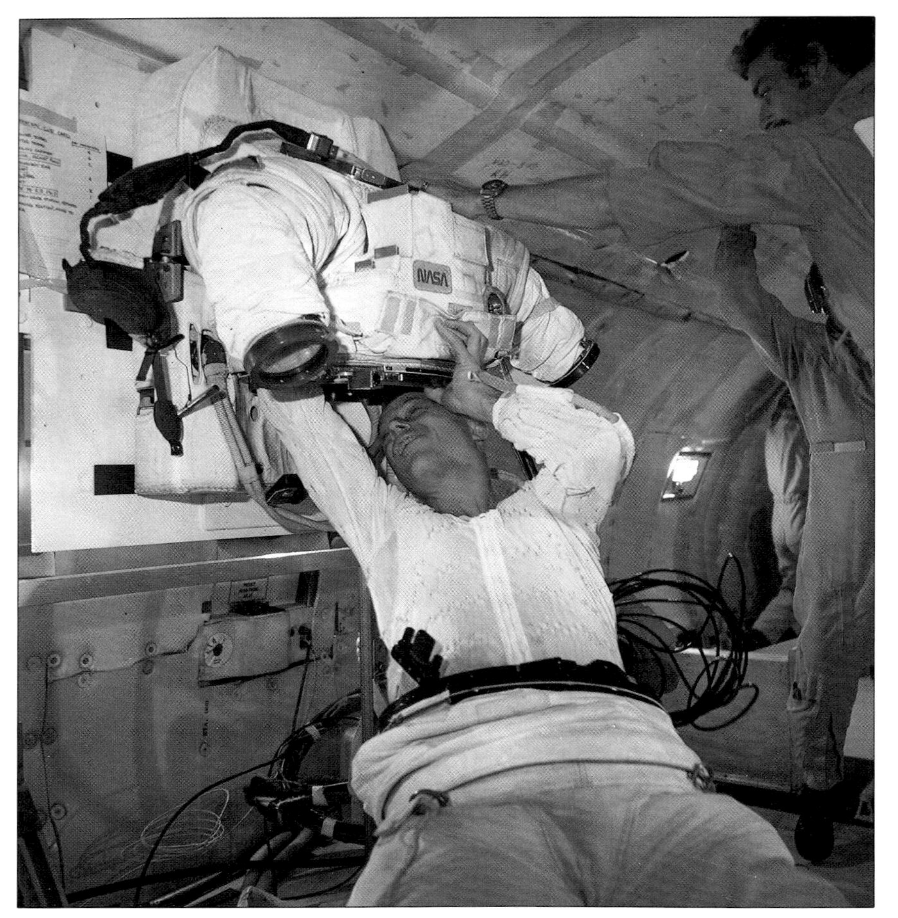

Left: In training for Shuttle 6, astronaut Story Musgrave practises suit donning in the weightlessness of a KC-135 'zero-gravity' aircraft.

The Portable Life Support Subsystem (PLSS) is designed to provide constantly refreshed atmosphere for breathing and suit pressurization, and to maintain suit temperature by removing metabolic heat. Measuring 19.75in (50.165cm) in depth, 23in (58.42cm) in width and 30.3in (76.96cm) in height, the PLSS weighs 160lb (72.58kg) and the rechargeable silver zinc battery provides 17 volts at 52W/hr for 7 hours. Attached to the back of the suit, the PLSS contains an oxygen supply of 1.217lb (0.55kg) at 850lb/sq in (58.6 bar) in the primary oxygen system, 2.6lb (1.18kg) at 6,000lb/sq in (413.7 bar) in the secondary pack, and 10lb (4.54kg) of water in three bladders. The primary oxygen system and water reserves provide sufficient expendables for a 7-hour EVA, including 15 minutes for checkout, 6 hours for EVA, 15 minutes for doffing and 30 minutes for reserve in event of primary system failure.

The EVA crew pre-breath using launch and entry helmets for one hour before entering the suits to enable them to clean their systems of nitrogen, thus preventing the 'bends' during EVA breathing pure oxygen. The suiting-up process is assisted by a fellow astronaut, and the airlock is entered to complete suiting-up while still connected to the spacecraft life support system: the EVA starts at the time the astronaut goes onto suit internal power, and is completed once he hooks up to orbiter power again. Exit and entry are effected through the payload bay airlock hatch, and there are enough consumables for three EVA periods of about 7 hours per mission for two persons: two are used in planned EVAs, and one is kept in reserve for any emergency EVA such as manual closing of the payload bay doors or restraint of equipment such as the RMS for re-entry. Mission specialists usually conduct EVAs, though commanders and pilots are trained for EVA operations to a lesser degree.

One of the most versatile items of Shuttle EVA equipment is the MMU, developed from the Gemini Astronaut Maneuvering Unit (AMU) and Skylab M-509 AMU experiment. The MMU provides its 'pilot' with free-flight capability away from the orbiter to travel across open space to inspect, construct, repair or retrieve satellites and other orbital hardware.

Providing six degrees of freedom and rotation through three axes, and translating in six directions using a system of 24 jet thrusters arranged in two sets of 12 (to provide a failsafe system of 12 prime and 12 back-up jets), the MMU is controlled through two hand controllers, one mounted on each of two arm rests.

Connected to the EMU by two latches on the back, the MMU provides an integral part of the EMU system and is rechargeable at its flight station in the forward part of the payload bay between EVAs. Two MMUs are carried on any one flight. The system uses a propellant of non-contaminating gaseous nitrogen, while the batteries are the same as those used in the EMU life support system and are thus interchangeable. The system has an independent flight capacity of 6 hours before recharging, though the batteries take about 16 hours to recharge.

The piloting of the MMU resembles that of the Shuttle, capitalizing on crew familiarity with both systems. The total nitrogen carried in the MMU allows an acceleration change of 66ft (20.1m) per second, which provides for several trips away from the orbiter out to a distance of 300ft (9.m). All propulsion and control systems are arranged in dual circuit systems to provide a redundancy of one system. Several orbiter rescue modes are available using the second EVA crewmember or the RMS system to retrieve a stranded MMU pilot.

Dimensions of the MMU unit include a height of 49.4in (1.25m), a width of 32.1in (81.53cm) and a depth of 44.2in (1.12m) with the control arms extended. Weight is 300lb (136.1kg) fully fuelled, and with a spacesuited crewmember and consumables on-orbit mass is about 740lb (335.7kg).

Challenger 4 astronauts were the first to demonstrate the MMU in flight in February 1984. This was followed by attempts to rescue the Solar Max by MMU methods in the following April, and spectacular activities to retrieve two stranded communication satellites on Discovery 2 (51-A) in November 1984. MMUs have not been used since 1984, but once the Shuttle resumes operations extended use of the units is an anticipated feature of future missions.

The mid-deck area provided ample space for small self-contained experiments and biological research. The

Left: Bruce McCandless makes an untethered EVA during Shuttle 10, this 'world first' being made possible by use of the Manned Maneuvering Unit.

Crew Cabin Arrangements

Below: Mid-deck has standard seats (D) and space for extra seats (A) plus airlocks (B and C), while the flight deck seats the pilot (1), MS (2), PS (3) and commander (4).

Bottom: Mid-deck has a table (A), bunks (B and C), lavatory (D), airlock (E) and galley (F), while the flight deck has the pilot's seat (1), MS (2), pilot (3), PSs (4) and commander (5).

Launch and Re-entry Phase (mid-deck left and flight deck right)

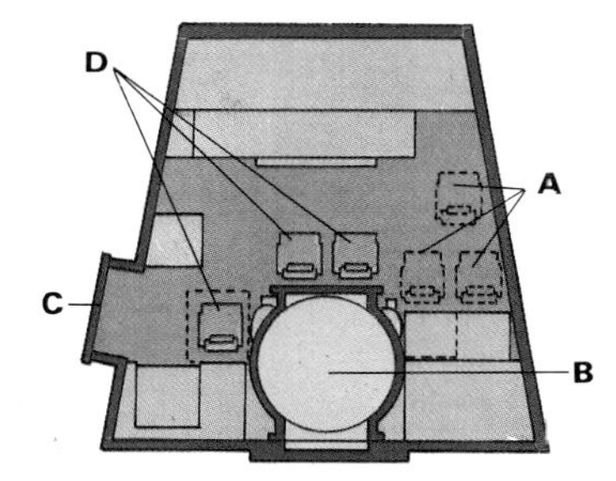

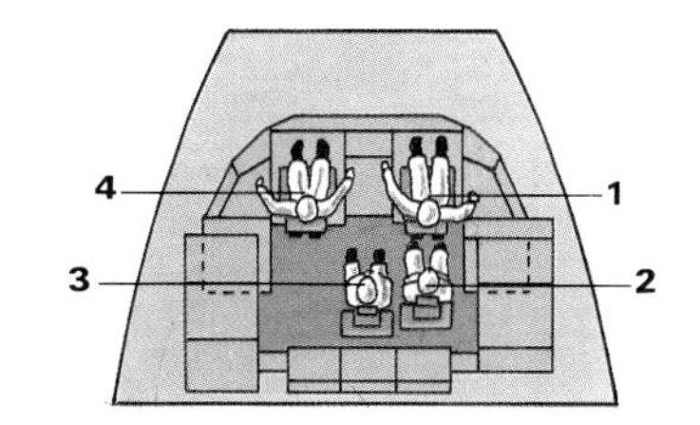

On-Orbit Phase (mid-deck left and flight deck right)

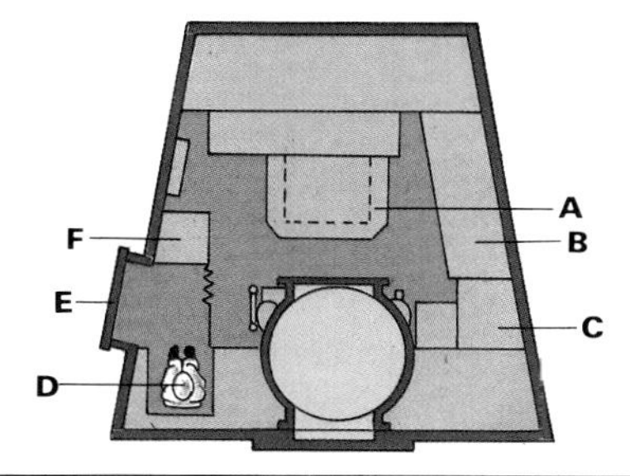

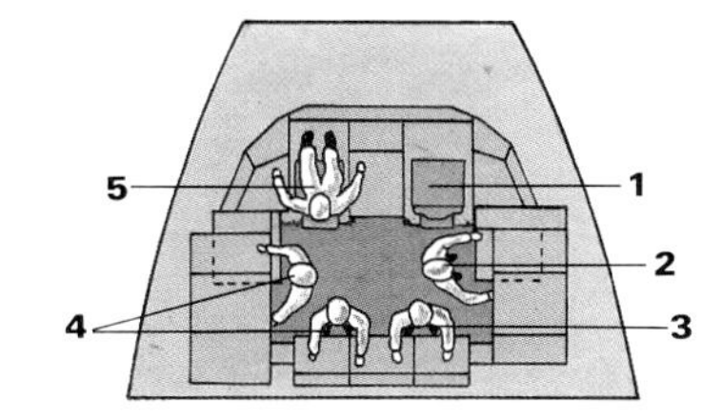

payload bay was also the location of simple GAS (Get-Away Special) experimental canisters; the spacelab range of modules and pallets, as well as deployable scientific payloads and Earth/Space observation equipment.

Living in space

Because of the short flight time of Shuttle missions (several days compared with the months which Soviet cosmonauts spend aboard their Salyut and Mir space stations), there is a limit to the time available to astronauts for gathering as much data and experimental results as possible, and for getting the most out of each flight. Crews work in shifts around the clock for Spacelab missions, and with satellite activities, EVAs and experiment operations there is not much time left for other more recreational events such as those undertaken on Skylab.

Shuttle flight crews usually number seven on normal missions, but can be as few as two and as many as eight. (A two-person crew can in theory fly a rescue mission bringing home a stranded eight-person crew, so by stripping sleeping compartments from the mid-deck a crew of 10 is theoretically possible.)

All crews fly a NASA team of commander in overall charge of the mission, a pilot responsible for orbiter systems and flight control etc, and one or more mission specialists who act as flight engineers for launch and re-entry, EVA crewmembers, operators of the RMS, experiments etc and for satellite deployments. The image of the hot-shot test pilot astronaut, possessor of the 'Right Stuff', has certainly been left with the early space programme. Payload specialists are usually flown with specific experiments and investigations, and come from the USA (including the services, who provide Manned Spaceflight Engineers) and foreign countries. Shuttle has also flown politicians, and pursued active programmes for teachers and journalists, while NASA expressed the desire to fly other specialists and 'ordinary citizens'. The loss of *Challenger* while carrying a Hughes engineer and the first Teacher-In-Space applicant has undoubtedly delayed for some time such an active Space Flight Participant programme.

Shuttle crews are usually formed about a year before they fly, and receive many hours of training and simulation work. The payload specialists and passengers do not receive so long a professional astronaut training programme. These astronauts need not learn to fly the Shuttle, but everyone who becomes a member of the Shuttle crew must learn what living facilities are available.

The orbiter's environmental control and the life support systems clean the cabin air, add fresh oxygen and remove moisture. Pressure is maintained at normal Earth sea-level scale at 14.7lb/sq in (1.01 bar) with 21% oxygen and 79% nitrogen. The system provides heat and cooling, and, as a byproduct of the associated electrical power system, drinking or washing water. (Because of the problems encountered with the Skylab mission, and of the limited duration of Shuttle flights, no shower is fitted on the Shuttle, whose crew members must make do instead with soap, wet wipes and towels.) Life onboard may still be cramped and makeshift, but it is a far cry from the confines of the Gemini and Apollo eras.

Return to Earth

After all the orbital activities have been finished, the crew stow all their equipment and prepare for their homecoming which, weather permitting, should take place at the landing strip alongside the launch site.

With all preparations for re-entry completed, the payload bay doors closed and the crew strapped into their seats, the mission is about 60 minutes from completion. The weather at the landing site is a major factor in deciding where to end the mission as there are a number of weather-dictated alternate sites available before the commitment to de-orbit burn is made. Indeed, the second and fifth *Challenger* landings experienced a last-minute switch from the landing strip at KSC to Edwards Air Force Base in California because of bad visibility at the Cape.

The orbiter is turned around against the direction of flight and the OMS engines are fired, slowing the vehicle and causing it to drop (as it is turned nose-first again) into the upper reaches of the atmosphere, at 110 mile (175km) altitude travelling at about 16,465mph (26,500km/h), one hour before landing and 12,695 miles (20,430km) from landing point. As the vehicle descends into the denser layers of the atmosphere, a glove of ionized gas envelops the orbiter and blocks all radio communications with the vehicle: this occurs at a height of 50 miles (80km), a speed of 16,700mph (26,875km/h), some 3,392 miles (5,459km) from landing and 25 minutes from touch-down.

Maximum heating is reached at 20 minutes from touch-down at a height of 43.5 miles (70km) at 15,045mph (24,212km/h) and 1,775 miles (2,857km) from landing. The Shuttle comes in for its entry belly-first, where the most effective thermal protection material is applied. The Shuttle employs a variety of TPS tiles and blankets, which protect the vehicle against the intense cold of space (−250°F/−157°C) during on-orbit operations and against the searing heat of re-entry (up to +3,000°F/+1,649°C). Internal insulation and heaters provide constant temperatures through purging techniques. Despite some problems, the TPS has proved an adequate system, though *Challenger* did lose some tiles during the launch vibrations of Challenger 5, and small particles of the TPS broke loose and damaged upper-surface insulation during the re-entry of Challenger 4. Post-flight inspection has revealed minor damage, the most serious after the Challenger 6 mission, when the waterproofing agent was found to be at fault.

Exit from the radio blackout occurs some 12 minutes from touch-down, at a height of 34 miles (54.7km), a speed of 8,275mph (13,317km/h) and a distance of 550 miles (885km). The Terminal Area Energy Management (TAEM) manoeuvre, in which the vehicle performs banked turns to assist in deceleration and lining up with the runway, occurs just over 5.5 minutes from landing at a height of 83,130ft (25,340m), a speed of 1,700mph (2,736km/h) and a distance of 60 miles (96.6km) from landing. The autoland sequence begins 7.5 miles (12.07km) out, at a height of 13,365ft (4,074m), a speed of 424mph (682km/h) and just 86 seconds from touch-down. The autoland interface is followed by a landing preflare 2 miles (3.2km) out from the landing site, reducing the glideslope from 22° to 1.5°. (The descent manoeuvres of the Shuttle owe a lot to the early X-15 and other rocket planes of the 1950s and 1960s, and to the lifting-body series of aerospace research vehicles of the 1960s and 1970s.)

At about 14 seconds to touchdown, the landing gear is gravity-lowered with the aid of springs and hydraulic power, ensuring rapid as well as safe lowering and locking. Touchdown occurs first on the two units of the main gear, the touch-down of the nose gear following in short order. After a rollout of several hundred yards the vehicle comes to a halt, its mission over. Braking has also proved to be a problem on several flights, and this was another area the *Challenger* inquiry team decided needed further investigation.

After the vehicle has stopped, close-out vehicles race to prepare the orbiter for transport back to the processing facilities to begin preparations for its next mission. The crew disembark and after a brief inspection of the exterior are taken to the debriefing room and the start of another mission training programme.

Note on designations

Up to September 1983 NASA identified the Shuttle missions as STS-1, STS-2 etc, and if a mission was cancelled the appropriate number designation was also cancelled (resulting in the sequence STS-9, STS-11 etc). As missions became cancelled and delayed, so the numbering sequence became more complicated (i.e. STS-9, [STS-10 cancelled], STS-11, STS-13, STS-12, [STS-14 cancelled] [STS-15 cancelled]etc). NASA then adopted a new identification system for missions from STS-9 (or Shuttle 9), which became 41-A, though the official use of the system came on Shuttle 11, otherwise 41-B. The first digit (4) denotes the U.S. financial year (October 1 to September 30) in which that flight/payload was originally manifested (i.e. 1984). The second digit (1) denotes launch site: (1 for Kennedy Space Center in Florida, and 2 for the Vandenberg AFB site in California). The letter denotes the sequence of launch planned from that site in that fiscal year: with 26 letters, a maximum of 26 flights can thus be accommodated at each of the two sites in the October-to-September period, totalling 52 missions per year! Even if the payload slips the designation remains unaltered (such as 51-L launched in January '86 *after* 51-J, 61-A, 61-B and 61-C). In this book the following designation has been adopted to determine respectively the flight within the programme, its prelaunch/payload identity and *Challenger* mission sequence thus:

Shuttle 6 (31-B) *Challenger* 1, or

Shuttle 13 (41-G) *Challenger* 6.

Below: Clearly visible in this landing shot are the main gear units, three SSMEs with two OMS/RCS pods flanking them, and the split rudder/speed brake.

Building the Vehicle

Challenger began life as the Structural Test Article 099, a vital but essentially Earthbound evaluation, test and systems rig for the many complexities of the Space Shuttle Transportation System. But the production of operational orbiters was cut from five to three for financial reasons, and in an effort to maintain an adequate capability in space NASA decided to refurbish _Challenger_ as Orbiter Vehicle 099. Between 1979 and 1982, therefore, STA-099 was rebuilt and revised as OV-099 to join the programme in which it soon became the best loved and most outstanding orbiter.

Part of the contract awarded to Rockwell in 1972 was to design and build a Structural Test Article (STA) (as well as four, possibly five, flight-worthy Shuttle orbiters) to serve as a ground test vehicle intended to provide data on the structural stresses and strains the final design of the orbiter would experience. When NASA was forced to cut its fleet of operational orbiters from five to three, losing OV-101 and OV-105 from the proposed operational manifest, it was decided to reduce the structural test programme of STA-099, employ OV-101 as a ground test and verification vehicle, and upgrade STA-099 to flight status as OV-099. Construction of OV-099 from earliest fabrication in 1975 through to final delivery as a flight vehicle, in 1982, was followed by the successful completion of nine spaceflights in its short but distinguished career.

Construction history

On January 6, 1975 at its Palmdale, California, plant Rockwell began the long-lead fabrication of STA-099 for the ground test programme. The assembly of the STA was completed by February 10, 1978 and STA-099 was transferred to the Lockheed facility at Downey, California, where a series of test preparations was completed by August 11. Between August 14 and September 29 a series of coefficient tests was completed on the STA before a series of structural tests was undertaken.

On January 25, 1979 STA-099 received the name *Challenger*, four days before the contract was signed confirming its conversion to spaceflight configuration by Rockwell. *Challenger* is an historic name in US maritime history (between 1872 and 1876 the US naval vessel *Challenger* conducted an extended exploration of the Atlantic and Pacific Oceans) and the Lunar Module of the Apollo 17 lunar landing mission in December 1972 had been given the callsign Challenger by its crew.

By August 6 the limited tests had been completed on STA-099, and this was followed by the completion of the set-up and thermal test programme on October 5. STA-099 was delivered to Rockwell's Palmdale facility on November 7, 1979 for the rework programme which would bring the vehicle up to operational standards. By October 23, 1981 the airframe had been modified to flight standard, and on October 26 the initial series of powered subsystems tests was started. An unpowered systems test was begun on November 2, and by January 29, 1982 the initial subsystems test series had been completed.

On April 16 the *Challenger*'s subsystems were cleared for operational use, and on April 30 the final acceptance test was completed at the Palmdale plant. In June *Challenger* received its final certifications before delivery. On June 4 the post-checkout operations were completed, and 17 days later the configuration inspection was successfully completed. On June 30 the vehicle was officially rolled out of the Palmdale facility, completing more than 7½ years work in the construction, testing and conversion of the vehicle, so bringing it up to operational standard as the second flight vehicle. *Challenger* was then installed on a low loader for its move to Edwards AFB.

On July 1, 1982, as its sister ship *Columbia* was orbiting the Earth during the fourth flight day of the fourth Shuttle mission, *Challenger* was transported by road in a 38 mile (61km) journey from the Palmdale plant to Edwards AFB for attachment to the Shuttle Carrier Aircraft (SCA) for its journey to KSC.

Shortly after *Columbia* landed at Edwards AFB, completing the fourth flight of the programme and its OFT series, *Challenger* was sent on its way to KSC by President Reagan, the vehicle taking to the air for the first time on the USA's 206th birthday, July 4, 1982. The SCA flew to Florida in two stages, taking the orbiter to Ellington AFB, Texas for an overnight stop and finally, on July 5, from Ellington to KSC, Florida and the Shuttle Landing Facility. Following demate from

Orbiter Main Sub-Assemblies

In its basic configuration and structure the orbiter follows orthodox aerospace practice. The core of the assembly is the mid-fuselage, to which are attached the payload bay doors, the wings, the upper and lower forward fuselage sections (complete with the attached forward RCS module and enclosed crew compartment plus its airlock modules), and the aft fuselage which is the structural core for the fin/rudder, the OMS/RCS pods and the body flap.

Left: Ecstatic send-off for the orbiter *Challenger* en route to Kennedy Space Center on July 4, 1982 atop the SCA ferry aircraft.

Right: Distinguishable by its gold foil insulation, the three-deck crew compartment of *Challenger* nestles in the lower forward fuselage section.

the SCA, *Challenger* was moved to the OPF to begin final preparations for its first flight on Shuttle 6 early in 1983.

Structural test programme

Following construction at the Rockwell facility, Palmdale in the construction bay next to that used for *Enterprise*, STA-099 was rolled across the road to the Lockheed facility where engineers attached about 2,700 pads to the aluminium skin of STA-099 (mostly on the wings) so that strain gauges and other data-recording instruments could measure the stresses applied to the vehicle by load jacks. The programme was designed to investigate dynamic loads and structural strength during critical phases of the ascent flight profile, and also during the descent stage of the mission, namely the periods of maximum aerodynamic load. During the latter stages of the planning for the STA programme the decision was made to use this orbiter shell for actual space flights, and a revision of the test programme led to a pattern of tests that could adequately apply the loads needed to demonstrate the strength and integrity of the airframe without causing damage to the vehicle.

Challenger main components

In basic configuration *Challenger* was similar to the other four vehicles constructed, the major components being the Forward Fuselage (comprising Upper and Lower Fuselage sections sandwiching the pressurized Crew Module), the Mid-Fuselage which was the major payload-carrying area of the vehicle, the Payload Bay Doors, the Wings, the Aft Fuselage (supporting the major propulsion systems and housing the SSMEs and Body Flap) and the Vertical Stabilizer. All of the structure's major elements were constructed of conventional aluminium protected by reusable surface insulation. These major structural assemblies were held together with rivets and bolts. The mid-fuselage was joined to the forward and aft fuselage assemblies primarily with shear ties, the mid-fuselage also overlapping the bulkhead caps at two points or stations. The wing assembly was attached to the lower sides of the mid-fuselage and aft fuselage by shear ties except in the wing carrythrough area, where the upper panels were attached with tension bolts. The vertical stabilizer was attached to the aft fuselage upper surface by bolts that worked in both shear and tension. Finally, the body flap, which incorporated aluminium honeycomb covers, was attached to the lower aft fuselage by four rotary actuators.

Below: With its otherwise blunt rear aerodynamically faired, the orbiter *Challenger* flies towards Houston and ultimately the Kennedy SC aboard the SCA, a modified Boeing 747.

Forward fuselage

Challenger's forward fuselage consisted of the upper and lower fuselages, housed the pressurized crew module (described separately), and provided support for the forward RCS module, nose cap, nose gear wheel well, nose gear and nose gear doors.

Initial fabrication of the forward fuselage for STA-099 began on February 16, 1976, and the final assembly was initiated on August 2. On April 1, 1977 the lower forward fuselage arrived at Palmdale, followed by the upper forward fuselage five days later. Following the structural test programme, the upper forward fuselage was demated on February 15, 1980 and arrived at Palmdale for rework on February 23. By May 30 preparations for the modification of the lower forward fuselage had been completed and work on bringing the section to spaceflight standards was conducted over the next six months, being completed on November 21. By July, 1981 the upper forward fuselage had also been modified and arrived back at Downey for integration with the lower forward fuselage.

The forward fuselage of *Challenger* was built of conventional 2024 aluminium alloy skin/stringer panels, bulkheads and frames. Each panel was made of single-curvature stretch-formed skins with riveted stringers between 3 and 5in (7.6 and 12.7cm) apart. Riveted to the skin/stringer panels, the frames were spaced between 30 and 36in (76.2 and 91.4cm) apart. The foremost bulkhead of the assembly was of flat aluminium and formed sections which were both riveted and bolted together in the upper forward fuselage, and machined for the lower forward fuselage. The bulkhead also provided the interface fitting for the nose assembly.

The nose section of the forward fuselage was constructed of machined beams and struts, and provided the structure for the nose landing gear supports and wheel well. Two support beams acted as the main structure for the wheel well, with closeout webs, support struts, a nose landing gear strut, actuator attachment fittings, and landing gear door fittings completing the structure.

The fuselage of *Challenger* was covered with TPS tiles except for the six windshields, the two overhead windows, the side hatch window, and sections around the forward RCS engines. There was provision in the structural skin of the forward fuselage for the installation of antennae, deployable air probes and two star trackers. Six outer-pane windshields were installed on the forward fuselage and were held by five-axis machined parts forming the window frame structure.

The forward fuselage also provided for the forward orbiter/External Tank attachment fittings located aft of the nose gear wheel well. Purge and vent control was achieved by the installation of flexible boots around the forward fuselage and crew compartment, all windows and the star-tracker opening.

Crew Module

For the STA programme a simulated crew module was built, and this arrived at Palmdale on January 28, 1977, just nine years before the loss of the vehicle. After the decision to configure STA-099 for operational flight, the construction of a space-worthy crew module design started with long-lead fabrication on January 2, 1979. This was followed by the start of crew module assembly on June 21, followed by the installation of initial systems on November 3, 1980. On July 14, 1981 the crew module arrived at Palmdale for integration into the vehicle structure.

The crew module was designed in three levels: the upper (or flight) deck, the mid-deck, and the lower (or equipment) bay. Construction of the compartment was of 2219 aluminium alloy plate with integral stiffening stringers and internal frames welded together to produce the desired pressure-tight unit. The compartment had two hatches. One, in the left side, was used for normal entry and exit to the vehicle, and led to the mid-deck area. The second hatch provided access, via the airlock, to the payload bay in the mid-fuselage, and was used for payload and other EVA tasks.

In all, some 300 penetrations in the crew compartment pressure shell were sealed with plates and fittings. The large removable panel in the aft bulkhead, used for access to the crew module interior during the initial fabrication of the module, was also used for the installation and removal of the airlock between missions.

The module supported the Environmental Control and Life-Support System (ECLSS), avionics, guidance and navigation, crew displays and controls and navigation star-tracker base, as well as crew facilities such as the sleep, waste management, galley and seat stations (see diagram on page 17).

Orbiter Flight Deck Windows

The flight deck has 10 windows (below right), of which six are on the forward flight deck (below left). Two panes are attached to the crew compartment, the inner of 0.62in (15.7mm) aluminosilicate glass and the outer of 1.3in (33mm) fused silica glass, while the single pane in the upper forward fuselage section is of 0.62in (15.7mm) silica glass. At the rear are two overhead and two rear windows (centre), the former identical in construction with the forward units though 0.45in (11.4mm) and 0.68in (17.2mm) thick for the inner two and outer panes. The rear windows are identical to the inner two panes of the forward windows.

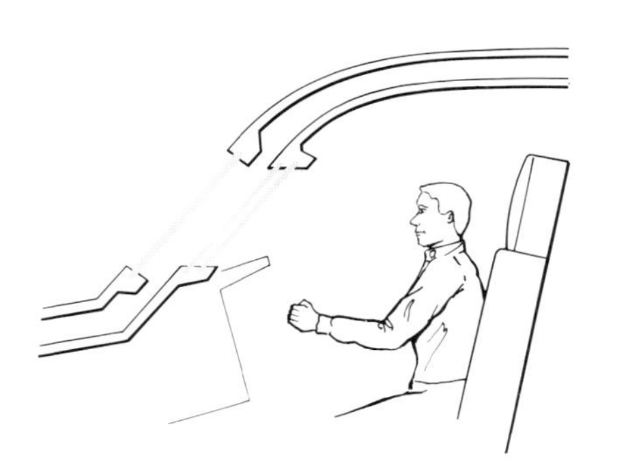

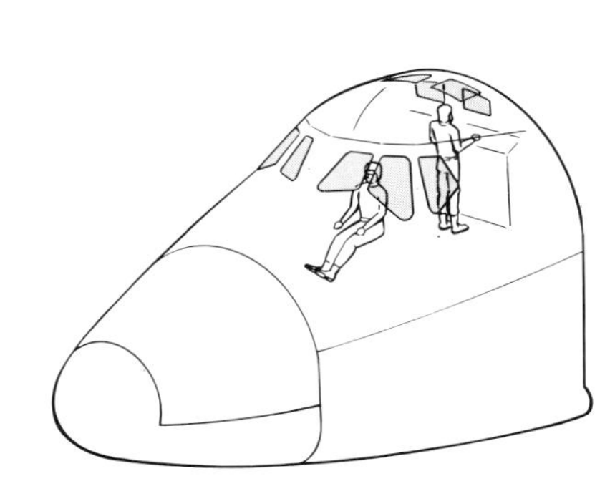

To reduce to a minimum the thermal conductivity between the compartment and the forward fuselage, only four attachment points were used to support the module within the forward fuselage. The major connections were located at the aft end of the compartment at flight deck floor level, with the vertical load link located on the centreline of the forward bulkhead and the lateral load reaction links on the lower segment of the aft bulkhead.

Pressurized to 14.7±0.2lb/sq in (1.01±0.013 bar), the compartment maintained an 80% nitrogen and 20% oxygen composition via the ECLSS, so providing a shirt-sleeve environment for the flight crew. The compartment was designed to a limit of 16lb/sq in (1.1 bar) and had a volume of 2,325cu ft (65.84m^3) with the airlock inside the compartment, rising to 2,625cu ft (74.33m^3) with the airlock in its alternative position in the payload bay.

The uppermost level of the crew compartment of the orbiter was the flight deck. The work stations for the commander (left) and pilot (right) were located in the forward section of the flight deck, with seats for two mission specialists behind the commander and pilot, farther from the centreline. The flight stations for the commander and the pilot had controls and displays for maintaining autonomous control of the orbiter through all phases of the mission.

To the right side of the aft flight deck was located the mission specialist station, which housed controls and displays for the monitoring of systems, communications management and payload operation management, as well as payload/orbiter interface operations. The payload specialist station was located on the left side of the aft flight deck, and contained controls and displays related to the specific mission payload.

Located between these two aft stations, and looking out to the rear, were the on-orbit pilot and payload-handling stations, which remained unoccupied during launch and re-entry phases. With visibility provided by the aft and overhead windows, the rear stations contained displays and controls for moving the orbiter during terminal phase rendezvous, stationkeeping and docking manoeuvres, and payload deployment and retrieval. The area of the forward flight deck, including the 5.2sq ft (0.48m^2) centre console and seats, was about 24sq ft (2.23m^2), the side console and displays adding another 3.5sq ft (0.325m^2). The area of the aft flight deck was 40sq ft (3.72m^2).

Over 2,000 separate displays and controls were located on the flight deck of the orbiter, these including toggle switches, circuit breakers, rotary switches, push buttons, thumbwheels, metered and mechanical readouts, and separate indication lights. These displays and controls available to the Shuttle crew represented about three times more than those on board the Apollo Command Module in the 1960s and early 1970s. The flight deck was arranged in the typical pilot/co-pilot configuration which allowed piloting of the vehicle from either station, and the controls were located so that a one-person emergency return was feasible. Each seat was provided with full manual flight controls, including rotational and translational hand controllers, rudder pedals, speed brake controls and facilities for the HUD (Heads Up Display) system.

At the payload-handling section of the on-orbit station, several displays and controls were located for the manipulation, release and capture of payloads. Also at this station were the displays and controls for the payload bay doors, radiators, RMS system, payload bay lights and TV cameras. Two closed-circuit TV monitors provided video pictures for payload-handling activities.

At the rendezvous and docking station were located the displays and controls needed for orbiter attitude and translation manoeuvres during terminal phase rendezvous and docking. Rendezvous radar displays and controls, pitch and roll cross-pointer displays for angles and rates were also found here, as well as rotational and translational hand controllers, flight control mode switches, and attitude direction indicators.

Located aft of the pilot's station on the right side of the orbiter, the mission station contained the displays and controls necessary for orbiter-to-payload interfaces and the subsystems of payloads. To provide the flight crew with adequate information on critical malfunctions detected in the payload systems, the station also housed an auxiliary caution and warning display. Orbiter subsystems which did not require immediate access for on-orbit housekeeping were managed from this station, which also featured a CRT (Cathode Ray Tube) screen and keyboard designed for the monitoring of payloads and orbiter subsystems. In addition, for the periods during the ascent and descent trajectories when the crew were strapped to their seats, payload conditions were displayed at the forward flight station by caution and warning as well as TV display means.

The seats used on the Shuttle were of two distinct types, the flight crew seats and the removable mission/payload specialist seats. Minimum crew complement on a normal Shuttle flight was two, but usually numbered between five and seven. *Challenger* was the first to fly an eight-person crew, and had in a rescue mode the capacity for 10 persons including either eight rescued astronauts, or eight passengers for a space station transfer accommodated for short periods by removal of the sleep stations in the mid-deck section.

The flight crew seats occupied by the commander and pilot were located at the forward position on the flight deck and were not removable during a mission. They were, however, adjustable fore and aft, up and down, and provided support for vertical launch and horizontal flight.

The specialist seats were not adjustable, but could be removed during the orbital phase of the mission and stowed to provide more habitable volume. Two specialist seats were usually carried on the flight deck: the first (located between and just behind the flight crew) was occupied by the MS designated as 'Flight Engineer' on the mission to assist and monitor the flight crew during launch and re-entry, but able to provide no active input in flight control of the vehicle. Two more such seats were located on the mid-deck just in front of the airlock, with the seventh adjacent to the mid-deck entry/exit hatch. If the sleep stations on the mid-deck were removed, three further seats could be located in that area. Each specialist seat measured 25.5in (64.8cm) in length, 15.5in (39.4cm) in width and 11in (27.9cm) in folded height.

As with each orbiter vehicle, *Challenger* had a total of 12 windows in the crew pressurized section (10 on the flight deck), these providing visibility for on-orbit, re-entry and landing. During the atmospheric phase of the mission the flight crew required visibility forward, left and right. During on-orbit operations these same windows were frequently used, while the aft-located windows were used for payload monitoring, rendezvous and docking manoeuvres, and payload handling.

Located directly beneath the flight deck, as on all orbiters, was the mid-deck, to which the crew gained access by two interdeck openings each measuring 26×28in (66.0×71.1cm) on the aft floor of the flight deck. For 1-g access a ladder was attached to the left interdeck access for easy passage between decks. This area of the orbiter was used for

Right: The forward flight deck of the orbiter. Notable are the flight computer and navigation aids console (between the seats) and three CRTs for data-display.

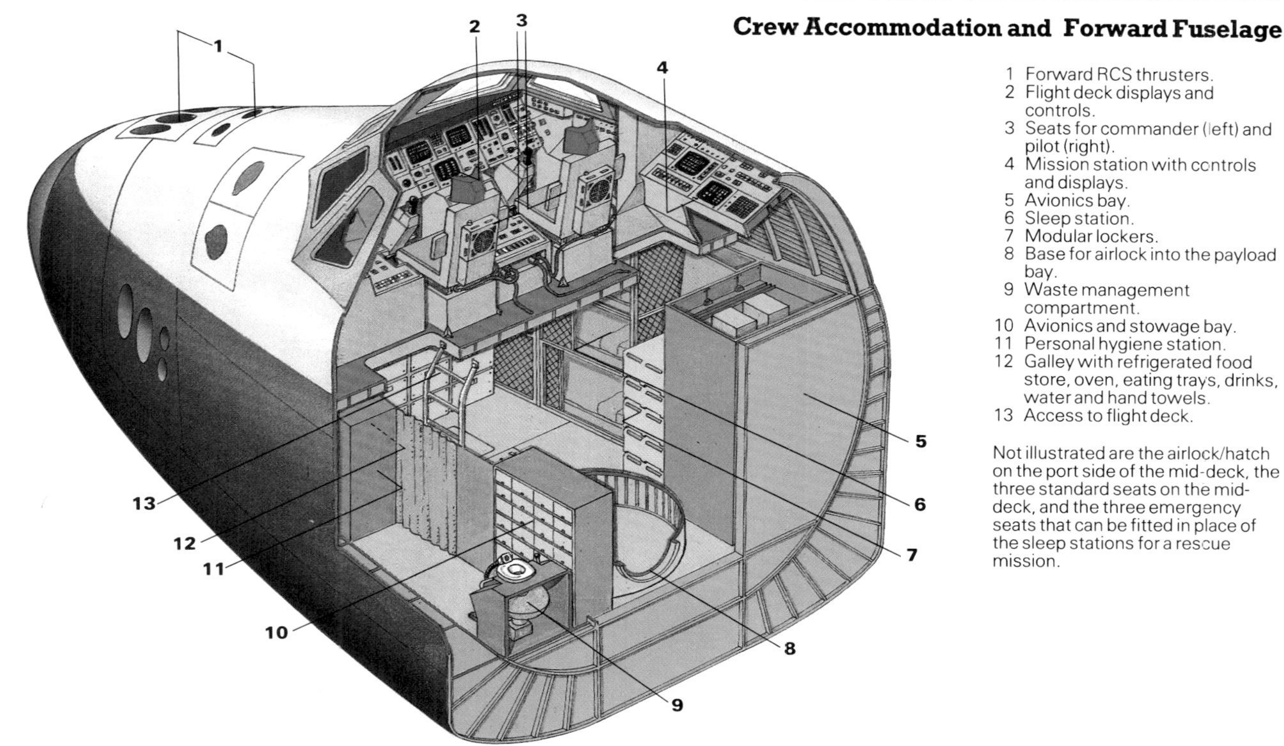

Crew Accommodation and Forward Fuselage

1 Forward RCS thrusters.
2 Flight deck displays and controls.
3 Seats for commander (left) and pilot (right).
4 Mission station with controls and displays.
5 Avionics bay.
6 Sleep station.
7 Modular lockers.
8 Base for airlock into the payload bay.
9 Waste management compartment.
10 Avionics and stowage bay.
11 Personal hygiene station.
12 Galley with refrigerated food store, oven, eating trays, drinks, water and hand towels.
13 Access to flight deck.

Not illustrated are the airlock/hatch on the port side of the mid-deck, the three standard seats on the mid-deck, and the three emergency seats that can be fitted in place of the sleep stations for a rescue mission.

on-orbit crew habitation, and also provided extra seating spaces for a maximum of six crew members.

The mid-deck area also housed three avionics equipment bays. The two forward bays occupied the complete width of the cabin and extended into the mid-deck 39in (99cm) from the forward bulkhead. The aft bay extended into the mid-deck 39in (99cm) from the aft bulkhead on the right side of the centrally located airlock. The side hatch (through which pre-launch entry to and post-landing exit from the orbiter were made) was located just forward of the waste management system on the left of the mid-deck. Completely stripped, the mid-deck area was 160sq ft (14.86m^2), while the gross mobility area was about 100sq ft (9.29m^2). The area was used for major stowage and crew living.

The side hatch, used for normal entry and exit of the orbiter, could be opened from inside or outside the vehicle. The assembly was attached to the cabin tunnel by hinges, a torque tube and support fittings, and was capable of opening outwards 90°. The hatch measured 40in (1.016m) in diameter, and included a 10in (25.4cm) three-pane glass viewing window. The hatch seal provided a pressure shell which was compressed by the latch mechanisms when closed, and a thermal barrier of Inconel wire mesh spring with a ceramic fibre braided sleeve was installed between the Reusable Surface Insulation (RSI) on the forward fuselage and the hatch. The hatch weighed 294lb (129kg).

The mid-deck area of the orbiter provided a stowage volume of 140cu ft (3.96m^3) and included stowage lockers which were used for storing flight crew personal gear, mission-necessary equipment and experiments, and were constructed of composite-structure panels (a sandwich of Kevlar/epoxy on a non-metallic core) to save weight. There were 42 identical boxes measuring 11×18×21in (27.9×45.7×53.3cm) available for stowage. In addition, provision was made in this area for dining, sleeping, maintenance, exercising, hygiene and data management.

The floor of the mid-deck contained removable panels providing access to the ECLSS equipment, changeable lithium hydoxide canisters, and waste stowage, while an opening in the ceiling provided access to the IMU (Inertial Measurement Unit) equipment.

The orbiter galley was also located in the mid-deck area and, with potable water provided as a byproduct of the fuel cells, the food and facilities carried were enough to support a crew ranging in size from two for one day to seven for 30 days, depending on requirements. The galley was a removable system that was not a mission requirement as food warmers, food trays etc could be carried. The galley provided food preparation facilities, stowage and food trays with facilities for oven inserts etc. It also contained a trash stowage area and a food oven which heated a meal for seven in about 90 minutes with a heating range of 145° to 185°F (62° to 85°C). On the side of the galley was the personal hygiene section, which included facilities for washing, shaving etc through water and soap dispensers, and had the facilities for holding towels and other equipment whilst in use.

In the area immediately aft of the mid-deck hatch was the waste collection system, located in an area 29in (73.7cm) wide. The unit measured 27×27×29in (68.6×68.6×73.7cm) and included two major independent and interconnected assemblies to deal with the collection, processing and storage or disposal of liquid and solid human waste products. This waste-collection system also included provision for dealing with perspiration and lung vapour in the atmosphere, as well as liquid waste from the galley and used EMUs, with solid waste of tissues etc also handled by these systems.

The opposite side of the mid-deck housed the main sleeping stations, which were 84in (2.13m) long but varied in width from 22 to 30in (55.9 to 76.2cm) tapering towards the front of the crew compartment. Sleeping bags, eye shades, ear muffs and restraints were also available, and the location of the restraints could be varied depending on the desires of the crew.

The largest item in the mid-deck area was the airlock, which allowed movement into and out of the payload bay by an EVA crewmember and, through the same hatch, into tunnels leading to the Spacelab modules. The airlock was used for inactive storage of EVA EMU equipment and for extra storage during the mission.

With an inside diameter of 63in (1.60m) and a length of 83in (2.11m), the airlock contained two 40in (1.016m) diameter D-shaped openings, 36in (0.914m) across, and two pressure sealing hatches and airlock support equipment. Volume was 150cu ft (4.25m^3), sufficient to contain two fully suited crew members. The hatches sealed the EVA crew from the mid-deck, so allowing direct exit into the payload bay for EVA activities. Airlock pressurization was controlled from inside the airlock or from the crew cabin, whilst depressurization was controlled from inside only. The hatches were designed to open towards the primary pressure source, the orbiter crew cabin, to assist sealing while closing. Each hatch contained a 4in (10.16cm) diameter viewing window constructed of dual panes of polycarbonate plastic mounted directly to the hatch with bolts through the panes. The primary structure of the airlock was of machined aluminium sections welded together to form a cylinder with hatch mounting flanges. The upper cylindrical aluminium section and the bulkheads were made of nonvented aluminium sections. The two semi-cylindrical aluminium sections were welded to the airlock primary structure to house the ECLSS and avionics support equipment. Three feedthrough plates on each section contained plumbing and cable routing from the orbiter to support the airlock subsystems. The airlock was designed to depressurize a volume of 133cu ft (3.77m^3) containing two suited crew members at 620 pascals/second in six minutes. Four depressurization modes were available (one normal, two emergency due to time constraints, and one rescue), and three EVA periods were available (two planned, one contingency) on each flight. The airlock could also be located outside the mid-deck in the payload bay, with or without the docking module/tunnel configurations.

Mid-fuselage

On October 15, 1976 the mid-fuselage for STA-099 arrived at Palmdale for integration with the rest of the vehicle's components for the structural test programme. Following the completion of the test programme preparations for the modifications to the mid-fuselage were begun on January 28, 1980, just six years to the day before the loss of the vehicle in a midair explosion.

Left: Flight deck scene during simulator training for 51-L, showing the fairly spacious launch positions for Michael Smith, Ellison Onizuka, Judith Resnik and Dick Scobee.

The mid-fuselage of the orbiter was joined to the forward fuselage, aft fuselage and wings, and was designed to support the payload bay doors and its associated systems, as well as the forward wing glove, and as such formed the payload bay area. Primarily an aluminium structure, it measured 60ft (18.29m) in length, 17ft (5.18m) in width and 13ft (3.96m) in height, and weighed approximately 13,502lb (6,125kg). Both the forward and aft ends were open, with reinforced skin and longerons interfacing with the bulkheads of the forward and aft fuselage.

The mid-fuselage skins were integrally machined by numerical control. The panels above both wing gloves and the wings for the forward eight bays had longitudinal T-stringers. The five aft bays had aluminium honeycomb panels, whilst the side skins in the shadow of the wing were also machined under numerical control but also had vertical stiffeners. The stabilization of the mid-fuselage was provided by 12 main frame assemblies consisting of both vertical and horizontal elements. The side elements were machined, whereas the horizontal elements were boron/aluminium tubes with bonded titanium end fittings, which provided a substantial weight reduction of about 49%, some 305lb (138kg).

The sill and door longerons formed the upper portion of the mid-fuselage, with the machined sill longerons constituting the primary body elements as well as absorbing the longitudinal loads from payloads in the payload bay. Attached to the longerons and associated structures were 13 payload bay door hinges on each side. These provided for the vertical reaction from the payload bay doors, and five of these hinges also reacted with the payload bay door shears. The sill longeron also provided supports and locations for the stowed RMS, the Ku-band rendezvous antenna and associated equipment. The side wall forward of the wing carrythrough structure also provided inboard support for the main landing gear, with the total lateral landing gear loads reacted by the mid-fuselage structure. The mid-fuselage also provided support for two electrical wire trays, containing wiring between the crew compartment and aft fuselage.

Payloads carried in the orbiter were classified as non-deployable or deployable, and were secured in a variety of ways. Non-deployable payloads were retained by passive retention devices, and those classed as deployable were secured by motor-driven active retention devices. Designed to provide three-axis support for a maximum five payloads of considerable size, the orbiter payload retention system was capable of securing payloads with the orbiter in either the vertical or horizontal mode.

Payload attachment points were located at 3.933in (0.99cm) distances along both longerons and the bottom centreline. Longeron attachment points totalled 172, with only 124 available as the other 48 were too close to orbiter hardware. Only 116 of the 124 points could be used for deployable payloads. Along the centreline a total of 89 attachment points was available, of which 75 could be used for deployable payloads. Totals of 13 bridges per side and 12 keel bridges were available per flight, but only the required structures were flown as mission requirements dictated. Longeron bridge fittings were attached to the payload bay frame at the longeron level at the side of the bay. Keel bridge fittings were attached to the payload bay frame at the bottom of the payload bay. Payload trunnions were the portion of the payload which interfaced with the payload bay and varied in size according to their location in the bay.

Orbiter/payload attachments were the trunnion/bearing/journal type, with split, self-aligning bearings for non-released payloads, and electric motor-driven hinged half-released latches for deployable payloads. Payload guides and scuff plates were used to assist in the deploying or berthing of payloads.

Some payloads were not attached directly to the orbiter, but rather the payload carriers for such payloads as IUS, Spacelab pallets, experiments etc.

Payload bay doors

On May 26, 1977 the aft payload bay doors for STA-099 arrived at Palmdale, followed by the forward doors on July 22. On December 7, 1979, after completion of the STA programme, the doors were demated from *Challenger* for rework to orbital certification. By January 25, 1980 the doors had arrived at Rockwell, Tulsa for rework operations, and were delivered for configuration on *Challenger* on July 10 1981.

The payload doors of *Challenger* consisted of a left-hand and a right-hand door assembly, which were hinged at each side of the mid-fuselage and latched mechanically at the forward and aft fuselage and split top centreline. The doors constituted protection during launch and re-entry phases of the mission, provided an opening for payload deployment and retrieval, and served as supports for the orbiter radiators.

Each door measured 60ft (18.29m) in length and was constructed of five segments interconnected by expansion joints. Each half-door had a chord of some 10ft (3.05m) and a diameter of 15ft (4.57m), with a surface area of 1,600sq ft (148.6m^2). The doors were constructed from subassemblies consisting of graphite/epoxy honeycomb sandwich panels, solid graphite/epoxy laminate frames, expansion joint frames, torque boxes, seal depressors, centreline beam intercostals, gussets, end fittings and clips. The use of graphite/epoxy reduced weight by 23% compared with aluminium honeycomb sandwich, resulting in a weight saving of 900lb (408kg) to 3,264lb (1,481kg) and making the doors the largest aerospace structure constructed from a composite material. The assembly also included 2024 aluminium shear pins, titanium fittings and Inconel 718 floating and shear hinges, joined by mechanical fasteners. In addition a protection measure against lightning was provided by bonding aluminium mesh wire to the outer skin.

Handholds and slidewires for EVA were attached in the torque box area, and the doors had the capacity for manual closing in the event of an emergency situation. The doors were also covered by Felt Reusable Surface Insulation (FRSI) thermal protection. The port (left-hand) door with attached systems weighed about 2,375lb (1,077kg), whilst the starboard (right-hand) door weighed some 2,535lb (1,150kg), the weight difference being attributable to the fact that the starboard door contained the centreline latch active mechanism. Each door's weight was also increased by 833lb (378kg) by the radiators.

When closed, the doors were locked by 16 bulkhead latches (eight aft and eight forward) and 16 centreline latches, each in groups of four latch mechanisms. Each door hinged on 13 (five shear and eight idler) Inconel 718 external hinges. The lower half of each hinge was attached to the mid-fuselage sill longeron, the hinges rotating on bearings with dual rotational surfaces.

On the forward 30ft (9.14m) sections of both doors deployable radiators were housed. These were hinged and latched to the inner surface of the doors, and exposed Freon-21 coolant loops from both sides of their panels when the doors were open. The capacity not to deploy the radiators (and thus radiate excess heat from only one side of the panel) was also available. In addition kitted, fixed panels could be added to the aft portions of the doors when required by specific mission requirements. The starboard door was always opened first and closed last, a sequence determined by the arrangement of the centreline latch mechanism and seal overlap.

Aft fuselage

On January 6, 1975 work began on the first major element of what became the *Challenger* Shuttle when long-lead

The Orbiter Vehicle

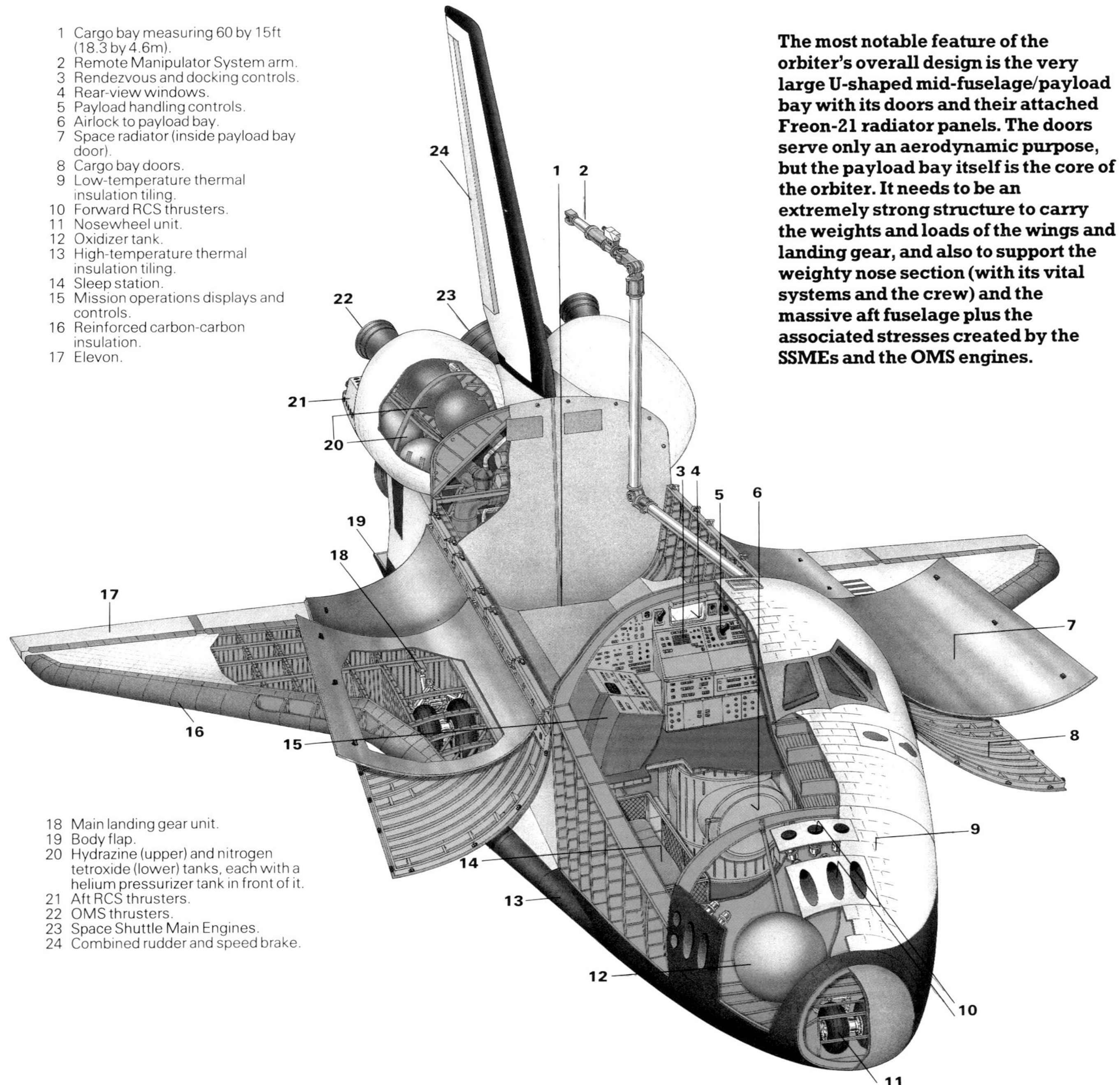

The most notable feature of the orbiter's overall design is the very large U-shaped mid-fuselage/payload bay with its doors and their attached Freon-21 radiator panels. The doors serve only an aerodynamic purpose, but the payload bay itself is the core of the orbiter. It needs to be an extremely strong structure to carry the weights and loads of the wings and landing gear, and also to support the weighty nose section (with its vital systems and the crew) and the massive aft fuselage plus the associated stresses created by the SSMEs and the OMS engines.

fabrication for the aft fuselage of STA-099 was started. On June 14, 1976 the assembly of the aft fuselage began, and on completion this was shipped to Palmdale on January 25, 1977. Following the completion of the STA programme the aft fuselage was demated by February 1, 1980 at Palmdale. The necessary rework on the construction was completed by December 12 of that same year, and was on dock at Palmdale on July 21, 1981 to be reinstalled on *Challenger*.

The aft fuselage of the Shuttle was designed to support and interface with the left- and right-hand OMS/RCS pods, the wing aft spar, the mid-fuselage, the orbiter/ET rear attachments, the SSMEs, the body flap, the vertical tail and the two launch umbilical panels. Constructed of an outer shell, a thrust structure and an internal secondary structure, the component measured 18ft (5.49m) in length, 22ft (6.71m) in width and 20ft (6.10m) in height.

Its design incorporated the design load path to the mid-fuselage main longerons, main wing spar continuity across its forward bulkhead, structural support for the body flap and vertical tail, and structural housing around all internal systems for protection from thermal, pressure and acoustic environments as well as controlled internal pressures during the flight.

The forward bulkhead of the aft structure was designed to close off the aft fuselage from the mid-fuselage, and was constructed of machined and beaded sheet aluminium segments. The upper portion of the bulkhead was attached to the front spar of the vertical tail.

The internal thrust structure's primary purpose was to support the three SSMEs, the upper section supporting the uppermost engine (No. 1) and the lower section the remaining two engines (Nos. 2 and 3). This structure included the three SSMEs' load reaction truss structures, engine interface fittings and the actuator support structure. It also supported the SSMEs' low-pressure turbopumps and propellant lines from the ET. The two aft Orbiter/ET attachment points were located at the longeron fittings beneath the structure.

The thrust structure was built of 28 machined, diffusion-bonded truss members, in which titanium strips were bonded together under heat, pressure and time in a process which fused the strips into a single, hollow, homogeneous mass both lighter and stronger than a forged unit and also lacking any weld lines. In selected areas the titanium construction was reinforced with boron/epoxy tubular struts to minimize weight by 21% or 900lb (408kg), while also increasing stiffness to a useful degree.

The upper thrust structure of the aft fuselage was constructed of integral machined aluminium with aluminium frames, except for the vertical fin support frame which was titanium. The skin panels were integrally machined aluminium and were attached to each side of the vertical fin to reduce drag and torsion loading. The outer shell of the structure was also built of integral machined aluminium, with access to installed systems provided in the shell.

The secondary structure was of conventional aluminium construction, except for titanium and fibreglass used in some thermal isolation of equipment. The aft fuselage secondary support consisted of brackets, built-up webs, truss members and machined fittings as determined by system loading and support constraints. Avionics shelves were shock-mounted to the structure, and provision was also made for other system components such as the APUs, hydraulics, ammonia boiler, flash evaporator and electrical wire runs.

Above: Most evident on the rear face of the aft fuselage are the holes for the three SSMEs. Not evident is the internal thrust structure.

Two umbilical areas interfaced with the ET's two aft attachment points for LO and LH feed lines as well as electrical wire runs. Following SSME cut-off, the umbilicals were retracted and closed off after ET separation by means of an electromechanically-operated beryllium door over the umbilical areas, which were sealed by thermal barriers. The exposed areas of the doors were covered by RSI thermal protection systems.

The heat shield and appropriate seal provided the base of the orbiter. The aft heat shield consisted of a base shield of machined aluminium, attached to which were domes of honeycombed construction supporting the flexible and sliding seal assemblies. The engine-mounted heat shield was of Inconel honeycomb construction which was removable for access to the SSME power heads. Except for the Inconel segments, the shield was covered with reusable surface insulation, as were all exposed areas of the aft fuselage.

Body flap

The body flap for the *Challenger* arrived on dock at Palmdale on May 31, 1977, and after the STA programme was demated by December 14, 1979 for rework, returning to Downey on January 25, 1980.

On September 1, 1980 modifications to the body flap were begun. The modifications were completed by July 17 and the unit was placed on dock at Palmdale on July 24, 1981 for final installation activities.

Designed to provide thermal shielding for the three SSMEs during re-entry, the hydraulically-actuated body flap also provided the orbiter with pitch control trim during the atmospheric flight phase following re-entry. Constructed of aluminium and covered with RSI, the body flap consisted of ribs, spars, skin panels and a trailing-edge assembly. The main upper and lower forward honeycomb skin panels were joined to the ribs, spars, and honeycomb trailing edge with structural fasteners. The structure was completed with removable honeycomb upper forward skin panels.

Vertical tail

The final assembly of the vertical tail began on October 1, 1976, the structure being delivered on dock at Palmdale on April 6, 1977. It was mated to STA-099 on September 30, 1977 and, after the structural test programme, was demated and delivered back to Fairchild New York on January 18, 1980 for rework. It was on dock at Palmdale again on March 26, 1981 for mating to *Challenger*.

Below: The aft fuselage also supports the vertical stabilizer (fin and rudder/speed brake) which must withstand great aerodynamic loads.

The vertical tail consisted of a structural fin surface, the rudder/speed brake surface, a tip and a lower trailing edge. The rudder split vertically into two halves to serve as a speed brake during the landing phase.

The structural fin and moving rudder/speed brake were made of aluminium, the main torque box being built up of integral machined skins and stringers, ribs and two machined spars. The fin was attached at the root of the front spar to the forward bulkhead of the aft fuselage by two tension tie bolts, and at the root of the rear spar to the upper structural surface of the aft fuselage by eight shear bolts.

The hydraulic power drive unit/mechanical rotary actuation system operated left and right drive shafts in the same direction for rudder control of ±27.1°. For speed-brake control, the drive shafts turned in opposite directions to a maximum of 49.3° each. The rotary drive actions were also combined for joint rudder/speed brake control. The hydraulic power drive unit was controlled by the orbiter's flight-control system, and a maximum deflection rate of 10° per second was available.

The vertical tail was designed for a 163dB acoustic environment and a maximum temperature of 350°F (176°C). An Inconel honeycomb conical seal housed the rotary actuators and provided a pressure and thermal seal capable of withstanding a maximum temperature of 1,200°F (648°C). The split halves of the rudder panels and the trailing edge contained a thermal barrier seal, and the vertical tail and rudder/speed brake were covered with RSI materials. A thermal barrier was also employed at the interface of the vertical tail and aft fuselage.

Wings

The final assembly of the STA-099 wings began at the prime contractor on October 1, 1976, and the units arrived on dock at Palmdale on March 16, 1977. Following the completion of the STA programme, the elevons were demated on December 21, 1979 and returned to the prime contractor for rework on February 1, 1980. Three days later the preparations for wing modifications were started, this part of the programme being completed by November 21 of the same year. By March 30, 1981 the rework on the elevons had been completed at Palmdale, and these units were installed on *Challenger*'s wings.

The wings of the Shuttle provided an aerodynamic surface that gave lift and control for the orbiter during the landing phases of the mission. The left and right wings consisted of the forward wing box and wing glove, the intermediate section which incorporated the main landing gear well, the torque box, the forward spar for the mounting of the reinforced carbon-carbon leading-edge structure TPS, the wing/elevon interface, the elevon seal panels and the elevons. Constructed of conventional aluminium alloy with a multi-rib and spar arrangement, the unit had stringer-stiffened skin covers or honeycomb skin covers. Each wing measured approximately 60ft (18.29m) in length at the fuselage intersection, with a maximum thickness of 5ft (1.52m).

The forward wing glove was designed for the aerodynamic blending of the wing leading edge into the mid-fuselage wing glove as an extension of the basic wing construction. The forward wing box was constructed to a conventional design of aluminium multi-ribs, aluminium tubes and tubular struts. The upper and lower wing skin panels were constructed from stiffened aluminium, the leading-edge spar being of corrugated aluminium construction. The intermediate wing section was also constructed of conventional aluminium multi-ribs and aluminium tubes. Both the upper and lower skin covers were of aluminium honeycomb, a portion of the lower wing surface skin panels being made up of the main landing gear door surfaces. This section housed the main landing gear units and absorbed some of the loads generated by that system in operation. A structural rib supported the outboard main landing gear door hinges and the leg's trunnion and drag link, whilst support for the inboard link was provided by the mid-fuselage. The doors were of conventional aluminium honeycomb configuration.

Right: The nosewheel guidance system caused some trouble during earlier Shuttle missions. An updated system was first used for the 61-A landing.

To minimize thermal loads the four major spars of the wing were fabricated of corrugated aluminium. The forward spar provided the attachment for the TPS reinforced carbon-carbon leading-edge structure. The rear spar provided attachment surfaces for the elevons, hinged upper seal panels and relevant hydraulic and electrical subsystems components. The upper and lower wing skin panels were made up of aluminium stiffened skins.

Elevons provided the vehicle with flight control during atmospheric flight. Designed as a two-piece unit on each wing, they were made from conventional aluminium multi-ribbed and beam components with aluminium honeycomb skins for compatibility with thermal and acoustic conditions. The elevons comprised two sections per wing, supported by three hinges per segment. Attachment to the flight-control system was effected by hydraulic actuators along the forward extremity of each elevon, all hinge movements being reacted at these points. Each elevon could move through an arc from 40° up to 25° down. The transition area on the upper surfaces between the torque box and elevons consisted of a series of hinged panels which provided a closeout of the wing-to-elevon cavity. The panels were built of Inconel honeycomb sandwich on the outer surfaces and titanium honeycomb sandwich inboard. In addition, the upper leading edge of each elevon incorporated titanium honeycomb rub strips (not covered by TPS) to provide a sealing surface area for the elevon seal panels.

Exposed areas of the wings, main landing gear doors and elevons were covered with the TPS RSI materials, the sole exception being the elevon seal panels. Thermal seals were provided on the elevon lower cover area, with thermal spring seals on the upper rub panels. On the main landing gear doors pressure seals and thermal barriers were incorporated.

Attached to the fuselage with a tension bolt splice along the upper surface, the wings were also attached by a shear splice along the lower surface in the area of the fuselage carrythrough structure, so completing the attachment interface.

Forward RCS Module

1 Electrical disconnect bracket.
2 Primary thrusters (14).
3 Oxidizer tank.
4 Fuel tank.
5 Service well.
6 Vernier thrusters (2).
7 Helium (pressurizer) tank.

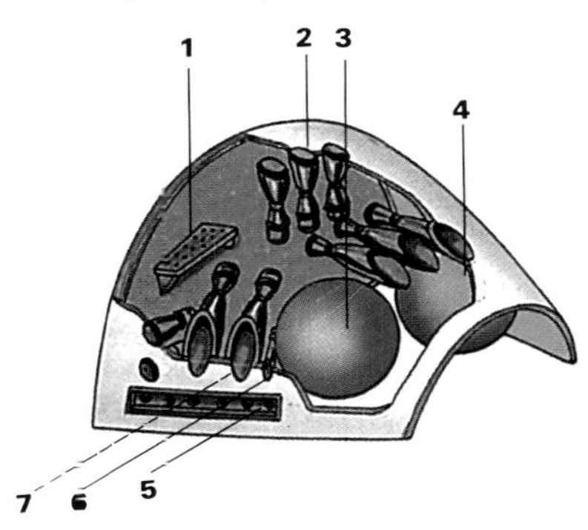

Above: The Reaction Control System is designed to control attitude and adjust velocity in space using 14 small thruster motors and two verniers.

Landing gear

The orbiter's landing gear was of the standard tricycle arrangement used by all modern aircraft, with a steerable nosewheel plus left and right main landing gear units. The system incorporated on each unit a shock strut assembly built of high-strength, stress- and corrosion-resistant steel alloys, aluminium alloys, stainless steel and aluminium bronze. Each unit terminated in two wheel and tyre assemblies, the nose unit being steerable and the main units each incorporating a brake assembly with anti-skid protection.

Each of the four main gear wheels had electro-hydraulic brakes and an anti-skid system. The disc brake assembly consisted of nine discs (four rotors and five stators). The carbon-lined beryllium rotors were splined to the inside of the wheel and rotated with it, while the carbon-lined beryllium stators were splined to the outside of the axle assembly and did not rotate. When brakes were applied, eight hydraulic actuators pressed the discs together to create

Orbital Maneuvering System and Space Shuttle Main Engines

1 6,000lb (2,722kg) thrust OMS rocket.
2 RCS helium tanks.
3 OMS fuel tank.
4 RCS fuel tank.
5 RCS oxidizer tank.
6 OMS oxidizer tank.
7 OMS helium tank.
8 RCS primary thrusters.
9 RCS vernier thrusters.

The detachable RCS pods flanking the SSMEs each contain one OMS engine and 14 RCS engines (12 primary and two vernier) together with 6,320lb (2,868kg) of fuel, 10,338lb (4,689kg) of oxydizer, and helium to pressurize the fuel and oxydizer tanks.

1 LH_2 engine inlet line.
2 LH_2 pre-valve.
3 LO_2 pre-valve.
4 LH_2 supply manifold.
5 LH_2 recirculation.
6 Orbiter/ET LH_2 disconnect.
7 LO_2 supply manifold.
8 Orbiter/ET LO_2 disconnect.
9 LO_2 engine inlet line.
10 Fluid system interface panel.
11 Engine gimbal bearing.
12 Heat shield.
13 SSME no. 3 (right).
14 SSME no. 2 (left).
15 SSME no. 1 (centre).

Propellants from the ET are pumped by low- and high-pressure turbopumps.

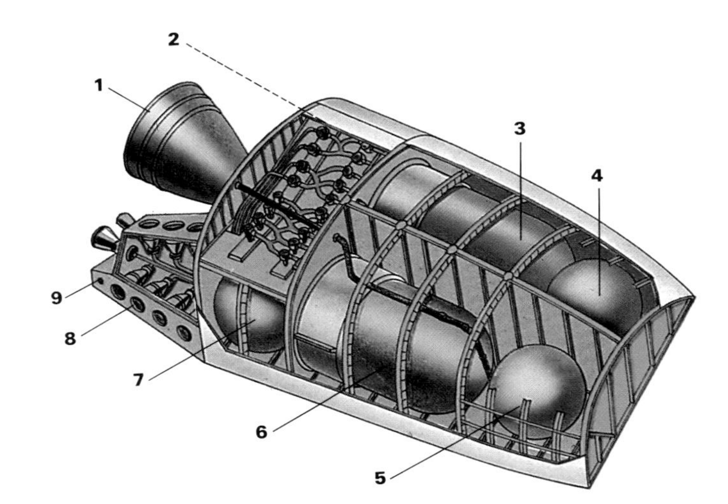

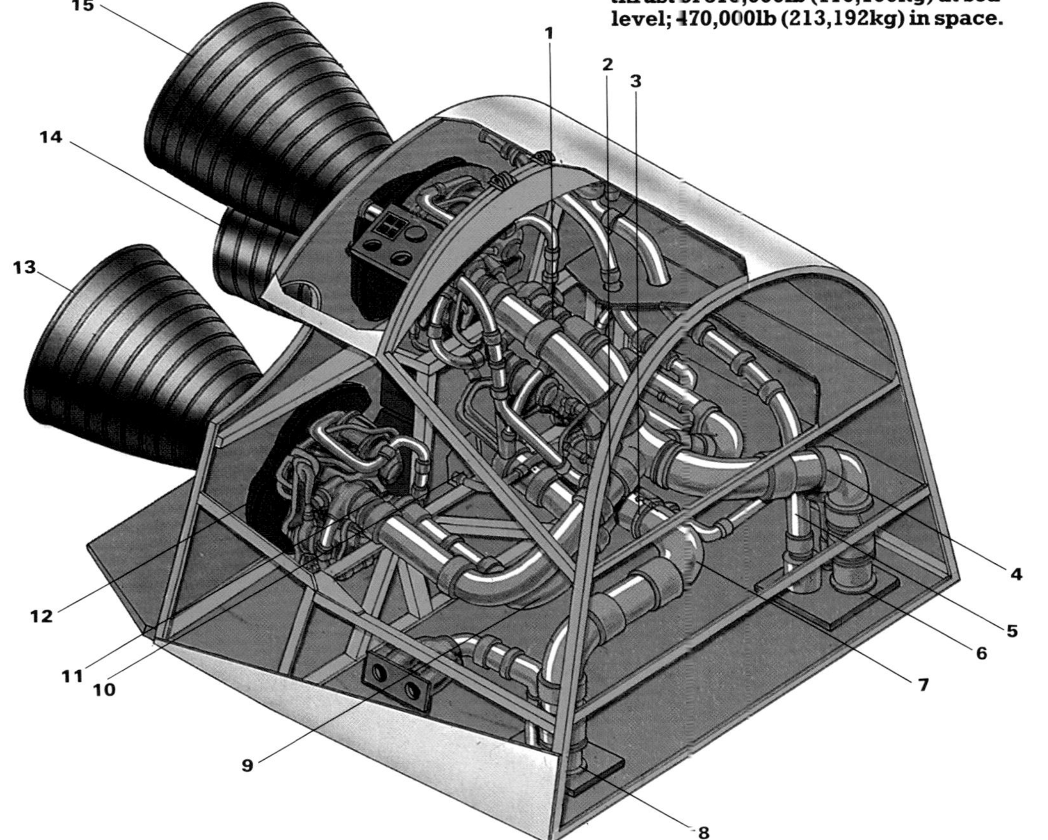

Below: The SSMEs each develop a thrust of 375,000lb (170,100kg) at sea level; 470,000lb (213,192kg) in space.

Above: A shot from *Challenger*'s aft windows captures a lateral RCS firing on Shuttle 6. Also visible is the vacated TRDS satellite support.

Above: SSME No. 2011 is dropped out of *Challenger* during February 1983 after the discovery of a small crack in the engine's combustion chamber manifold.

braking torque to slow the orbiter.

The nosewheel unit was steerable upon landing, by electro-hydraulic automatic commands through the General-Purpose Computer (GPC) and flight-control autoland mode. The gear could also be steered by the commander's or pilot's rudder pedals in control stick steering mode. The doors had High-temperature Reusable Surface Insulation (HRSI) tiles bonded to their outer surfaces and operated mechanically, the gear being deployed by hydraulic pressure at any airspeed below 300kts (556km/h) at the command of the flight crew. Extension took 10 seconds, and the units were extended by gravity (assisted by springs and hydraulic systems) before locking into position.

Forward RCS package

On November 7, 1977 the forward Reaction Control System (RCS) for STA-099 arrived on dock at Palmdale, and was demated by February 8, 1980 following completion of the STA programme. By March 21, 1980 the forward RCS had arrived on dock at Downey for rework to flight standards. On February 2, 1981 installation of the system components started, the package finally arriving at Palmdale on January 31, 1982 for installation in *Challenger*.

Constructed of conventional 2024 aluminium alloy stringers, panels and frames, the package was composed of single curvature, stretch-formed skins with riveted stringers, the frames being riveted to the skin-stringer panels. The forward RCS module was secured to the forward fuselage nose section and forward bulkhead of the fuselage with 16 fasteners to permit removal and re-installation of the system between flights. Components of the RCS were attached to the module forming a separate unit in the nose section.

The orbiter RCS provided thrust for velocity changes along the axis of the orbiter and attitude control (pitch, yaw and roll) during orbital insertion, on-orbit and re-entry phases of the flight. The complete system consisted of three modules totalling 38 bi-propellant primary thrusters and six vernier thrusters, each module being independent and containing its own pressurization system and propellant tanks. One set was located in the nose and the remaining two in the OMS pods.

The forward module provided 14 primary thrusters and two vernier thrusters, the use of multiple primary thrusters facing in each direction providing redundancy for mission safely. The propellants were nitrogen tetroxide (N_2O_4) as the oxidizer and monomethyl hydrazine (MMH) as fuel, with a mixture ratio of 1:6 (oxidizer: fuel), permitting the use of identical tanks for both propellants. The configuration of the internal screen for the forward tank varied from that used in the aft RCS tanks, because of the operational requirements needed from the two systems. The capacity of the tanks was 930lb (422kg) of MMH and 1,488lb (675kg) of N_2O_4. A system of heaters maintained temperatures in the propellant lines and other associated equipment.

Usable propellant quantities for the nose RCS module were 1,369lb (621kg) of N_2O_4 and 856lb (388kg) of MMH. The propellants were sprayed under controlled pressure by the injector into the combustion chamber, where they combined hypergolically to produce hot gases. These gases then expanded and accelerated though the required nozzles to produce a thrust of 870lb (395kg) per primary engine in the required direction and velocity. Primary thrusters were used for normal translation and attitude control, while the vernier thrusters, each developing 24lb (10.9kg) thrust, were employed for fine attitude control and payload positioning, away from plume contamination.

Orbital Maneuvering System

The first set of OMS pods for *Challenger* arrived early 1982 at Palmdale for installation of the TPS. The right-hand pod was delivered on February 15, and the left-hand pod on March 3. Following this activity the pods were transported to KSC on September 3 for installation on *Challenger* for its first mission. As with the SSMEs, the pods were designed for interchanging with other pods on the inventory as flight turnaround activities increased.

The pods were attached to the upper aft fuselage on the left and right sides, and were fabricated primarily of graphite/epoxy composite and aluminium. The dimensions of each pod included a length of 21.8ft (6.65m), and a width of 11.37ft (3.47m) at the after end declining to 8.41ft (2.56m) at the forward end, for a surface area of about 435sq ft (40.4m^2). Housing all OMS and aft RCS propulsion components, the pods were each attached to the aft fuselage with 11 bolts, and were each divided into a OMS housing and a RCS housing. The skin of the pods was of graphite/epoxy honeycomb sandwich, machined aluminium 2124 being used for the forward and aft bulkheads, the aft tank support bulkhead and the floor truss beam. The centreline beam was 2024 aluminium sheet with titanium stiffeners and graphite/epoxy frames. The thrust structure was of conventional 2124 aluminium construction, while the cross braces were of aluminium tubing, the frames of graphite/epoxy, and the attachment fittings at the forward and aft ends of 2124 aluminium; the intermediate fittings were of corrosion-resistant steel. The attached RCS housing, containing the RCS thrusters and associated propellant feed lines, was of aluminium sheet construction, including the flat outer skins, while the curved outer skin panels were of graphite/epoxy honeycomb sandwich construction. Ground access was provided by 24 doors in the skins.

Using the materials selected a weight reduction of 10% or 450lb (204kg) was achieved, the pods being able to withstand 162dB acoustic noise and a temperature range of −170° to +135°F (−112° to +57°C). All exposed areas of the pods were covered with RSI, and pressure/thermal seals were installed on the pod/fuselage interface. Thermal barriers were also used between the RCS thrusters and TPS.

Employed for orbit insertion, on-orbit manoeuvring, transfer, rendezvous and de-orbit, the OMS could provide a velocity change of 1,000ft/sec (305m/sec) with a payload weight of 65,000lb (29,484kg). A total of 23,876lb (10,830kg) of usable propellant was carried in the OMS pods. The propellant system in the OMS pods comprised one high-pressure helium storage bottle; a tank pressurization, regulation and control system; a tank containing 7,433lb (3,372kg) of nitrogen tetroxide, a tank containing 4,505lb (2,043kg) of monomethyl hydrazine, and a pressure-fed regeneratively-cooled rocket engine.

Each engine developed a vacuum thrust of 6,000lb (2,722kg) using a hypergolic propellant combination of nitrogen tetroxide (N_2O_4) and monomethyl hydrazine (MMH), burned at a nominal oxidizer:fuel ratio of 1:65 at a chamber pressure of 125lb/sq in (8.6 bar).

With the capacity of gimballing by electromechanical pitch and yaw actuators at the forward end of the combustion chamber, the engine was designed for 100 missions with a service life of 10 years, and to be capable of sustaining 1,000 starts and 15 hours' cumulative firing. Measuring 77in (1.96m) in length, each engine weighed 260lb (118kg) and had an engine bell extending 80% outside the structure.

Each aft RCS module housed 12 primary and two vernier thrusters, and retained the capability of high-g operation during re-entry. Using similar design and propellant as the nose RCS set, the aft set had 2,905lb (1,318kg) of N_2O_4 and 1,815lb (823kg) of MMH in each of the aft compartments.

Space Shuttle Main Engines

A cluster of three Space Shuttle Main Engines (SSMEs) was located at the rear of the orbiter on the aft fuselage to provide the main propulsion for the launch phase of the mission in conjunction with the twin SRBs. Using liquid oxygen and liquid hydrogen as propellants, the reusable engines provided throttlable capability and variable thrust levels depending on mission requirements. Ignited a few seconds before launch, the SSMEs were fed from the ET and continued to fire for a nominal 8.5 minutes, continuing for some 6 minutes after the SRBs' burn-out and separation. By use of modified airline-type maintenance procedures, the servicing of the engines was possible without removal, most components being replaced as needed by line replaceable units without the need of extensive testing and qualification. The engines were mounted in a one-above-two arrangement, and were capable of replacement between flights as needed.

Using a LO/LH mixture ratio of 6:1 and producing a sea level thrust of 375,000lb (170,100kg) and a vacuum thrust of 470,000lb (213,190kg), the engines could be throttled between 65 and 109% (though this latter figure was never achieved; 104% being recommended as the limit in future). This made possible maximum thrust during the early ascent, a throttledown through the period of maximum dynamic pressure (Max Q) and the sustaining of a limited 3-g acceleration during the closing stages of powered ascent. All three engines were designed to gimbal (in pitch yaw and roll) during firing, allowing fine refinements to the angle of thrust during ascent. Each engine was designed for over 7.5 hours of cumulative firing spread over a life span of 55 starts. Each SSME was 14ft (4.27m) long and 8ft (2.44m) in diameter at the nozzle exit, and weighed 6,900lb (3,130kg).

Orbiter Thermal Protection System

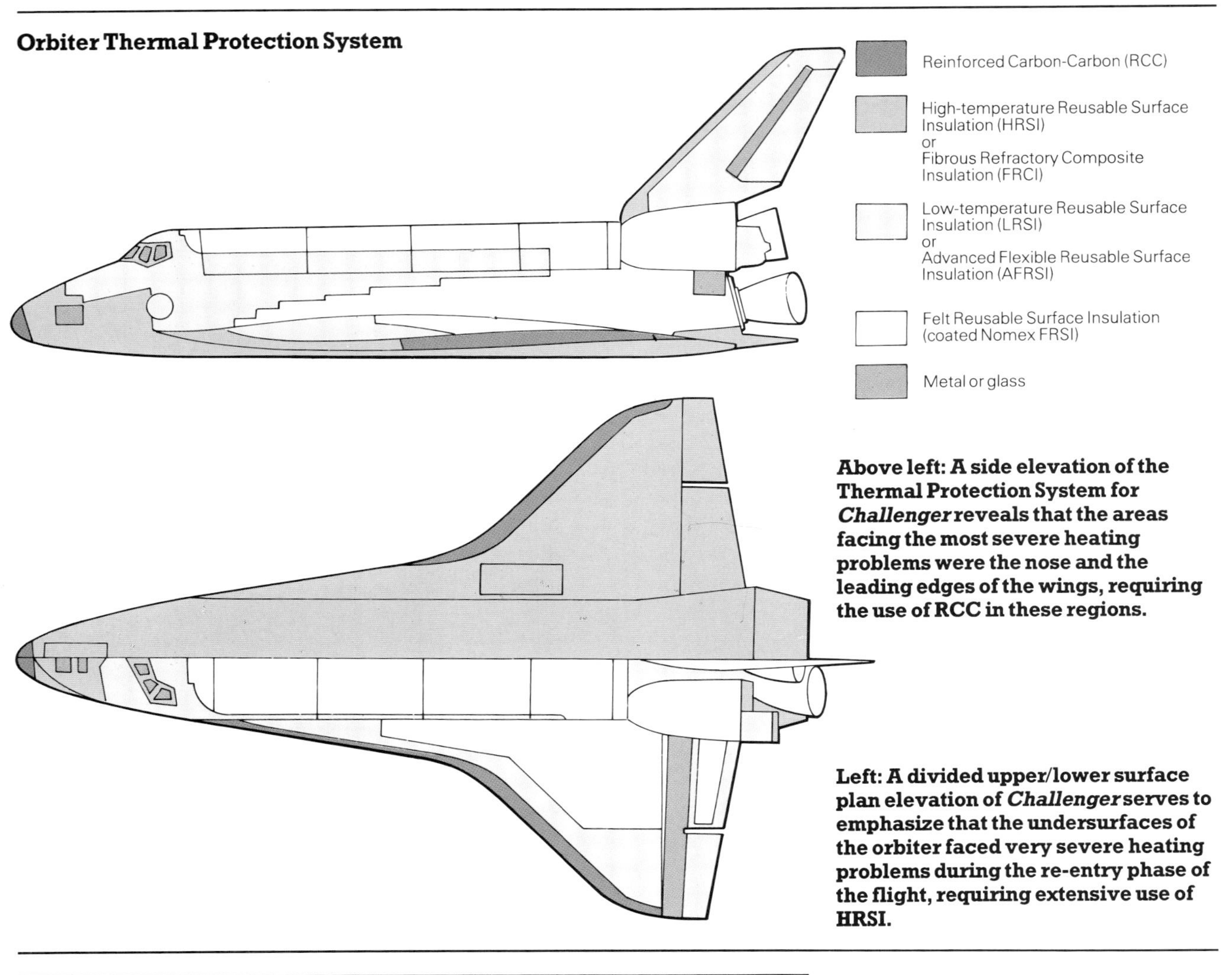

Above left: A side elevation of the Thermal Protection System for *Challenger* reveals that the areas facing the most severe heating problems were the nose and the leading edges of the wings, requiring the use of RCC in these regions.

Left: A divided upper/lower surface plan elevation of *Challenger* serves to emphasize that the undersurfaces of the orbiter faced very severe heating problems during the re-entry phase of the flight, requiring extensive use of HRSI.

Left: In practice the Shuttle's Thermal Protection System worked well, though there were numerous instances of tiles coming off. This shot of the area of the port wing glove illustrates the complexity of fitting and fixing the rigid tiles to a three-dimensional structure.

Fed by flow valves in the engines, the LO and LH entered the system from the ET and, through a complex system of valves and turbopumps, circulated around the engine so that their cryogenic properties could cool the engine. The liquid hydrogen was also used to assist in the cooling of the engine through the nozzle loops, and was routed to drive the turbine for the low-pressure turbine; it additionally cooled the preburners, hot-gas manifold and main injector. The LO was also used in part to drive high-pressure oxidizer turbines and then routed back into the main flow system.

Spark igniters (in the dome of both preburners and in the main chamber) were used to initiate combustion, the gases and steam from this action again being used to drive components of the engine system. The gases then passed through the hot-gas manifold and into the main ejector, where the combined thrust was directed down and out of the nozzle providing the required thrust for launch.

Thermal protection system

One of the major areas of importance in the Shuttle programme, to ensure economic system reusability, was adequate thermal protection of the orbiter vehicle, which experienced a wide variety of thermal and aerodynamic environments during every mission. Designed to protect the surfaces of the orbiter during all stages of the mission, the Thermal Protection System (TPS) was also designed to require a minimum of ground refurbishment and attention between missions. The TPS was intended to protect the aluminium and graphite epoxy skin of the orbiter proper to a nominal value of 350°F (177°C) during ascent and re-entry. Maximum surface temperature could vary from 2,750°F (1,510°C) on the wing leading edge during re-entry to less than 600°F (316°C) on the upper fuselage. In addition the TPS had to withstand the extremes of intense heat, deep cold and heat again as the vehicle ascended into and descended from orbit, and to react to mechanical forces induced by the airframe as it responded to the environment. The system was designed to withstand 100 ascents and re-entries with the minimum refurbishment or maintenance.

Despite several early problems with the TPS system, it proved a reliable system of protection for the Shuttle. Though not as long-wearing as first planned, the system adopted on *Challenger* differed from those of the first orbiter *Columbia* and of the later vehicles (*Discovery* and *Atlantis*). This section deals with the TPS attached to *Challenger*. The TPS consisted of material attached to the exterior of the orbiter's skin to maintain airframe temperature within design limits whilst internal temperatures were maintained by a system of heaters, internal insulation and purging facilities.

Felt Reusable Surface Insulation (FRSI) of coated Nomex was used where temperatures were less than 700°F (371°C), and as such was used on the upper part of the payload bay doors, the mid and aft fuselage sides, the upper surface of the wing, and sections of the OMS pods. Low-temperature Reusable Surface Insulation (LRSI) tiles were used where temperatures between 700°F (371°C) and 1,200°F (649°C) were expected and were attached to the lower portions of the payload bay doors; the forward, mid and aft fuselage, the outer portions of the wing upper surface, and the vertical tail. These tiles had a white surface coating to provide better on-orbit thermal characteristics. On *Challenger*, in addition to the LRSI tiles on the OMS pods the orbiter carried a sewn composite blanket (Advanced Flexible Reusable Surface Insulation, or AFRSI), a quilted fabric blanket that improved durability as well as reducing production costs and installation time, and improving weight-reduction targets. High-temperature Reusable Surface Insulation (HRSI) tiles were used on areas where temperatures between 1,200°F (649°C) and 2,300°F (1,260°C) were expected, such as the forward fuselage, lower mid-fuselage, under side of the wing, selected areas of the vertical tail, portions of the OMS pods, and around the forward windows. The HRSI weighed 9lb/cu ft (4kg/m^3), and was used in all these areas except the landing gear doors, nosecap interface, wing leading edge, reinforced carbon-carbon/HRSI interface, vertical stabilizer leading edge and umbilical/vent doors. These areas incorporated HRSI tiles of 22lb/cu ft (9.9kg/m^3) density, and distinguishable by their black coating for maximum emittance during re-entry. As these denser tiles needed replacement *Challenger* was fitted with Fibrous Refractory Composite Insulation (FRCI) HRSI tiles. These FRCI-12 tiles had a density of 12lb/cu ft (5.4kg/m^3) with improved strength and resistance to coating cracking, as well as providing further weight reductions. For the wing leading edges and nose insulation, where temperatures

Left: A shot looking aft along the mid-fuselage reveals white LRSI and black HRSI tiles, with a number yet to be fitted. Tiles were bonded to the orbiter structure but not to each other, the inter-tile gaps being filled with a special agent. The payload bay doors were Nomex-coated.

exceeded 2,300°F (1,260°C), Reinforced Carbon-Carbon (RCC) was employed. The same material was also used in the forward orbiter/ET structural attachment point on *Challenger*.

In addition, thermal panes were used on all forward windows and the mid-deck hatch window, metal was used for forward RCS fairings and the elevon seal panels on the upper elevon interfaces, and black and white pigmented silica cloth was used for thermal barriers and gap fillers around operable penetrations such as the landing gear doors, the side hatch, umbilical doors, the rudder/speed brake, and vent doors.

The FRSI Nomex felt was between 0.016 and 0.40in (0.41 and 1.016cm) thick and consisted of sheet about 3 by 4ft (0.91 by 1.22m) bonded directly to *Challenger*'s exterior by room temperature vulcanizing silicon adhesive; the felt was basic Nomex (aramid) 2-denier fibre. The HRSI tiles were manufactured from a slurry containing fibres and water, framecast into a soft porous block to which a colloidal silica binder solution was added. When solid, the block was cut and machined to the precise dimensions required for individual tiles, varying in thickness from 1 to 5in (2.54 to 12.7cm). After the tiles had been shaped, a glass-mixture coating of tetra-silicide and boro-silicate glass (in powder form, mixed with a liquid carrier) was sprayed to a thickness of 16 to 18 mils. Oven heating to 2,300°F (1,260°C) resulted in a black waterproof gloss covering. The tiles could then be heated to 2,300°F (1,260°C) and immersed in cold water without damage, and also hand-held seconds after removing from the oven without the protection of a glove. They were attached to *Challenger* in a manner similar to that used for the FRSI.

The OMS blankets were made from low-density fibrous silica batting, formed from high-purity silica (glass) in the form of amorphous silica fibres. The batting was sandwiched between an outer woven high-temperature silica fabric and an inner lower-temperature woven glass fabric, sewn with silica thread resulting in the quilt-like look. Treated with a material to provide water-repellency, the blankets varied in thickness from 0.45 to 0.95in (1.14 to 2.41cm), had a density of about 11lb/cu ft (4.9kg/m^3), and were bonded by a room temperature vulcanizing silicon adhesive.

RCC panels were used on the nose cap and wing leading edges. The nose cap was produced in one piece, whilst the wing portions were made-up of 22 RCC panels each (44 in total). Comprising layered and pyrolized nylon cloth, graphitized and impregnated with a phenolic resin. This was layered up as a laminate, cured, heated to convert the resin to carbon in a pyrolization process, then impregnated with furfural alcohol before again being cured and pyrolized. The repetition of the process three times completed the operation, and the panels were then mechanically attached to the wing by a series of floating joints.

Some 23,000 HRSI tiles were used under *Challenger*, with about 7,000 LRSI tiles applied to the upper surfaces, and several 3 by 3ft (0.91 by 0.91m) thermal blankets on the OMS pods. Generally the TPS system on *Challenger* stood up well to requirements but, as the mission reports reveal, several difficulties were encountered with maintenance.

Right: The Shuttle programme was always envisaged as a high-profile operation of great international prestige, so national and NASA markings were featured strongly.

Orbiter subsystems

In addition to the previous described components of *Challenger*, the orbiter also was equipped with the following subsystem assemblies: a power-generation system supplied by three fuel cells for electricity, three independent hydraulic pumps for hydraulic power, an environmental control and life support system, a water and waste management system, and a purge vent and drain system to remove gases and liquids from the orbiter and so prevent hazardous build-up of unwanted consumables.

Markings

The basic colour scheme of *Challenger* was made up from the pattern of the TPS system (white upper surfaces and black lower surfaces), and as missions increased the weathering effect on the outer surfaces of *Challenger* became more pronounced.

Looking at *Challenger* upright on the pad, the USA designation and US flag appeared on the upper side of the left wing of the vehicle. The new stylized NASA logo and the name CHALLENGER appeared on the right wing. The name of the vehicle was also positioned beneath the cockpit windows on the side of the forward fuselage, which remained visible with payload bay doors open for on-orbit identification.

Right: Resplendent in pristine condition and markings, the newly completed *Challenger* is seen outside the Rockwell plant at Palmdale. The overhead view emphasizes the flight deck forward and top windows, the basically modular design, and the size of the orbiter's cargo bay.

The Missions

After a first career as the Static Test Article 099 and then remanufacture as Orbiter Vehicle 099, *Challenger* was ready by 1982 for its second career as an operational spacecraft. Delays forced the postponement of the first launch to April 1983, but in the next 34 months *Challenger* built up an unrivalled record of eight more missions plus a number of successes within the SSTS programme and as the parent vehicle for three Spacelab missions. There had been some problems, but these did not appear to pose any real threat as *Challenger* was readied for its tenth flight. But the full implications of the problems had not been appreciated, and the 51-L mission ended in disaster.

In early manifests the mission of Shuttle 6 was the final Orbital Flight Test (OFT) before qualification as an operational system. However, when the OFT programme was cut to four missions the sixth flight of the programme became the second operational mission. Shortly after the first Shuttle mission in April 1981, the sixth flight was scheduled for a two-day flight in December 1982, its primary purposes being the deployment of the first Tracking and Data Relay Satellite (TDRS-A) and shakedown of the new orbiter *Challenger* on its first mission. The TDRS was to support the communication coverage of the Spacelab 1 mission later in 1983 and the requirements for Landsat 4 Earth-resources satellite and the Space Telescope programme.

However, as the mission slipped into 1983, NASA decided to extend the mission to five days and add an EVA in the flight plan, following the abandonment of the initial Shuttle EVA planned for Shuttle 5 in November 1982, when both suits suffered hardware failures during EVA preparations.

The crew for the sixth flight of the programme and the maiden launch of *Challenger* consisted of four veteran NASA astronauts, though only one had flown in space. The commander was Paul Weitz, 50, a retired US Navy captain who had joined NASA in 1966 and flown a 28-day mission on Skylab in 1973. Boasting the oldest average age yet for a US space mission (48 years 3 months), the crew busied themselves with their new flightplan, and used the extra time to simulate the newly acquired EVA experiment. The mission called for a deployment of TDRS on Flight Day 1 and the EVA on Flight Day 4. The four-man crew had been named to the mission on March 2, 1982.

Launch preparations

Final preparations for the launch of Shuttle 6 began with the arrival of *Challenger* atop the Shuttle Carrier Aircraft (SCA), a modified Boeing 747, at the KSC on July 5, 1982. The vehicle was removed from the back of the Model 747 and transferred to the OPF, where a full pre-flight check was performed.

For the first time in the programme the second MLP was to be used for this mission, as the first platform was still occupied by *Columbia* in the final stages of preparations for the fifth mission in November. The assembly of the twin SRBs on the MLP began on October 1 and was completed on October 14; seven days later the ET for the sixth mission was mated to the SRBs.

The SRBs used on mission six were of the newer and lighter-weight variety designed to increase the payload capacity of the Shuttle by about 800lb (363kg). The motor cases for this and subsequent missions each weighed about 98,000lb (44,453kg), some 4,000lb (1,814kg) less than those used for the first five missions, the saving being achieved by reducing the thickness of the casing's steel skin by 0.02 to 0.04in (0.51 to 1.02mm) in the cylindrical attach and stiffener segments.

The ET for this mission, designated ET6 or Lightweight 1 (LWT-1), was the first of the improved versions of the ET which weighed some 10,000lb (4,536kg) less than that used on Shuttle 1. Each future tank would weigh approximately 67,000lb (30,391kg). Again the loss of weight on the ET allowed extra payload weight in the Shuttle.

Meanwhile *Challenger* was undergoing a series of processing activities in the OPF, including a dynamic stability test, and the installation of the three SSMEs (Nos 2011, 2012 and 2015) and the two OMS pods, which arrived at KSC on September 3 and had been fitted by October 8. This was followed by an Orbiter Integrated Test (OIT), successfully conducted on November 5-7 to verify the compatibility of various orbiter subsystems. On November 23, after spending 141 days in the OPF the *Challenger* was moved to the VAB and attached to the ET and SRBs.

After spending seven days in the VAB, the *Challenger*/Shuttle 6 combination was rolled out of the VAB atop the MLP on November 30 and taken the 3 miles (4.8km) to Launch Pad 39A in 3.5 hours, 30 minutes less than planned. Once the vehicle had been secured at the pad the final pre-launch checkout and propellant servicing activities began. The hypergolic propellant pre-flight servicing of *Challenger* was conducted on December 8-11, upon completion of which the preparations were started for the 20-second static test firing of the three SSMEs.

This Flight Readiness Firing (FRF) was conducted on December 18. It was designed to verify the integrity of the *Challenger* and its new, more powerful engines. In addition the firing also provided the means to test the outer insulation of the new lightweight ET and an opportunity to run *Challenger*'s APUs, so certifying them for flight. It was during this 20-second firing that a level of excess gaseous hydrogen was detected (in the orbiter's aft compartment) beyond the normal operating limits and, following the FRF, extensive post-firing inspections began to pinpoint the source of the hydrogen leak.

A mock launch and re-entry test was performed on December 23 and, after the Christmas break, the payload for Shuttle 6 was prepared for delivery to the launch pad. The TDRS-A satellite with the IUS was moved to the Pad 39A Payload Changeout Room (PCR) on December 27. Functional tests were performed on the TDRS-A/IUS combination, and preparations were made in early January to service the TDRS attitude control system with hydrogen fuel.

Above: A 'trick' double-exposure photograph on February 3, 1983 shows the TDRS satellite in *Challenger*'s payload bay, ready for the long-delayed launch of STS-6, *Challenger* 1.

Right: Launch of *Challenger* on its first mission, the sixth of the Shuttle series. As always there were some anomalies, but nothing serious.

Far right: The TDRS-A and its IUS are loaded into their container on December 23, 1982 for transport to the Payload Changeout Room at LC 39A.

As analysis of the FRF continued early in January, engineers were unable to locate the source of the hydrogen leak, forcing a NASA decision, on January 7, to postpone the launch from the scheduled day (January 20, 1983) into March. A second FRF would be conducted to identify the leak by adding instrumentation both inside and outside the aft engine compartment of *Challenger*.

The final Countdown Demonstration Test (CDT) was performed on January 11, the four members of the flight crew participating in a final demonstration of the vehicle, flight software and flight crew readiness for the launch.

As a safety measure the TDRS-A/IUS payload was removed from the PCR within the RSS on January 15, and returned to the VAB until after the second FRF.

On January 25 the engines of *Challenger* again burst into life for just over 20 seconds as the engineers conducted the second FRF. Once again a high level of gaseous hydrogen was detected in the aft compartment in a repeat of the problem experienced during the first FRF. With the addition of the extra instrumentation on this firing, however, it was determined that the hydrogen source was inside the aft compartment. Over the next few days engineers painstakingly searched the hardware and test data for identification of the exact source of the leak, and finally a 0.75in (19mm) crack was discovered in SSME No. 1's main combustion chamber coolant outlet manifold. Subsequent tests were performed to check that the crack discovered was the only source of the leak for the amount of hydrogen detected. The TDRS-A/IUS was returned to the pad on February 4 and installed in the PCR during the following day.

The removal of No. 1 engine (2011) was conducted on February 4, and the replacement arrived at the Cape the same day. Engine 2016 was delivered to the VAB to undergo its receiving inspection, and whilst there the new engine received the low-pressure oxidizer turbopump from engine 2011. During the inspections of the new engine a leak in an inlet line to the liquid oxygen heat exchanger (used to convert the liquid oxygen into gaseous oxygen, which is then routed back through the Main

MISSION DATA CHALLENGER 1

Sequence: Shuttle 6
Designation: 31-B
OV-099 Mission: One
Launch Date: April 4, 1983
Launch Time: 13:30 EST
Launch Site: Pad 39A, Kennedy Space Center, Cape Canaveral, Florida, USA
Launch Weight: 4,490,498lb (2,036,856kg)
Maximum Altitude: 185 miles (298km)
Inclination: 28.5°
Orbits: 80, landing during 81st
EVA Duration: 4 hours 17 minutes
Mission Duration: 5 days 0 hours 23 minutes 42 seconds; travelled 1.82 million miles
Landing Date: April 9, 1983
Landing Time (main gear): 10:53:42 PST
Landing Site: Runway 22, Edwards AFB, California, USA
Rollout Distance and Duration: 7,180ft (2,190m) & 49 seconds
Crew: (Commander) Captain P. J. Weitz, USN (Ret), 50, NASA; (Pilot) Colonel K. J. Bobko, USAF, 45, NASA; (MS-1) Dr F. S. Musgrave, 47, NASA (EV-1); (MS-2) Colonel D. H. Peterson, USAF (Ret), 49, NASA (EV-2)
Payload: TDRS-A/IUS (deployed Day 1, GET 10:00); EVA Task Simulation Devices; Continuous-Flow Electrophoresis System (CFES); Mono-disperse Latex Reactor (MLR); Optical Survey of Lightning; Getaway Specials (3).

FLIGHT LOG CHALLENGER 1

1 (APRIL 4, 1983) **00:00:00** SRB ignition from GPC (lift-off*) **00:00:30.6** SSME throttle-down command to 81% thrust **00:01:02.70** SSME throttle-up command to 104% thrust **00:01:10.96** Max Q **00:02:09.38** SRB separation command **00:07:22.75** SSME throttle-down command for 3-g acceleration **00:08:19.6** MECO **00:08:37.45** ET separation **00:10:19.9** OMS-1 ignition **00:12:35.3** OMS-1 cut-off **00:13:43** APU deactivation **00:43:37.7** OMS-2 ignition **00:45:35.7** OMS-2 cut-off **01:34:57.6** Payload bay doors open **10:00:01** TDRS-A/IUS deployed **10:20:53.27** OMS-3 ignition **10:21:14.27** OMS-3 cut-off
2 (APRIL 5, 1983) **25:30:47.27** OMS-4 ignition **25:31:08.87** OMS-4 cut-off
3 (APRIL 6, 1983) **49:27:58** APU No. 2 activation **49:03:09** APU No. 2 deactivation **74:00:50** EVA start **78:17:00** EVA complete
6 (APRIL 9, 1983) **116:06:20** Payload bay doors closed **119:25:00.06** De-orbit manoeuvre ignition (OMS-5) **119:27:25.22** De-orbit manoeuvre cut-off **119:40:30** APU Nos 2 and 3 activation **119:53:27** Entry interface **120:01:23** End blackout **120:17:29** TAEM (Terminal Area Energy Management) **120:23:42** Main landing gear contact **120:23:54** Nose landing gear contact **120:24:31** Wheel stop

(*Lift off time has been rounded off from 13:30:00.016 EST)

Propulsion System for ET pressurization) was discovered, and the engine could not be qualified for this flight.

It was therefore decided to replace the engine with No. 2017. The second replacement completed its certification firings at the National Space Technology Laboratories (NSTL) in Bay St Louis, Mississippi, on February 15 and was shipped to KSC. As engineers continued performing pre-flight checks on the two remaining engines a leak was discovered, on February 26, coming from the No. 2 (2015) engine. After further examination the source of the leak was found to be a hairline crack in a 0.5in (12.7mm) fuel line leading into the injector's augmented spark igniter chamber. After the discovery of this fault the No. 3 engine (2012) was borescoped and revealed a crack in the same location as the one found in Engine 2015.

The cracks were found at the place in the line where a metal sleeve was brazed to the line, the sleeve acting as a shock absorber to prevent the chaffing of the line at the point where it passed through a cover over the injector. This time the fault was in a place that prevented on-pad repairs, so both engines were removed from the vehicle, returned to the VAB and underwent repairs to eliminate the sleeve.

First to be repaired was the Engine 2015 (No. 2) which was reinstalled on *Challenger* on March 8. Engine 2012 (No. 3) was installed on March 10, and Engine 2017 (No. 1) was fitted during the next day. A final verification of the three *Challenger* engines for flight was begun again on March 14. The engines used on the maiden flight of *Challenger* would deliver 104% of rated thrust, somewhat more than those on *Columbia*, which reached 100%. Again the increased power meant that the orbiter could deliver to orbit 1,000lb (454kg) more payload per 1% of additional thrust. A wide range of design changes and modifications in the design, construction and testing of SSMEs had allowed for the increase in rated thrust, and redesigned engine parts were incorporated into the original design.

As KSC engineers wrestled with the problem of the engines, the payload *Challenger* was scheduled to carry was also having its own problems. The TDRS-A/IUS system was stored in the PCR of the RSS on February 28, when strong winds whipped across the Cape area to breach the weather seal between the RSS, PCR and *Challenger*. Inspection of the payload after the event revealed a fine layer of particle matter on the TDRS-A. The Goddard Spaceflight Center and TRW (the TDRS prime contractor) investigated the satellite and determined that a cleaning operation would be needed, inevitably causing a second launch delay. TDRS-A cleaning began on March 14 and was completed on March 19, and the satellite was reinstalled in the PCR on the same day. As work on the engines continued a second series of functional tests on the IUS and TDRS-A was completed, and the attitude-control system of the satellite was serviced before the TDRS-A/IUS combination was loaded into the payload bay of *Challenger* on February 22. On February 24-25 electrical tests were performed to verify orbiter-to-payload interfaces, so completing the Shuttle 6 payload checkout.

Between March 28 and March 31 precountdown activities included final ordnance operations, checks of the Shuttle Range Safety System (SRSS) and the pressurization of the OMS propellant tanks to regulator lock-up.

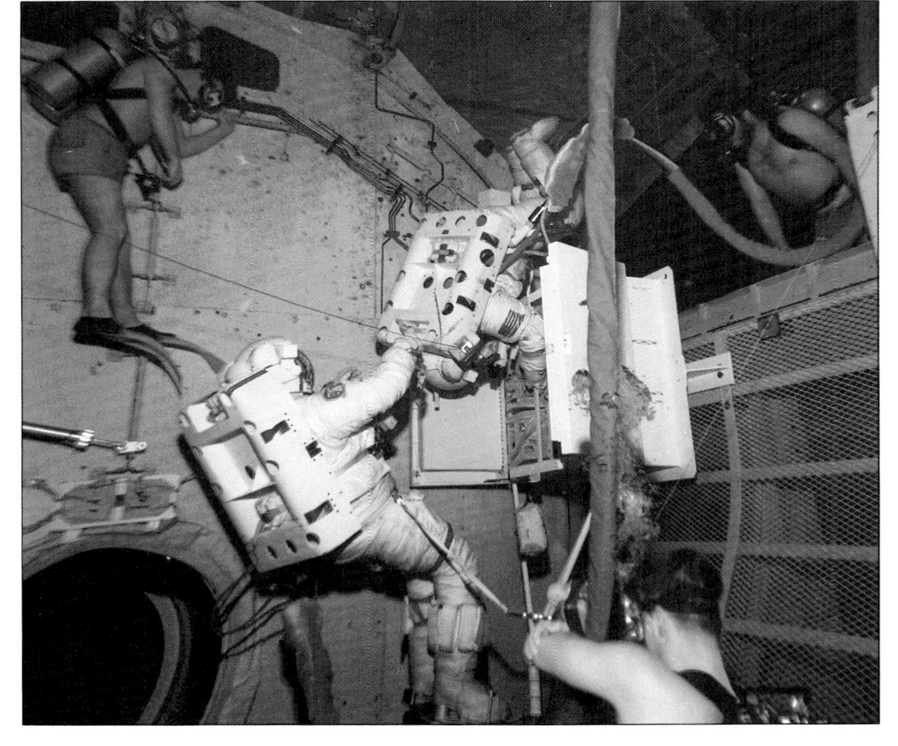

Left: Story Musgrave and Donald Peterson practise EVA activity in JSC's Weightless Environment Training Facility for Shuttle 6.

Launch phase

On March 31, 1983 the 111-hour long count-down was started. The terminal count-down was in fact 93 hours, with a total of 18 hours of built-in hold time added resulting in a 20-minute launch window in the afternoon of April 4, the duration of the window being dictated by sunset at the TAL site in Dakar, Senegal. Sitting on the pad *Challenger* resembled *Columbia*, the sister craft which had flown the first five Shuttle missions. The heaviest mass lifted since the days of the Saturn V in the early 1970s by an American vehicle, the Shuttle 6 assembly with ET and SRBs weighed 4,490,498lb (2,036,856kg) at SRB ignition, just 1,939lb (880kg) heavier than the previous mission at launch. Other additions to the vehicle for this flight included two flight deck seats for the mission specialists and the installation of the McDonnell Douglas CFES biological processing experiment in the mid-deck.

The countdown was described as the smoothest experienced in over 20 years of manned launches. Only two minor problems occurred, the more serious of them concerning the weather. Only 17 hours before the scheduled launch the high-altitude winds were still too high to allow the launch, the jetstream at 45,000-47,000ft (13,715-14,325m) being recorded at 122-166kts (140-191mph; 225-307km/h). A series of five USAF weather balloons was launched to monitor wind velocity, which dropped to 94kts (108mph; 174km/h) shortly before launch. The countdown thus continued. The second problem was the inadvertent activation of the No. 1 fuel cell by a pad worker, who tripped a master unit switch placing the unit in parallel with the DC power supply.

The crew exited the crew operations building, travelled to the pad and entered the vehicle on time and without difficulties. Weitz took up his position in the left seat, Bobko in the right, Peterson in the centre aft seat to perform launch duties as flight engineer, and Musgrave in the seat to the right of and a little behind Peterson, with no launch duties other than to enjoy the ride.

Just 0.0884 seconds after its planned launch time of 13.30 Eastern Standard Time (EST) on April 4, 1983, *Challenger* lifted off after spending 126 days on the pad, to begin its historic first mission, with the three engines rated at 100% thrust and the SRBs burning nominally. As the vehicle cleared the launch tower the engines were throttled up to 104% thrust some 6.5 seconds into the flight. As the *Challenger* climbed into a clear blue sky it rolled 90° to the right to a 090° heading out over the Atlantic Ocean, taking it into its planned 28.5° orbital inclination. The changes incorporated in the vehicle and engines resulted in a slight change of launch velocity and altitude timings compared with previous flights. As the vehicle approached Max Q the engines were throttled down to 81% thrust at GET 30.6 seconds, the vehicle passing through Max Q at just over 70 seconds into the flight and encountering dynamic pressure much less than that of the test flights before it. This was a reflection of flying an operational rather than a data-gathering ascent. As the mission duration clock passed the Max Q point the engines were again throttled up to 104%, and shortly afterwards the crew received the information that the trajectory was slightly depressed over planned data.

The separation of the SRBs occurred some 3,000ft (915m) lower than the planned 153,100ft (46,665m) level, a result of the depressed trajectory, at GET 2 minutes 09 seconds and in full view of the crowds watching from the Cape. *Challenger*, flying at Mach 4.4, was following a path angle 1° lower than planned, but this was not considered a safety issue. As the SRBs separated a layer of soot was deposited on the orbiter's windows, much to the annoyance of the crew but posing no hazard to their viewing capabilities. Despite the lower trajectory, first-stage performance was given as nominal, vehicle reserves making up the deficit. The SRBs splashed down in the Atlantic about 7 minutes after launch, within 1.5 miles (2.4km) of each other at a point some 188 miles (303km) due east of the Cape.

Main Engine Cut-Off (MECO) was achieved at 8 minutes 20 seconds into the flight, some 2 seconds later than planned, at a height of 65.6 miles (105.6km) but travelling 1ft (0.305m) per second faster than predicted. Separation of the ET was achieved as planned, but the separation manoeuvre took about a half minute longer than envisaged because of the reduced engine impulse, and the overspeed situation reduced the burn velocity of the first OMS manoeuvre by 7ft (2.13m) per second. As *Challenger* climbed to orbit, the ET fell back towards Earth, re-entering the atmosphere and burning up as planned, and its debris falling into the Indian Ocean.

OMS-1 burn was initiated at GET 10 minutes 19 seconds and, lasting just over 2 minutes 16 seconds, increased velocity by 218ft (66.4m) per second. The improved engines had allowed a MECO to be achieved some 20 seconds earlier than on the five previous missions, despite the heavier payload. Shutdown of the three APUs at GET 13 minutes 43 seconds was followed by the OMS-2 burn at GET 43 minutes 38 seconds. This lasted 1 minute 57 seconds, resulting in a velocity increase of 185.8ft (56.6m) per second. By the 45th minute of the mission *Challenger* was safely in its operational 185 mile (298km) circular orbit, inclined at 28.5° to the Equator with an orbital period of 1 hour 30 minutes 22 seconds.

TDRS Geosynchronous Satellite Deployment

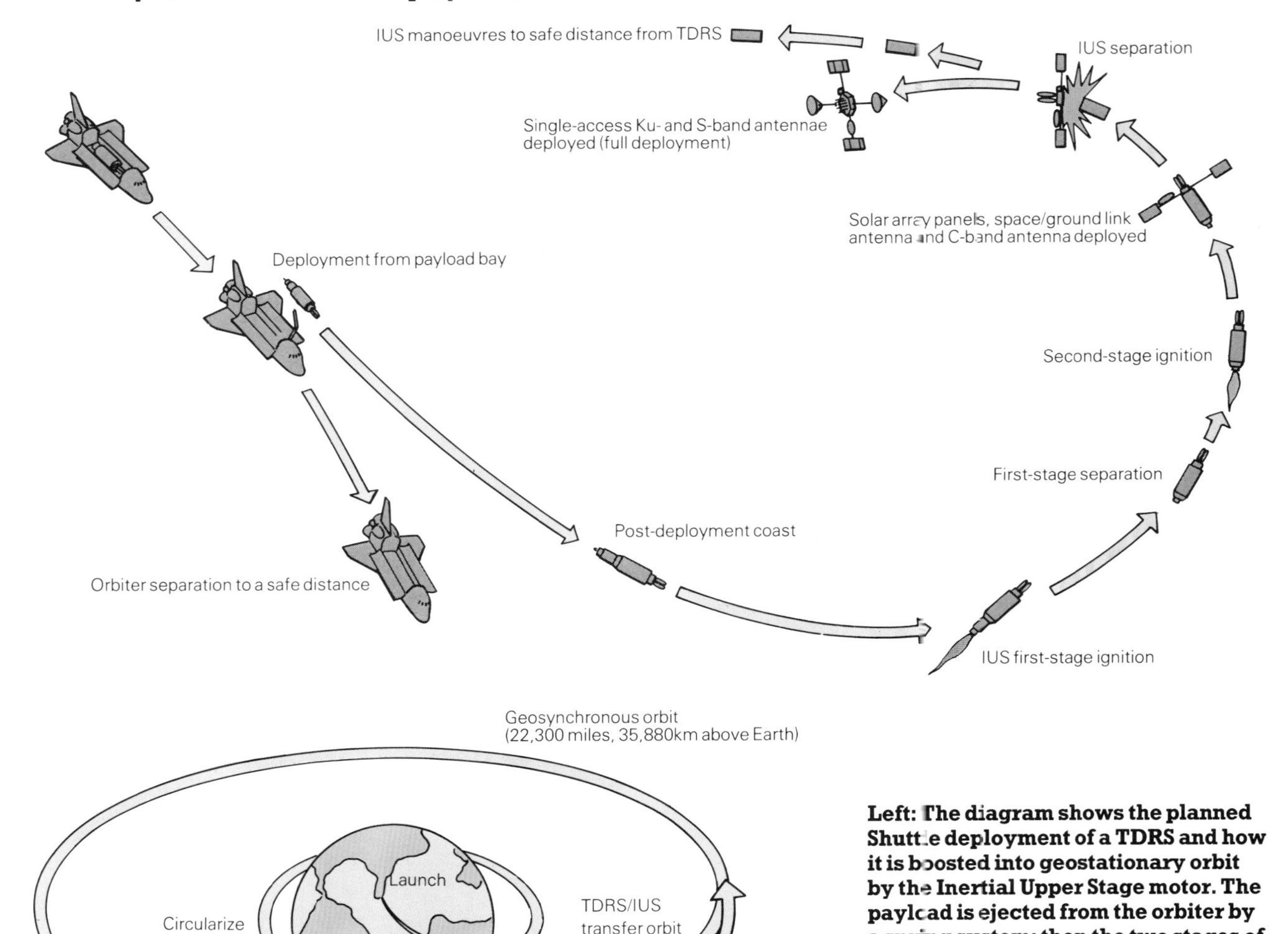

Left: The diagram shows the planned Shuttle deployment of a TDRS and how it is boosted into geostationary orbit by the Inertial Upper Stage motor. The payload is ejected from the orbiter by a spring system; then the two stages of the IUS burn for 141 and 103 seconds respectively to fire TDRS into a geostationary transfer orbit. Once on station, IUS separates and TDRS deploys its antennae to achieve final operating configuration.

Below: Hanging between the two slide wires, Musgrave tests the reel-in safety tether, while Peterson works on the port side of the payload bay.

According to the crew the launch was very smooth, with no unexpected events: in fact it was a much easier ride than that of the simulators during training!

Following the launch, an inspection of the pad revealed little damage, whose repair would pose no problem to the planned launch date of Shuttle 7 in early June. The pad washdown was completed within 24 hours of the launch, after which the damaged circuit box was repaired. NASA officials commented that each launch resulted in less damage to the pad and that modifications were continuous.

Orbital activities

As the mission clock reached GET 1 hour 34 minutes and *Challenger* began its second orbit, the crew activated the payload bay doors, which opened very smoothly. TV pictures showed the TDRS-A/IUS payload lying in the bay, but also patches of the FRSI thermal protection system hanging loose off the starboard OMS pod, the result of launch stresses. The damage to this least critical of the TPS components was not thought to pose a re-entry problem, and the crew prepared for the deployment of the payload.

The crew completed a full systems checkout of the new orbiter before concentrating on the payload deployment, which took several hours to prepare. A long series of hardware and communications checks was necessary to ensure that the payload had survived the launch phase, it being anticipated that the payload package be returned to Earth if serious problems were found. All four astronauts were involved in the deployment, though Musgrave as MS had responsibility for checkout and deployment preparations. After some concern with the three of the five IUS gyros, the 'go' for deployment was given some 39 minutes before the scheduled deploy point. Nineteen minutes later the countdown for deployment began, and shortly afterwards the crew raised the IUS tilt table carrying the payload combination to its required 59° deployment position and disconnected the IUS/orbiter connections.

Some 20 minutes later, at a GET of just over 10 hours after launch and as the spacecraft flew south over Ascension Island in the Atlantic Ocean during the eighth orbit, the satellite was pushed out of the bay over the top of *Challenger*'s flight deck at a speed of 39.4ft (12m) per second and illuminated in the payload bay floodlights. At GET 10 hours 20 minutes the crew fired the OMS engines for the third time to increase separation distance from the payload, a burn time of 21 seconds imparting a velocity change of 39.4ft (12m) per second to *Challenger*, modifying its orbit slightly to a more elliptical shape 204×178 miles (328×287km) and separating it some 36.67 miles (59km) from the TDRS-A/IUS combination. Some 55 minutes after deployment, the first-stage motor of the IUS ignited, pushing the satellite on its way to operational location.

Despite the successful first-stage burn of 2 minutes 31 seconds by the IUS, and the separation of the second stage, the planned 1 minute 43 second second-stage burn lasted only 70 seconds. This was caused by the deflation of an oil-filled seal, which crippled the second-stage steering mechanism and resulted in a 30rpm tumble indicating a probable loss of the vehicle. The system was carrying more fuel than actually needed, however: ground control safely separated the satellite and over the next 58 days performed a series of delicate manoeuvres to coax the crippled satellite in its required synchronous orbital position at 41°W, after expending some 817lb (371kg) of the 1,318lb (598kg) of propellant. This action saved the following Spacelab 1 mission, but placed serious doubts on the reliability of the IUS system scheduled for a second TDRS deployment on Shuttle 8 and for a DoD deployment on Shuttle 10.

Most of the crew's activities on Days 2 and 3 concentrated on the scientific programme and preparations of hardware for the EVA on Day 4. Before that, though, the crew conducted two manoeuvres as part of a programme of simulations for the Solar Maximum rescue mission rendezvous the following year. The first burn was conducted by the RCS engines and the second by the OMS engines. OMS-4 lasted for 21 seconds, and was followed by a series of smaller burns over the coming days as the simulation tests continued. By now *Challenger* was

in a 176 by 175 mile (283 by 282km) orbit inclined at 28.5° with a 90.25-minute period. *Challenger's* crew carried out their science programme with the CFES and other onboard experiments.

The crew performed a further RCS burn on Day 3, and Weitz and Bobko completed a one-hour checkout of the controls of *Challenger*, including the activation of one of the three APUs (No. 2) but for only just over five minutes to check movement of all the spacecraft's aerodynamic control surfaces.

On Day 4 Musgrave and Peterson completed the USA's first EVA in over nine years and the first in the Shuttle programme. After a 3.5 hour prebreathe they exited the airlock at GET 3 days 2 hours 50 minutes during the 51st orbit. The two astronauts spent the next 3 hours evaluating the series of slide wires, tethers and restraints that had been developed for later more complicated EVAs, but available on every Shuttle flight in the event of the need for an emergency EVA. A series of tether dynamics by Musgrave across the open payload bay was followed by an evaluation of the tools in the EVA tool box and then a simulated wind-down of a stranded IUS tilt table, the actual Shuttle 6 tilt table not being attached for this simulation. As the EVA progressed smoothly only minor problems hindered the astronauts, in no way interfering with their pace of work or safety outside the vehicle. After an evaluation of the Payload Retention Device (PRD) used to restrain loose cargo in an emergency, Musgrave carried a bag containing about 33lb (15kg) of tools down to the aft of the payload bay to test the ease of moving large articles in the new suit. After a full and very successful work-out of the new EVA suit and hardware, the two men climbed back into the airlock after just over 3.5 hours outside and 4 hours 17 minutes on the EMU units.

On the last full day in space the crew stowed equipment and prepared for re-entry during the next day. Despite the TDRS-A/IUS problem (the fault of neither *Challenger* nor her crew, who had performed their duties exactly as planned), the vehicle was performing flawlessly with only a few minor problems of the type to be expected with a brand new vehicle on its first flight.

Re-entry and landing

Early in the morning of Day 6, April 9, the crew were awakened and began final preparations for entry. Weather was excellent at the Edwards landing site, where the new orbiter would make its first landing to take full advantage of the almost limitless runways in the Californian desert. The crew powered-up the landing instruments and closed the payload bay doors, and as the vehicle flew over south of Mauritius Island, the 2 minute 26 second OMS-5 burn against the direction of flight provided a retrograde velocity of 292.2ft (89.1m) per second at 400,000ft (121,920m) altitude some 4,656 miles (7,492km) from Edwards. Flying an entry angle of 40°, *Challenger* entered the blackout period at GET 119.53.27 and exited about 8 minutes later.

Weitz flew *Challenger* through a series of hypersonic and supersonic manoeuvres which expanded data in the three areas where hard flight data was lacking: orbiter lateral stability, RCS capability and rudder authority. In all, *Challenger* completed the normal three hypersonic S-turns that all previous flights had completed to reduce energy and refine the guidance for the final landing phase, and in addition flew eight flight test manoeuvres, which required about 30 separate jet firing or control surface inputs to gather required data.

Left: Tucked into the payload bay, the TDRS-A/IUS assembly gives scant indication of the satellite's deployed configuration with two solar arrays and a number of antennae.

The first Programmed Test Input (PTI), as the eight flight tests were called, began at 261,000ft (79,553m) altitude with the vehicle flying at 16,700mph (26,875km/h). Weitz applied a right aileron pulse manoeuvre, followed by a right roll jet burn then a right yaw jet input. As *Challenger* responded to Weitz's commands and automatic software, it flew through the denser layers of the atmosphere. The vehicle slowed and dropped as test inputs followed almost immediately after each other, turning the vehicle to the left then the right then back to the left again, using RCS jets in the higher reaches of the atmosphere and the control surfaces in the lower areas. *Challenger* flew a slightly higher angle of entry during the fall from Mach 12 to Mach 3 in order to provide a wider range of test data than that supplied from the first five flights. A manoeuvre at Mach 9 failed, but the other PTIs were successful.

Using manual control for the final approach and from 5,000ft (1,520m) altitude the new Heads Up Display (HUD) console on the windscreen as a landing aid, Weitz brought *Challenger* around the last few thousand feet towards the concrete Runway 22 at Edwards. As *Challenger* approached Weitz manually retracted the speed brake in the vehicle tail, due to a sharp increase in wind velocity as the vehicle approached 2,500ft (760m) altitude, so allowing a full energy landing, which was adjusted to allow Weitz to aim his touchdown point 6,500ft (1,980m) from the threshold. As *Challenger* approached, the landing gear had to be dropped manually when the primary system failed to engage the system by computer.

Challenger touched main landing gear 2,026ft (618m) down the runway at GET 5 days 0 hours 23 minutes 42 seconds, the nose gear following 12 seconds later, at 4,972ft (1,515m) along the runway. *Challenger* rolled for another 49 seconds some 7,180ft (2,190m) along the runway as Weitz applied 140kt (161mph; 259km/h) braking power for 4 seconds while building to maximum pressure. He eased off at the 80kt (92mph; 148km/h) point to a deceleration rate of 4-8ft (1.2-2.4m) per second, which he held until wheel stop 5 days 0 hours 24 minutes 31 seconds after launch.

Post-landing activities

Challenger had successfully completed its first mission and was back on Earth. Post-flight activities indicated that only 22 flight plan anomalies had been recorded against 82 on the first flight of *Columbia*. As the orbiter was being safed before being prepared for return to KSC, the crew exited and began their series of debriefings.

The safing of *Challenger* ran about 5 minutes ahead of schedule, and the orbiter was towed to the mate/demate device only 3.5 hours after wheel stop, 30 minutes sooner than expected. The lack of ejection seats on this vehicle enabled ground crews to work on system shutdown on the flight deck with much more ease. One of the few flight anomalies included a random propellant leakage of an RCS thruster during the mission, and this dictated drainage of the No. 2 manifold before the ferry flight back to KSC. It took some 6 hours to unload the 6 US gal (22.7 litres) of monomethyl hydrazine and nitrogen tetroxide, but a 12-15 hour deservicing operation on the whole manifold area was accomplished to enable extensive leak checks on the system. It was thought that KSC ground-based quick-disconnect equipment had damaged the onboard unit, but evaluation found no traces of hardware damage to the connection. The investigations would continue back at the Cape, so *Challenger* was prepared for loading on the SCA. The orbiter had suffered only minor scorch marks and tile damage from re-entry, but had lost several pieces of the quilted insulation blanket from the front of each OMS pod. Two blankets on each pod had been completely destroyed, with a further three on each pod eroded. The installation of the Advanced Flexible Reusable Surface Insulation (AFRSI) blankets was not expected to delay the next launch (then set for June 9) seriously, and a possible quick-fix remedy for Shuttle 7 was being considered before a more permanent fix with new blankets for Shuttle 8.

In addition about 5sq in (32.26cm²) of FRSI on the *Challenger* body flap was eroded. The damage on the OMS pod was thought to be caused by encountering Max Q during the launch. As with the *Columbia* flights, there was some discolouration of the white-tile Low-temperature Reusable Surface Insulation (LRSI) surface of *Challenger*, though not so marked as on *Columbia*.

On April 14, 1983 *Challenger* was flown atop the SCA to Kelly AFB, Texas, the first leg of its return to Kennedy. After a one-day stopover, *Challenger* was transferred from Kelly AFB, Texas to Kennedy Space Center on April 16, arriving 12 days after leaving on its first mission.

Below: Just above the runway at Edwards AFB, *Challenger* comes in for its first landing at the conclusion of the successful Shuttle 6 mission.

With one successful flight in the log book, the preparations for *Challenger*'s second flight were made easier by the achievements and results of Shuttle 6. In the second quarter of 1983, NASA had only two operational orbiters available (OV-102 and OV-099), with OV-103 and OV-104 in various stages of construction. After flying the first five missions *Columbia* was undergoing a series of modifications which would bring the vehicle up to current operational flight standards and configure it for its sixth flight carrying the first Spacelab payload later in that year. Until then two missions remained on the flight schedule, Shuttle 7 in June and Shuttle 8 in August. Lack of confidence in the performance of the IUS used on Shuttle 6 eventually led to the decision to remove the IUS from Shuttle 8 and to cancel the Shuttle 10 mission, a dedicated DoD flight, which would have been *Challenger*'s fourth mission.

As these events highlighted the problems in the SSTS, engineers and programme managers continued with the final preparations for the launch of *Challenger* on its second (and the programme's seventh) mission. Scheduled to deploy two communications satellites and a free-flying retrievable pallet satellite, the mission also featured the first five-person launch, the first members of Shuttle-era astronaut selection to fly, and the first spaceflight by a US woman, 20 years after Soviet cosmonaut Valentina Tereshkova flew in Vostok 6.

The crew was commanded by Bob Crippen, who had flown the first Shuttle flight in April 1981 aboard *Columbia*, and was selected on April 20, 1982 for Shuttle 7. Originally the crew consisted of four members, but on December 21, 1982 Dr Norman Thagard was assigned as third payload specialist to study Space Adaptation Syndrome (SAS) first hand, and its effect on the other members of the crew. Like his three Group 8 companions, this was Thagard's first flight.

MISSION DATA CHALLENGER 2

Sequence: Shuttle 7
Designation: 31-C
OV-099 Mission: Two
Launch Date: June 18, 1983
Launch Time: 07:33:00 EDT
Launch Site: Pad 39A, Kennedy Space Center, Cape Canaveral, Florida, USA
Launch Weight: 4,485,597lb (2,034,633kg)
Maximum Altitude: 195 miles (314km)
Inclination: 28.45°
Orbits: 97, landing during 98th
EVA Duration: None
Mission Duration: 6 days 2 hours 23 minutes 59 seconds; travelled 2.22 million miles
Landing Date: June 24, 1983
Landing Time (main gear): 06:56:59 PDT
Landing Site: Runway 15, Edwards AFB, California, USA
Rollout Distance and Duration: 10,450ft (3,185m) & 75 seconds
Crew: (Commander) Captain Robert L. Crippen, USN, 45, NASA; (Pilot) Captain Fredrick H. Hauck, USN, 42, NASA; (MS-1) Colonel John M. Fabian, USAF, 44, NASA (EV-1); (MS-2) Dr Sally K. Ride (Hawley), 32, NASA; (MS-3) Dr Norman E. Thagard, 39, NASA (EV-2)
Payload: Remote Manipulator System; Anik C/PAM-D (deployed Day 1, GET 09:29); Palapa B/PAM-D (deployed Day 2, GET 22:00); Shuttle Pallet Satellite, or SPAS-01 (deployed & retrieved Day 5); MAUS (3 West German GAS experiments); Mission Peculiar Experiment Support Structure (for OSTA-2); OSTA-2 (Materials Experimental Assembly); Mono-disperse Latex Reactor (MLR); Continuous-Flow Electrophoresis System (CFES); Getaway Specials (7); OAST Orbiter Experiments Program (ACIP, HRAP); GAS experiments.

Launch preparations

As workers at KSC prepared *Challenger* for its first mission, elements of the payload scheduled for its second mission were also arriving at the Cape. The first PAM module arrived on November 4, 1982 and was scheduled to deploy the Anik comsat, which arrived at KSC on November 30; the Palapa satellite also arrived on the same day, being followed by its PAM on January 3. All four elements underwent separate inspection and processing before the satellites were mated to their boosters in the Delta Spin Test Facility, and then installed in their launch cradles.

The SPAS-01 payload arrived on January 15, 1983 and was moved to Hangar S at Cape Canaveral for assembly and checkout. The OSTA-2 payload had arrived on January 2, and was also taken to the Operations and Checkout Building (OCB) for assembly and systems checkout.

The assembly of the Shuttle 7 vehicle began on February 9 when engineers began the stacking of the twin SRBs on MLP-1 in the VAB. The SRB stacking was completed on February 23, and was followed by the mating of the ET to the SRBs on March 2.

The Palapa/PAM was transferred to the Vertical Processing Facility (VPF) on April 7, followed by Anik/PAM on April 21. The SPAS-01 pallet satellite was transferred to the VPF the same day, and together the three major elements of the cargo underwent a Cargo Integration Test Equipment (CITE) checkout. The OSTA-2 payload, which did not require CITE in the VPF, was the first element of the cargo to be put into the payload canister on May 16, and the canister was transferred to the VPF on May 18, whereupon the three major satellite payloads were installed. The cargo was then transferred to the PCR in the RSS at Pad 39A on May 23 to await the arrival of *Challenger* on the pad a few days later.

Challenger arrived back at KSC from its first mission on April 16, and was taken off the SCA and to the OPF on April 17, to begin preparation for its second launch. The remaining elements of the Shuttle 6 cargo were removed, and a regular post-flight maintenance programme of leak and functional checks of the SSMEs and subsystems began.

One of the major areas of inspection and processing for Shuttle 7 was the TPS on *Challenger*. Engineers thought that the thermal blankets, after the hottest part of the Shuttle 6 entry, had been eroded by aerodynamic flow as the vehicle dropped below Mach 5. Further analysis of the TPS indicated that individual tile injection with waterproofing agent had to be implemented to prevent water corrosion, which had been experienced in *Columbia* after only five missions. Some 14,000 of *Challenger*'s tiles were injected, and further investigation into the blanket damage was undertaken to reveal if changes in the blanket material occurred in space or during re-entry and so occasioned the damage. About 170 thermal tiles were replacing 44 thermal blankets on the OMS pod areas, with a further 120 tiles added to replace blanket damage on the elevons.

Above: On-orbit scene as Sally Ride floats between the pilot's and commander's seats amid items free-falling or velcroed to the walls.

Right: Perfect deployment for the Palapa B/PAM-D assembly as it spins up and out of the payload bay well clear of the vertical stabilizer.

After spending 34 days in the OPF, *Challenger* was moved to the VAB on May 21 and mated to the SRBs and ET. The SIT was accomplished on May 24-25 and, following less than 24 hours of preparation for the move, the combination was carried by the MLP to Pad 39A on May 26 after only five days in the VAB. Pad/vehicle verification tests were begun on that same day and, following the transfer of the cargo to the payload bay on May 28, a series of payload/vehicle integration tests was completed.

As work continued on the pad, final preparations were hampered by thunderstorms in the area, twice delaying the propellant loading preparations and, following the CDT on June 3, the replacement of a faulty Inertial Measurement Unit (IMU) and No. 2 engine interfacer unit.

By June 13 the pressurization of the OMS and RCS propellant and helium tanks, and the servicing of the orbiter fuel cells' LO and LH storage tanks (all terminal countdown activities on previous missions) had been completed. Servicing of the CFES equipment was completed on June 14, and closeout of the OMS and RCS systems by June 15.

Launch phase

On June 16 at 03:00 EDT NASA started the countdown for the Shuttle 7, whose launch was another 52 hours 33 minutes away at 07:33 EDT on June 18. The actual count lasted for 40 hours with built-in holds totalling 12 hours 33 minutes, a useful reduction from the 93-hour count on Shuttle 6. The hold periods were not needed during the countdown, in which only three incidents were recorded.

Challenger had been fitted with three sets of cryogenic oxygen and hydrogen tanks for the fuel cells, and the payload was arranged (from the aft bulkhead) in the order Palapa B-1, Anik C, OSTA-2 and SPAS-01, with six GAS canisters mounted along the left longeron, forward of the SPAS, and the seventh bolted amidships on the right longeron. An extra seat was added to the middeck and the RMS used on *Columbia* had been installed along the left door hinge line.

At exactly 07:33:00.03 EDT on June 18, 1983 the SRBs of Shuttle 7 ignited, followed by the ignition in sequence of the three SSMEs, the same engines which had been used on Shuttle 6. *Challenger* flew a near-perfect ascent trajectory, reaching Max Q in 1 minute 3 seconds after launch, at 104% thrust on the three SSMEs and an almost perfect performance from the SRBs, which separated at GET 2 minutes 06.12 seconds. Falling into the Atlantic, the SRBs were subsequently retrieved for later reuse, though the parachutes (as on most missions) suffered some scorch damage. The on-time cut-off of the three SSMEs was achieved at GET 8 minutes 20 seconds, with nominal separation of the ET achieved at 8 minutes 38 seconds, the tank impacting the ocean only 12 miles (19.3km) from the predicted point. A 2 minute 19 second OMS-1 burn was followed by a 1 minute 57 second OMS-2 burn which 'kicked' *Challenger* into an approximate 184 mile (296km) orbit, at an inclination of 28.5°, almost 47 minutes after launch.

The crew reported a very smooth and enjoyable ride, with Crippen comparing this ride to his first aboard *Columbia*. A few particles were noted coming from the ET and again the windows were slightly streaked.

At 4.8 lb/sq in (0.33 bar), *Challenger*'s

FLIGHT LOG CHALLENGER 2

1 (JUNE 18, 1983) **00:00:00.03** SRB ignition command from GPC (lift-off) **00:00:27.92** SSME throttle-down to 81% thrust **00:01:01.40** SSME throttle-up to 104% thrust **00:01:03** Max Q **00:02:06.12** SRB separation command **00:07:23** SSME throttle-down for 3-g acceleration **00:07:23.60** 3-g acceleration **00:08:20.24** MECO **00:08:38.24** ET separation **00:10:20.36** OMS-1 ignition **00:12:39.81** OMS-1 cut-off **00:13:13.0** APU deactivation **00:44:30.53** OMS-2 ignition **00:46:28.05** OMS-2 cut-off **09:29:00** Anik C deployed **09:46:29.41** OMS-3 ignition **09:46:34.41** OMS-3 cut-off
2 (JUNE 19, 1983) **26:00:00** Palapa deployed **26:08:10.45** OMS-4 ignition **26:08:15.37** OMS-4 cut-off
3 (JUNE 20, 1983) **51:17:10.97** OMS-5 ignition **51:17:14.09** OMS-5 cut-off **52:02:33.41** OMS-6 ignition **52:02:44.37** OMS-6 cut-off
5 (JUNE 22, 1983) 1st SPAS release; final SPAS capture
6 (JUNE 23, 1983) **115:50:52** OPS-8 checkout started **123:18:08** OPS-8 checkout accomplished
7 (JUNE 24, 1983) **145:23:00.21** De-orbit ignition manoeuvre (OMS-7) **145:25:46.21** De-orbit manoeuvre cut-off **145:28:01** APU No. 1 activation **145: 40:04** APU Nos 2 and 3 activation **145:52:58** Entry interfaced (400,000ft, 121,920m) **146:09:59** End blackout **146:17:31** TAEM **146:23:59** Main landing gear contact **146:24:19** Nose landing gear contact **146:25:14** Wheel stop

Above: The SPAS-1 platform captures *Challenger* orbiting 180 miles (290km) above Earth with the RMS arm parked over the row of six GAS canisters. The retrieval of SPAS-1 provided simulation data for the Solar Max mission.

Max Q was some 0.097lb/sq in (0.0067 bar) higher than that of Shuttle 6, which was achieved by targeting *Challenger* at a shallower trajectory from 25 to 75 seconds into the mission at a 4.5° angle of attack. This resulted in faster acceleration at lower altitude (and thus denser atmosphere), resulting in the higher dynamic loads.

Orbital activities

First activities in the flight's orbital programme were the opening of the payload bay doors and configuration for orbital flight. Despite some initial closing and opening problems with the satellite sunshield doors, the satellite deployments were achieved without major incident, both satellites reaching their intended operational orbits after launch on the first and second flight days. The Anik C was deployed 9 hours 29 minutes into the mission. After nominal power-up and spin-stabilization to 50rpm, the PAM motor ignited exactly on time and placed the satellite into its required transfer orbit. Anik C arrived on station during June 24. The Palapa B satellite was deployed in a similar way on the second day (at GET 26 hours) with a further successful PAM ignition and transfer to operational orbit.

Flight activities for the first half of the mission included a complete systems check on the RMS system and SPAS pallet satellite, the activation of the OSTA-2 experiments, and operation of the other scientific experiments, including the MLR and CFES experiments on the middeck. Throughout the mission Thagard continued his experiments and investigations into SAS, and the crew completed a 30-hour experiment which lowered the cabin pressure in *Challenger* from the standard 14.7lb/sq in (1.01 bar) to 10.2lb/sq in (0.70 bar) as part of the evaluation of a new scheme which could delete the need for a pre-EVA prebreathe of 3.5 hours before each excursion.

Despite some early SPAS overheating problems, the major activity later in the mission was the deployment and retrieval of the pallet satellite, which was equipped with a TV camera and gave a spectacular first complete view of an orbiter in space above an Earth backdrop. The first release, which lasted just over 60 seconds, was achieved as *Challenger* flew over Australia at 8.05 CDT on June 22, the fifth day of flight.

For a total of about 9 hours the SPAS flew free from the orbiter, while the crew conducted simulated approach and proximity operations, designed to provide simulation data for the planned Solar Max repair mission (also to be commanded by Crippen) scheduled for the next year. A distance of 1,000ft (305m) was the maximum range between the orbiter and SPAS, which successfully demonstrated the ability of an orbiter's crew to monitor other spacecraft with radio and radar, as well as by optical methods, and to approach, fly in formation with and safely grapple it. Future applications included the Solar Max, Space Telescope and Space Station missions. After the crew had completed a complicated series of approaches to the SPAS, the pallet was eventually grappled for the last time and safely berthed in the payload bay. Whilst in free flight the SPAS had conducted a range of experiments and investigations designed to evaluate the near-orbiter environment envelope for contamination, again with future experiments and payloads in mind. The day after the free flights, the SPAS was again manoeuvred around the bay (this time attached to the RMS) in a series of arm/payload/vehicle motion studies.

Throughout its week in orbit *Challenger* again proved a clean and reliable vehicle, only minor problems occurring. The CRT-3 failed late in Day 3, but because it was near an emergency cockpit roof escape hatch release handle on the flight deck, it was decided not to repair-exchange the unit with a working unit as had been achieved on Shuttle 2.

Re-entry and landing

Shuttle 7 was originally planned to perform the first landing at KSC, which would help turnaround time for Shuttle 8 (due for launch less than two months later), and so provide proof that it could be done. With Shuttle 8 and 9 programmed for Edwards landings, and Shuttle 10 cancelled, NASA's next opportunity for a KSC landing would not occur until Shuttle 11 (later 41-B) early in 1984. But severe weather problems at KSC indicated a change to Edwards. Originally the mission planners decided to have *Challenger* attempt the landing, or even remain in orbit for a couple of extra days until the weather cleared. When the APU No. 3 played up, however, they decided that *Challenger* should come home on time, though to Edwards AFB, rather than remain flying with a running but suspect APU.

The OMS burn lasted 2 minutes 46 seconds and *Challenger* began its second descent through the atmosphere at just before 06.00 PDT. Flying the largest cross-range distance yet by an orbiter (849 miles, 1,367km), Crippen brought *Challenger* safely through the descent across the Pacific, deleting four planned test manoeuvres in order to conserve fuel and energy for the long approach flight. A normal descent was flown, despite a further problem with APU No. 3, and *Challenger* encountered no other difficulties during descent. After flying a descent of 56 minutes *Challenger* again touched its main landing gear down on solid ground as Crippen brought the vehicle to a landing on Runway 15 at Edwards AFB, the vehicle rolling some 10,450ft (3,185m) before wheel stop.

Post-landing activities

Challenger had come through its second mission fairly well. The orbiter had logged 6 days 2 hours 23 minutes 59 seconds in flight, and completed 97 full orbits, landing during orbit 98. Some 57 of 58 flight test objectives had been met, and the lowest-yet number of anomalies was logged: post-landing checks revealed 27, though this figure later rose to 42 before declining to 21. They included a damaged exterior window pane on the forward flight deck of the orbiter.

Challenger was subsequently made safe, but during the towing operations noises and chatter came from the right-hand wheel. This necessitated the jacking-up of the orbiter, removal of the wheel, extraction of the faulty braking assembly and replacement of the wheel before the towing could be completed. The landing at Edwards, a contingency site, meant that certain equipment had to arrive from KSC before safing could be completed. This put a further delay in the transfer of *Challenger* to KSC, a move which began on June 28 with a ferry flight from Edwards to Kelly AFB, Texas. On the next day *Challenger* was transferred from Kelly AFB to KSC by the SCA for Shuttle 7 payload removal, and for preparations for its third mission on Shuttle 8.

In the original flight schedule for 1983, the third flight of *Challenger* and the eighth of the programme was manifested to carry into orbit the small Indian Insat 1B comsat and the TDRS-B tracking satellite. However, the problems encountered during the Shuttle 6 mission with the malfunctioning IUS stage forced a NASA decision to dely the launch of TDRS-B until the problems with the IUS had been identified and cleared. Only four months before the scheduled launch, therefore, the mission had a sudden weight loss of 81,201lb (36,833kg) with the removal of the TDRS-B satellite, its IUS upper stage and support equipment.

Instead of cancelling the entire mission NASA decided to launch as planned with the Insat satellite, 260,000 commemorative postal covers (which thus finally found a flight place in the manifest) and the Payload Flight Test Article (PFTA), a large 7,450lb (3,379kg) dumbbell-shaped structure designed to evaluate RMS exercises with a large payload. Originally planned for Shuttle 11, the structure was brought forward, with the retention of the RMS and the addition of the extra GAS canisters to fill the nearly empty payload bay.

Despite criticism for flying the mission with substituted payloads, the space agency needed to fulfil the agreement to deploy the Insat on time, and test the operational TDRS-A satellite before Shuttle 9 flew Spacelab 1 in October, for the Spacelab required TDRS communications links during its data-gathering and dumping programme. Commanded by Shuttle 2 veteran Dick Truly, the crew of four was chosen on April 24, 1982 and on December 21, 1982 was supplemented by Bill Thornton, who was to investigate Space Adaptation Syndrome (SAS) in a continuation of the experiments began by Thagard on the previous flight.

MISSION DATA CHALLENGER 3

Sequence: Shuttle 8
Designation: 31-D
OV-099 Mission: Three
Launch Date: August 30, 1983
Launch Time: 02:32:00 EDT
Launch Site: Pad 39A, Kennedy Space Center, Cape Canaveral, Florida, USA
Launch Weight: 4,491,622lb (2,037,400kg)
Maximum Altitude: 172 miles (277km)
Inclination: 28.45°
Orbits: 96, landing during 97th
EVA Duration: None
Mission Duration: 6 days 1 hour 8 minutes 43 seconds; travelled 2.22 million miles
Landing Date: September 5, 1983
Landing Time (main gear): 00:40:42 PDT
Landing Site: Runway 22, Edwards AFB, California, USA
Rollout Distance and Duration: 9,200ft (2,805m) & 50 seconds
Crew: (Commander) Captain Richard H. Truly, USN, 45, NASA (EV-1); (Pilot) Commander Daniel C. Brandenstein, USN, 40, NASA; (MS-1) Lieutenant-Commander Dale A. Gardner, USN, 34, NASA (EV-2); (MS-2) Lieutenant-Colonel Guion S. Bluford, USAF, 40, NASA; (MS-3) Dr William E. Thornton, 54, NASA
Payload: Remote Manipulator System; Insat 1B/PAM-D (deployed Day 2, GET 01:01:16.54); Payload Flight Test Article (PFTA); US Postal Service philatelic covers (in 8 GAS canisters & 2 DFI pallet boxes); Continuous-Flow Electrophoresis System (CFES); Development Flight Instrumentation Pallet; Shuttle Student Involvement Program Experiment; Animal Enclosure Module (6 rats); GAS Canister Experiments (4); Space Adaptation Syndrome Investigation Experiments

Launch preparations

In order to meet the original mid-August launch date set by flight planners, and make possible a gap of at least 30 days between launches of Missions 8 and 9 to provide sufficient simulator time for the Spacelab crew, NASA adopted a three-shift operation in the OPF and allowed overtime and a non-standard week, in which workers toiled for five days starting and ending on any day according to job speciality, in order to launch Shuttle 8 on time.

The stacking of the twin SRBs on MLP-2 began on June 3, MLP-1 at that time being occupied by the STS-7 vehicle. SRB stacking was completed on June 20, and was followed by the mating of the ET on June 23. Meanwhile the payloads had begun arriving at KSC for installation in *Challenger* following its second mission.

Insat had arrived at the Cape Canaveral Air Force Station on May 2, and had then been mated to its PAM and installed in its support cradle in Area 60A facilities at the Cape Canaveral AFS.

Challenger arrived back at the Cape on June 29 following the Shuttle 7 mission, and was delivered to the OPF during the following day. For the next 26 days the vehicle was processed for its third mission, the processing crews working round-the-clock shifts, seven days per week.

By now the payloads were ready for installation in the payload bay of *Challenger*. The GAS experiments arrived at the Cape on various dates, were checked and mounted inside their respective canisters, all 12 being mounted inside *Challenger*'s payload bay during July 15 and 16. The PFTA payload and Development Flight Instrumentation (DFI) pallet arrived on July 12, and were stored in the OPF until installation in the spacecraft on July 21. On July 19 the Insat/PAM combination was moved to the VPF, where the satellite underwent a checkout programme to verify all orbiter-to-payload interfaces (as they were to be operated in flight) in the CITE stand.

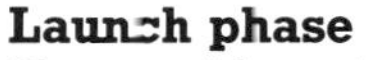

After setting a record for the fastest turnaround in the OPF, *Challenger* was moved to the VAB on July 26, carrying almost all its Shuttle 8 payload (including the same RMS used on Shuttle 7) for mating to the ET/SRB combination on that same day. The SIT was performed on July 29-30, and was followed on August 2 by the move to Pad 39A after only 7 days in the VAB. Pad to vehicle connection checks were also accomplished on that day.

For the next 28 days *Challenger* sat on the pad, nose pointed skywards as the final preparations for the spacecraft's third launch continued. The Terminal CDT was conducted on August 4, and was followed by the delivery of the Insat/PAM cargo to the PCR on August 8. On the following day the satellite was installed in *Challenger*'s payload bay, and several electrical interface checks were concluded.

Shuttle ordnance activities began on August 13, with a nine-day hold from August 15 to 25 in all other activities, as the hypergolic propellants were loaded aboard the vehicle. Pressurization of the OMS and RCS propellant and helium tanks was conducted on August 18, followed by the completion of closeout of OMS and RCS systems by August 20. Following a planned hold in the preparations for contingency work, the major clearance of pad activities resumed on August 24.

FLIGHT LOG CHALLENGER 3

1 (AUGUST 30, 1983) **00:00:00** SRB ignition command (lift-off at 02:32:00.009 EDT) **00:00:24.6** SSME throttle-down to 69% thrust for Max Q **00:00:49.7** Maximum dynamic pressure (Max Q) **00:01:01.2** SSME throttle-up to 100% thrust **00:02:05** SRB separation command **00:07:50.3** MPS throttle-down for 3-g acceleration **00:08:42** MECO command **00:09:00** ET separation **00:10:14.9** OMS-1 ignition **00:13:00.7** OMS-1 cut-off **00:14:14** APU deactivation **00:44:53** OMS-2 ignition **00:46:47.3** OMS-2 cut-off
2 (AUGUST 31, 1983) **25:16:54** Insat-1B/PAM deployment **25:31:54.2** OMS-3 ignition **25:32:00.6** OMS-3 cut-off
3 (SEPTEMBER 1, 1983) **69:56:28.2** OMS-4 ignition **69:57:05.6** OMS-4 cut-off **70:52:24.8** OMS-5 ignition **70:53-11.4** OMS-5 cut-off
5 (SEPTEMBER 3, 1983) **118:06:17** Flight control system OPS-8 checkout; APU No. 3 start **118:14:17** FCS OPS-8 checkout; APU No. 3 shutdown
7 (SEPTEMBER 5, 1983) **144:10:30** APU No. 1 activation **144:15:30.2** De-orbit manoeuvre ignition **144:18:01** De-orbit manoeuvre cut-off **144:25:31** APU activation **144:38:24** Entry interface (400,000ft, 121,920m) **144:55:00** End blackout **145:02:23** TAEM **145:08:43** Main landing gear contact **145:08:50** Nose landing gear contact **145:09:33** Wheel stop

Launch phase

The countdown to the third *Challenger* mission began on August 27, 1983, and apart from a 17-minute delay due to weather at the launch site (including severe lightning storms for 18 hours before the launch) the count-down was one of the smoothest in the programme to date.

At 02:32:00.009 EDT August 30, 1983, the SRBs and three SSMEs of *Challenger* lifted the vehicle into the sky for the third time, so beginning the eighth flight of the programme. The mission was the fourth operational flight in the programme, and was the USA's second manned night launch (the first having been the Apollo 17 lunar mission in December 1972), and as *Challenger* cleared the pad and headed on out over the Atlantic the area around the Cape lit up in a brilliant spectacle as the dazzling light from the *Challenger*'s engines illuminated the scene. The spectacle was shortlived, however, as the vehicle entered the low cloud and disappeared from ground view.

All aspects of the ascent phase of Challenger 3 occurred without incident, the SRB separation, SSME cut-off, ET separation, and two OMS burns occurring on time and resulting in *Challenger* entering its preplanned 172 mile (277km) orbit.

Left: Mission 31-D was the first night launch of the Shuttle, a highly impressive sight as *Challenger* left the pad in a blaze of light.

Shuttle 8 was flying the new high-performance SRB motors which provided an additional 3,000lb (1,361kg) payload capability compared with the motors used on the first seven missions. With both burn rate and nozzle modifications providing greater ascent capabilities, the vehicle could use just 100% throttle rather than the 104% of *Challenger*'s previous missions despite the vehicle's lighter weight.

Both SRBs were recovered intact from the Atlantic shortly after their parachute landing following the nocturnal launch from the Cape. The SRBs were then towed back to the Cape and, upon return to the processing facility, were destacked, cleaned and inspected before component re-use on other missions. It was not until September 27, over three weeks after the return of the Shuttle 8 crew, that indications of a potentially disastrous accident came to light. Morton-Thiokol, prime contractor of the SRBs and their processing, reported excessive corrosion on one of the carbon-phenolic resin liners of the SRB nozzles used for Shuttle 8. This liner was designed to sustain a burn-down to about 1-1½in (2.54-3.81cm) from a pre-flight thickness of 3in (7.62cm) as a means of protecting the nozzle's aluminium and steel structure from the 5,800°F (3,204°C) temperature of the booster's exhaust gases. Examination of the recovered Shuttle 8 boosters revealed that this liner had burned down to a thickness of only 0.2in (0.51cm) in some parts of the nozzle, and though no official time was revealed on how long remained until burnthrough, a figure of just 14 seconds has been mentioned.

Examination of the Shuttle 9 SRB liners revealed nothing unusual, but a subsequent test firing on a scale model initially duplicated the problem, though other tests did not. It was eventually determined that an anomaly during the curing process for this batch of nozzle liners was responsible for the excessive corrosion on Shuttle 8. The SRB problems forced a cancellation of the Shuttle 9 launch whilst the investigation was under way.

Orbital activities

Meanwhile, back in orbit the *Challenger* crew prepared to begin their week-long mission, unaware of the near disastrous launch they had just endured. Just 3½ hours after launch MS Bluford, the first US negro in space, powered up the CFES for its first biological runs of the mission, and MS 'Dr Bill' Thornton, now the oldest man in space at 54, set up his medical investigation gear which he operated on the mid-deck throughout the mission. The flight crew of Truly and Brandenstein oriented *Challenger* to a nose-to-Earth attitude with the starboard side pointing in the direction of flight, allowing a study of the orbiter's 'glow' phenomenon in the ISAL (Investigation of STS Atmospheric Luminosities) experiment.

Deployment of the Insat 1 satellite occurred on the second flight day at GET 25 hours 16 minutes 54 seconds. And unfortunately some damage was sustained to the satellite which caused later problems. With the major activity of the mission behind them, the crew settled down to completing the remaining research tests of their mission. During the third to fifth flight days the crew worked with the RMS and PFTA around the payload bay area of *Challenger*. For a total of over 12 hours the crew successfully grappled, manoeuvred and stowed the RMS and PFTA during these three days.

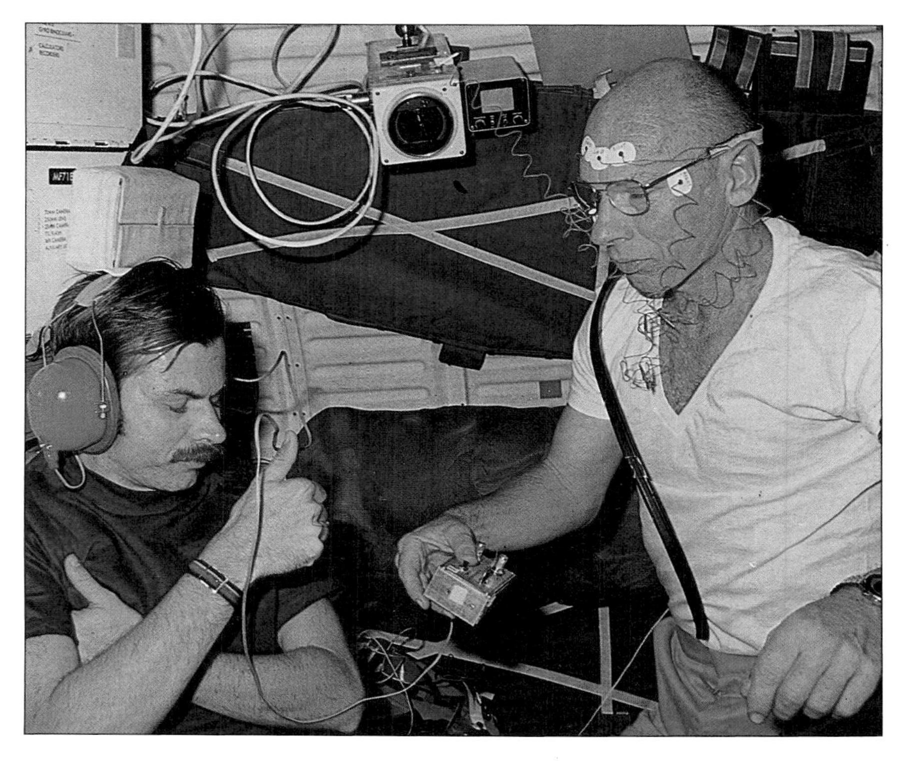

Right: Himself wired for medical readings, William Thornton conducts an audiometry experiment on Dale Gardner in the mid-deck area.

Tests with the TDRS satellite during the mission were performed between the first and sixth flight days, and encountered several difficulties including a 3-hour loss of telemetry link (corrected by the crew being awakened to switch data over to S-band link) though the crew voice commlink was not affected, and the failure of the Text And Graphics System after the transmission of five good pages of data.

Throughout the mission the crew continued work with the medical experiments and the CFES, and on the fourth flight day lowered *Challenger*'s orbit to investigate the Oxygen Interaction Experiment which allowed a higher density of oxygen molecules to impact on various test materials located in the payload bay, which was thought to erode certain materials in lower Earth orbits.

Despite difficulties with the TDRS test programme, *Challenger* itself was performing beautifully and had recorded only minor malfunctions during the week in space. On Flight Day 1 the no. 2 hydraulic circulation pump failed to start, recording a high temperature and excessive current rates during start-up attempts. This was the most significant failure of the mission, but was resolved by workarounds and maintenance of a higher temperature level in the hydraulic systems, which made it possible for the rest of the flight to be completed without the no. 2 pump but without adverse effect. Finally, during the sixth flight day two significant problems occurred. The first was the failure of data flow between GPC nos. 1 and 2. A review of GPC-1 dumped data revealed a failure-to-synchronize mode, and although the data were recovered for use they were exchanged for those in GPC-4 and placed in the least critical redundant set for re-entry. The second problem occurred with IMU no. 2, which failed in standby: the unit was successfully realigned and incorporated back into the navigational set, without the cause being identified in flight.

Re-entry and landing

Following a day of cabin stowage and configuration for landing, the crew initiated the 160-second de-orbit burn early in the morning of September 5. Using a descent profile which recorded new data on hypersonic profiles and reduced pressures on TPS tiles, Truly flew the programme's first night landing with the aid of HUD instrumentation, and guided *Challenger* to a safe landing at Edwards AFB, California. The mission descent flight plan called for nine test manoeuvres requiring 30 thruster firings or control surface inputs. All were successfully accomplished, with Truly taking manual control below Mach 1.

At GET of 6 days 1 hour 8 minutes 43 seconds, the main landing gear of *Challenger* again hit the surface of the Earth for the third time after a space mission, and after a rollout of 9,200ft (2,805m) the vehicle stopped, its third mission and the first night landing successfully completed. The success of the night operations opened a potential second 12-hour launch/landing period for future flights. In all, the third mission accomplished 54 out of 54 test objectives as well as additional tests involving two star-tracker sunlit-horizon limit tests and the ability of the star-tracker to acquire a 'rendezvous' star target.

Post-landing activities

Preliminary inspection of *Challenger* following the landing again showed the orbiter had stood up to a third mission very well, with all the tiles in place and the effects of no heat scars on its surfaces. Turnaround time at Edwards was delayed 16 hours as a result of the need to drain manifolds associated with the left-aft RCS thruster and one in the forward RCS package, which had both experienced minor leaks on orbit. This potentially hazardous activity could not be done when other post-flight ground activities were being accomplished. Whilst the orbiter was still at Edwards, the experiments hardware was removed from *Challenger*, as were the vehicle's brakes which were returned to the manufacturer: a brake rotor had shattered on Shuttle 7, but it was found that this time the brakes were fine and even the tyres showed no sign of wear.

On September 9, 1983 *Challenger* left Edwards atop the SCA for the flight back to Florida. Following a stop at Sheppard AFB in Texas, the combination continued its journey, finally arriving at the east coast launch site later on the same day. *Challenger* was now removed from the 747 and moved to the OPF for a well earned rest until flying the Shuttle 10 mission early in 1984. *Challenger* had logged over 17 days in flight in three successive missions. *Columbia* was slated to fly the ninth mission, and *Challenger* would return in February 1984. Its next mission was destined to be one of the most dramatic.

Below: Mission 31-D ended with another 'first', namely the SSTS's initial night landing, successfully accomplished by Richard Truly on Runway 22 at Edwards AFB with the aid of *Challenger*'s head-up display.

The 10th flight of the programme and the fourth for *Challenger* opened 1984 with a spectacular mission that generated both good and bad media coverage for the Shuttle. The loss of two satellites early in the mission (as a result of faulty upper-stage motors) was unnecessarily branded as a Shuttle failure, while the dramatic and very important EVAs (flying the MMUs for the first time) and the KSC landings were labelled outstanding programme successes. This then was the 10th mission, a mission which saw *Challenger* orbit the Earth for a fourth time, and astronaut Ron McNair play his saxophone in space.

Launch preparations

On September 11, 1983 *Challenger* returned from Edwards AFB atop the SCA at the end of its third mission. The orbiter was removed to the OPF for the turnaround operation for its next mission. Following its third flight, *Challenger* was planned for launch on its next mission on January 29, 1984 but was delayed for five days when the three APUs were exchanged with those from *Discovery*, on December 23, 1983. Two of the three APUs had failed on Shuttle 9 (Columbia 6), so it was decided to replace *Challenger's* units with three new and unflown units before the next mission. *Challenger* occupied Bay 1 of the OPF for 67 days of preparations. During this stay in the OPF, engineers removed the remains of the Shuttle 8 payload and began installing the Shuttle 10 configuration, which included over 70 modifications to the vehicle as part of a normal interflight turnaround programme, in addition to the removal and replacement of the SSME No. 1 engine (No. 2017) for No. 2109, all five GPCs (General Purpose Computers), the three APUs, the main landing gear brakes, the RMS elbow TV camera, the waste-collection system, RCS forward thruster R3D, payload bay TV camera D, and another 16 major items. Only then could the loading of Shuttle 10 equipment begin. On December 10, 1983 and on MLP-2 in the High Bay 3 area of the VAB, the twin SRBs for the Challenger 4 mission were stacked. After the seasonal holiday this was followed by the attachment of the ET to the SRB units on January 3, 1984.

Meanwhile the finishing touches were being made to *Challenger*. These included the installation of the MMUs, which had arrived at the Cape in September, during November 1983. Finally, on January 6, 1984, *Challenger* was moved to the VAB for mating to the ET/SRB stack, and following combined systems checks the whole vehicle was rolled out to Pad 39A on January 12. On January 20 the major payloads of the mission were transported to the pad and installed in the vehicle. *Challenger* had spent six days in the VAB, and would remain 22 days on the pad.

Before the countdown had started, contamination was discovered in two HPU units in one of the SRBs: this was found to be a chloride material which was coating the valve and hydrazine lines in the booster. The second SRB was not affected, and the situation was corrected without any delay in the launch preparations, or any slippage of the planned launch date.

At 02:00 on February 1 the countdown for the fourth *Challenger* mission began. The countdown was to last 43 hours (not including an additional nine hours of built-in holds), one hour less than that of Shuttle 9 during the previous November as a result of the shifting of a number of pre-launch activities. The subsequent events in the countdown sequence were performed without major interference to the launch preparations.

MISSION DATA CHALLENGER 4

Sequence: Shuttle 10
Designation: 41-B
OV-099 Mission: Four
Launch Date: February 3, 1984
Launch Time: 06:59:59.998 EST
Launch Site: Pad 39A, Kennedy Space Center, Cape Canaveral, Florida, USA
Launch Weight: 4,504,350lb (2,043,173kg)
Maximum Altitude: 165 miles (266km)
Inclination: 28.5°
Orbits: 127
EVA Duration: EVA—1 (February 7): 05 hours 55 minutes; EVA-2 (February 7): 06 hours 17 minutes. Total EVA: 12 hours 12 minutes
MMU Flight Duration: Unit 2: 2 flights totalling 1 hour 31 minutes; Unit 3: 3 flights totalling 3 hours 39 minutes. Total MMU Flight Duration: 5 flights totalling 5 hours 10 minutes (2 hours 31 minutes on EVA-1 and 2 hours 39 minutes on EVA-2)
Mission Duration: 7 days 23 hours 15 minutes 55 seconds; travelled 2.87 million miles
Landing Date: February 11, 1984
Landing Time (main gear): 07:16 EST
Landing Site: Runway 15, KSC, Florida, USA
Rollout Distance and Duration: 10,815ft (3,295m) & 64 seconds
Crew: (Commander) Vance D. Brand, 52, NASA; (Pilot) Lieutenant-Commander Robert L. Gibson, USN, 37, NASA; (MS-1) Lieutenant-Colonel Robert L. Stewart, US Army, 41, NASA (EV-2, MMU trained); (MS-2) Captain Bruce McCandless II, USN, 46, NASA (EV-1, MMU trained); (MS-3) Ronald E. McNair, 33, NASA
Payload: Remote Manipulator System; 2 Manned Maneuvring Units (Units 2 and 3) and Flight Support Structures; Westar VI/PAM D (deployed Day 1, GET 00:07:59.00); Integrated Rendezvous Target (deployed Day 3, GET 01:22:51.00); Palapa B2/PAM D (deployed Day 4, GET 03:02:13.16); Shuttle Student Involvement Program (6 rats in Animal Enclosure Module); GAS Canisters (5); Shuttle Pallet Satellite (not planned for deployment on this mission); 2 Cinema 360 Cameras; Mono-disperse Latex Reactor; Acoustic Containerless Experiment System; Ion Electric Focusing Experiment

Launch phase

The terminal countdown of the 10th Shuttle mission and the fourth flight of *Challenger* progressed smoothly once the APUs had been replaced, and resulted in an on-time launch at 06:59:59.998 EST from Pad 39A at the Kennedy Space Center, Florida. The ascent phase of the mission was nominal, with ontime separation of the SRBs and ET, and subsequent planned recovery of both SRBs and ET impact within the preflight footprint.

Performance of the twin SRBs indicated that their operation was well within the design specifications and that head pressures and propellant burn rates were both almost to the pre-flight levels predicted. Reviews of the separation times and thrust vector controls revealed no anomalies or hydrazine leaks. In addition, SRB power data

Above: Ronald McNair is seen in the mid-deck during Mission 41-B, his right hand near the cylindrical Mono-disperse Latex Reactor experiment.

Right: Bruce McCandless becomes the world's first 'human satellite' as he makes an untethered EVA with the aid of the Manned Maneuvering Unit.

recorded within design limit rates: one rate gyro ('C' serial number 29) had a slight deviation compared with the other rate gyros, but was still well within the design limits. The only launch-related anomaly occurred during the SRB recovery phase: one main parachute on each SRB casing failed to open, resulting in an impact rate faster by 15mph (24km/h). This did not cause serious structural damage, and all components were subsequently recovered for refurbishment.

Performance of the ET both during the countdown and launch phase was as planned, with consequent separation, re-entry and tumble activities close to the preplanned guidelines so that the ET impacted in the Indian Ocean as desired. In addition, the performance of the three SSMEs was nominal, with no anomalies occurring in the launch countdown or during the boosted phase of the launch profile. All events happened as predicted with the sole exception of the shutdown of the three SSMEs, which took place about 0.1 seconds later than predicted!

Two OMS burns kicked *Challenger* into orbit for the fourth time, and as the spacecraft flew through its first orbits of the mission, the crew prepared for a very active and demanding series of mission objectives.

FLIGHT LOG CHALLENGER 4

1 (FEBRUARY 3, 1984) **00:00:00.002** SRB ignition command (lift-off) **00:00:29.4** SSME throttledown to 73% thrust (No. 3) **00:01:00.8** SSME throttleup to 100% thrust (No. 3) **00:01:07** Maximum dynamic pressure (Max Q) **00:02:08.6** SRB separation command **00:07:50.1** MPS throttledown for 3-g acceleration (No. 3) **00:08:41.76** MECO **00:09:00** ET separation **00:10:41.8** OMS-1 ignition **00:13:12** OMS-1 cut-off **00:14:43** APU deactivation (APU No. 3) **00:45:24.8** OMS-2 ignition **00:47:29.8** OMS-2 cut-off **07:59:00** Westar/PAM satellite deployment **08:13:53.7** OMS-3 ignition (separation firing) **08:14:06.2** OMS-3 cut-off
3 (FEBRUARY 5, 1984) **45:23:23.2** OMS-4 ignition (orbit adjust firing) **45:23:54.4** OMS-4 cut-off **46:51:00** Integrated Rendezvous Target deployed/failed
4 (FEBRUARY 6, 1984) **76:13:16** Palapa/PAM satellite deployment **76:28:16.2** OMS-5 ignition (separation firing) **76:28:28.6** OMS-5 cut-off
5 (FEBRUARY 7, 1984) **95:10:00** Start first EVA (EVA-1) **101:05:00** End EVA-1
7 (FEBRUARY 9, 1984) **141:24:00** Start second EVA (EVA-2) **147:41:00** End EVA-2
8 (FEBRUARY 10, 1984) **163:58:59** OPS-8 flight-control system checkout
9 (FEBRUARY 11, 1984) **190:11:19** APU No. 2 activation **190:16:15.2** De-orbit manoeuvre ignition **190:19:03.4** De-orbit manoeuvre cut-off **190:32:27** APU Nos 1 and 3 activation **190:45:12** Entry interface (400,000ft, 121,920m) **191:01:29** End blackout **191:09:30.2** TAEM **191:15:55** Main landing gear contact **191:16:06** Nose landing gear contact **191:17:02** Wheel stop

Orbital activites

Following the opening of the payload doors, the crew prepared for the commercial part of the mission, the deployment of the first of two HS-376 communication satellites by PAM D upper stages. Following nominal predeployment activities, the first satellite (Westar VI) was deployed from the bay at GET 7 hours 59 minutes and slowly spun clear of the payload bay. Following the normal separation manoeuvre by the Shuttle, the PAM ignited some 45 minutes after deployment, but after only about 10 seconds rather than the planned 80 seconds of burn time the engine shut down, sending the satellite into an orbit of 186 by 754 miles (299 by 1,213km) instead of its planned geosynchronous one, rendering the satellite inoperable. Despite the perfect operation of the *Challenger* vehicle and crew in the deployment sequence, the failure was wrongly attributed to the Shuttle rather than to the faulty rocket stages, which could in any event have failed following a launch on an unmanned launcher. The news coverage of the mission was not helped when the Integrated Rendezvous Target balloon experiment exploded shortly after deployment on the third flight day, seriously limiting the proposed rendezvous experiments linked to the Solar Max mission planned for the following flight. Despite this loss, the crew was able to manoeuvre *Challenger* to track debris from the IRT for some time and perform useful visual observations.

Following the delay of the deployment of the second commercial satellite (Palapa B2) from *Challenger*, so that the ground teams could investigate the failure of the Westar PAM, the second satellite was smoothly deployed from *Challenger* during the fourth flight day at GET 76 hours 13 minutes: but it too was promptly sent into the wrong orbit by a faulty PAM upper stage! Later analysis of the malfunctions indicated that the trouble centred on faulty treating material, which caused the exit cones to shatter during the intense heat of the

finally touching the runway at the 5,800ft (1,768m) point down the runway. Applying light braking, Brand gradually brought the spacecraft to a halt amongst the fog-covered scrub and rivers of the KSC area, the 10th flight of the programme and the fourth for *Challenger* finally coming to an end after almost eight days away from Earth. *Challenger* had returned to a spot within a few miles of its starting point, a notable achievement in the development of the Shuttle system. While engineers continued working out the method of recovering the two stranded satellites deployed from *Challenger*, workers at the Cape began almost immediately the transport of the orbiter from the landing runway to the OPF to begin the rapid turnaround for the next mission and a rendezvous in space with Solar Max.

Post landing activities

The crew left *Challenger* only 40 minutes after the landing, and as close-out units moved around the stationary vehicle the crew returned to the KSC facilities to begin their debriefings. Following repeated problems with the Shuttle brake system it was decided to jack up the *Challenger* and remove the brakes on the landing strip before towing the vehicle to the OPF. Removal of the brakes was accomplished faster than planned, and *Challenger* was back in the OPF just 8 hours after landing. Post-flight inspections revealed only minor damage to *Challenger*. The right-hand main brakes were damaged and returned to the manufacturer. At least 31 TPS tiles would need replacement, including four lost or damaged on the left OMS pod during the mission. The pod and one main engine (No. 2, 2015) had received slight heat damage and would be replaced from *Discovery*, then undergoing preparation for its first flight. An unpromoted 'first' for the mission was that of a small bird, which collided with the *Challenger* at 500ft (150m) in the first such incident with a spacecraft, leaving some feathers near the windscreen.

firing. Almost immediately plans were put forward to attempt a rescue mission to retrieve the two stranded satellites, a feat which was successfully accomplished during the Shuttle 14 (51-A) *Discovery* mission in November 1984.

Despite these setbacks, the flight of *Challenger* itself progressed smoothly as the crew got ready for the demanding EVA programme. Preparations took several days, and included a 72-hour reduction of cabin pressure to modify the need to prebreathe for three hours at 14.7lb/sq in (1.01 bar) to only one hour at 10.2lb/sq in (0.7 bar). Following the suiting up activity and depressurization of the airlock, astronauts McCandless and Stewart began the first EVA at GET 95 hours 10 minutes, and for the following 6 hours provided some of the most spectacular and stunning visual images of the space programme to date as both men took turns in performing the first untethered EVAs in free space, flying the MMUs out to 300ft (91m) distance from *Challenger* in evaluations of the newest item of Shuttle hardware.

A second EVA followed on Flight Day 7, lasting for just over six hours and again featuring evaluation flights on the MMUs. During the two EVAs the astronauts also performed a variety of tasks which provided useful information for future planned EVA activities. These included docking operations with the SPAS-01 berthed in the payload bay, and practising with the MMU and TPAD which would be used in retrieving the Solar Max satellite on the next mission, as well as working on the mock-up Solar Max main electronic box. Also demonstrated successfully was the satellite refuelling technique, using a mock-up Landsat fuelling port and red-dyed freon as the fuel to confirm seal integrity. The astronauts also rode the mobile foot restraint on the RMS in further evaluations of manoeuvrable work stations for EVA astronauts.

In addition to the planned activities of the EVAs, several unscheduled events were also undertaken. The EVA astronauts removed the payload bay TV camera D for inflight maintenance within the cabin on EVA-1, and reinstalled it during EVA-2. The crew reported a slight 'chatter' with the MMU during +X translations, experienced some difficulty with locking their feet into the foot restraints, and encountered some communication problems, though none of these was serious in nature. One significant problem was encountered with the RMS during a checkout before EVA-2: it operated normally except for the wrist joint, which had functioned perfectly on EVA-1. Despite repeated crew attempts to recover use of the arm, the system was stowed and all planned RMS and deployed SPAS-01 activities for the second EVA were cancelled. The EVA astronauts also repaired a slide wire linkage, and McCandless retrieved a foot restraint that had come loose.

The contrast of lost satellites with spectacular EVAs was supported by the programme of experiments, some of which needed the attention of the crew while others operated automatically.

On February 7 the five Shuttle astronauts were joined in space by three Soviet cosmonauts aboard Soyuz T-10, resulting in a record of eight persons in space at the same time.

Despite some nagging problems of the type that plague every mission including the recurring problem with the management of trash, *Challenger* performed well during its fourth trip around the world. As the mission drew to a close the crew prepared for the first landing at KSC, delayed from the seventh mission.

Re-entry and landing

Following a go for landing and a weather-clear call from chief astronaut John Young, the crew initiated the OMS burn for 168 seconds to begin the long descent to KSC. Re-entry was nominal in all respects, and during the descent phase the crew undertook 10 independent flight test manoeuvres as *Challenger* streaked across the USA, finally arriving over KSC with a double sonic boom and flying out over Launch Pad 39B before alighting on the Shuttle Landing Facility 1,930ft (588m) down the runway on its main gear, the nose gear

Right: Another pioneering effort on Mission 41-B was the validation of the Mobile Foot Restraint attachment for the RMS arm, allowing a flight deck controller to move the EVA astronaut without effort to any point in the payload bay, so maximizing EVA work capabilities.

On February 18, 1983 NASA announced the names of a five-man Shuttle crew which was to fly a rescue/repair mission to the ailing Solar Max satellite. This had been launched by an unmanned vehicle from the Cape on February 14, 1980 to conduct an extensive programme of solar observations from Earth orbit. However, on November 23, 1980 three fuses in the attitude-control system blew and the satellite was left without attitude-pointing capability for four of the six on-board telescopes: despite limited data return by spin-stabilization of the satellite, all important information coming from the satellite was lost or could not be gathered. On the plus side, however, Solar Max had been designed with the Shuttle in mind and had the facilities for on-orbit retrieval and repair. Even before the Shuttle had logged time in space detailed plans were formulated early in 1981 to allow a 1984 mission to rendezvous with the stricken satellite, capture it, repair the faulty equipment and redeploy it once more into operational orbit. *Challenger* was assigned the mission, originally labelled STS-13 but redesignated Shuttle 11 after the cancellation of Shuttles 10 and 12.

Launch preparations

Challenger was towed to the OPF shortly after landing after its fourth mission, Shuttle 10 (41-B), on February 11, 1984 to undergo turnaround activities for an April 6 launch to meet the rendezvous requirements for the Solar Max repair. During the next 32 days the processing teams worked hard to extract the Challenger 4 payload and insert the Challenger 5 payload plus all the equipment needed to support the Solar Max repair mission.

On February 17, 1984 SSME No. 2020, which had been installed on *Discovery*, was removed for reinstallation on *Challenger*: it would fly in the No. 2 position, replacing SSME No. 2015 which had received slight heat damage during re-entry on the Shuttle 10 mission. Only SSME No. 2012 remained attached to the No. 3 position which it had occupied since 1982 and the initial pre-maiden flight processing of *Challenger*.

On February 17, and again three days later on February 20, the OPF Bay 2 location had to be evacuated when minor leaks of dangerous nitrogen tetroxide were detected in the ground servicing units draining the propellants from *Challenger*'s tanks. No injuries were sustained as only a small quantity of gas escaped into the atmosphere, but the incidents resulted in about 7 hours of lost processing time, a factor significant because of the tight constraints on the launch turnaround between the two missions. Adequate safety procedures were met each time, and the problems were soon corrected to allow the processing to continue without major delays.

The first leak was caused by a B-shaped nut on the ground servicing plumbing, which came loose and allowed an escape of sufficient nitrogen tetroxide to trigger the gas sensors and force an evacuation of the OPF bay. This first mishap occurred as KSC technicians were preparing the equipment necessary to drain *Challenger*'s left OMS pod lines as part of the pod removal process to exchange the system with the left-hand OMS pod from *Discovery*, which was undergoing preparations for its maiden flight at the same time that *Challenger* was being prepared for its fifth mission. The second incident occurred with a leaking O-ring seal in a ground filter assembly which sprang a leak during the completion of OMS deservicing operations.

On February 22 an unflown RMS arm was installed on *Challenger* after ground crews were unable to repair the wrist yaw motor failure which had curtailed the use of the original *Challenger* RMS in the second EVA of the previous mission. Delivered in December 1983, this arm was to have been installed on *Chal-*

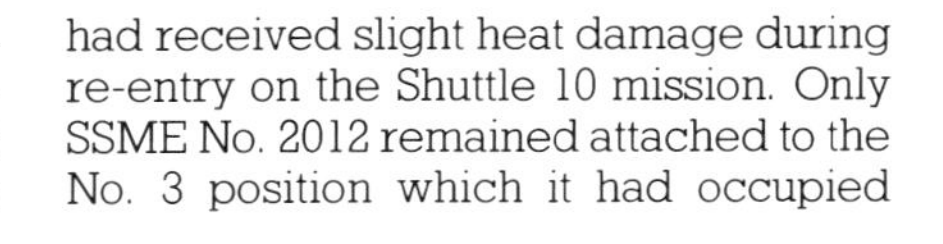
Below: Van Hoften (left) and Nelson pre-breathe before an EVA, the object being to purge the astronauts' bodies of the nitrogen that might otherwise cause spatial 'bends'.

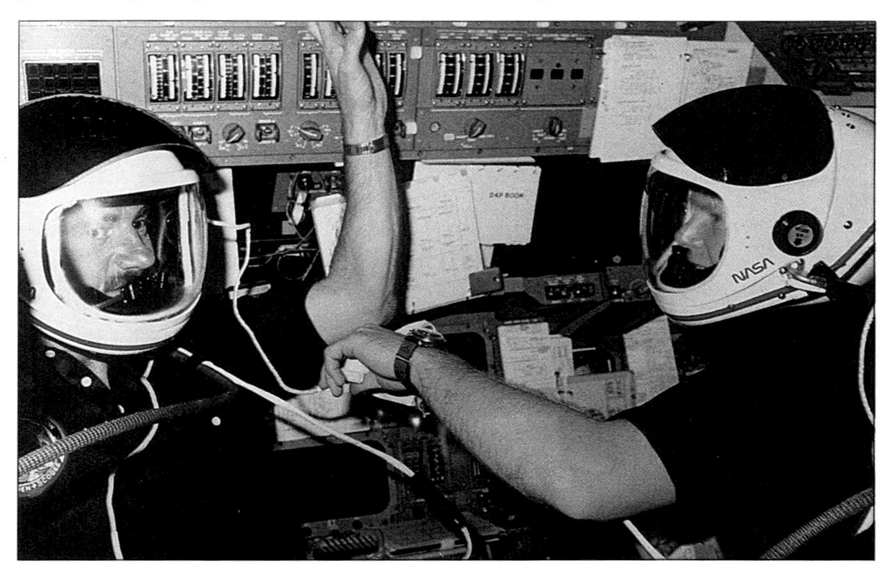

MISSION DATA CHALLENGER 5

Sequence: Shuttle 11
Designation: 41-C
OV-099 Mission: Five
Launch Date: April 6, 1984
Launch Time: 08:57:59.999 EST
Launch Site: Pad 39A, Kennedy Space Center, Cape Canaveral, Florida, USA
Launch Weight: 4,508,234lb (2,044,901kg)
Maximum Altitude: 290 miles (467km)
Inclination: 28.5°
Orbits: 106, landing during 107th
EVA Duration: EVA—1 (April 8): 02 hours 57 minutes; EVA-2 (April 11): 06 hours 16 minutes. Total EVA: 09 hours 13 minutes
MMU Flight Duration: Unit 2: 1 flight totalling 42 minutes; Unit 3: 1 flight totalling 28 minutes. Total MMU Flight Duration: 2 flights totalling 1 hour 10 minutes (42 minutes on EVA-1 and 28 minutes on EVA-2)
Mission Duration: 6 days 23 hours 40 minutes 7 seconds; travelled 2.88 million miles
Landing Date: April 13, 1984
Landing Time (main gear): 05:38:07 PST
Landing Site: Runway 17, Edwards AFB, California, USA
Rollout Distance and Duration: 8,716ft (2,657m) & 48 seconds
Crew: (Commander) Captain Robert L. Crippen, USN, 46, NASA; (Pilot) Major Francis R. Scobee, USAF (Ret), 44, NASA; (MS-1) Terry J. Hart, 37, NASA; (MS-2) Dr George D. Nelson, 33, NASA (EV-1, MMU trained); (MS-3) Dr James D. Van Hoften, 39, NASA (EV-2, MMU trained)
Payload: Remote Manipulator System; 2 Manned Maneuvering Units (Units 2 and 3) and Flight Support Structures; LDEF containing 57 experiments (deployed Day 2. GET 01:03:21.27); Fixed Service Structure (for Solar Max satellite); Shuttle Student Involvement Program (study of 3,000 honey bees in zero-g); IMAX camera; Cinema 360 Camera

FLIGHT LOG CHALLENGER 5

1 (APRIL 6, 1984) **00:00:00.001** SRB ignition command (lift-off) **00:00:25.8** SSME throttledown to 67% thrust (No. 3) **00:00:50.5** Maximum dynamic pressure (Max Q) **00:00:57.6** SSME throttleup to 104% thrust (No. 3) **00:02:06** SRB separation command **00:07:30.4** MPS throttledown for 3-g acceleration (No. 3) **00:08:31.2** MECO **00:08:49.3** ET separation **00:12:11** APU deactivation (APU No. 3) **00:42:54.1** OMS-2 ignition (OMS-1 not made: direct ascent) **00:44:29.3** OMS-2 cut-off
2 (APRIL 7, 1984) **27:21:27** LDEF deploy by RMS
3 (APRIL 8, 1984) **48:20:00** Start first EVA (EVA-1) **51:17:00** End EVA-1
5 (APRIL 10, 1984) **95:54:20** Solar Max RMS grapple
6 (APRIL 11, 1984) **115:00:00** Start second EVA (EVA-2) **121:16:00** End EVA-2
7 (APRIL 12, 1984) **139:28:29** Solar Max RMS release **143:55:29** OPS-8 flight-control system checkout
8 (APRIL 13, 1984) **166:26:33** APU No. 1 activation **166:31:30.9** De-orbit manoeuvre ignition **166:35:32.8** De-orbit manoeuvre cut-off **166:56:58** APU Nos 2 and 3 activation **167:09:51.6** Entry interface (400,000ft, 121,920m) **167:26:12** End blackout **167:33:54.5** TAEM **167:40:07** Main landing gear contact **167:40:23** Nose landing gear contact **167:40:55** Wheel stop

Left: *Challenger* waits on Launch Complex 39A for its eventual fuelling after roll-out for the 41-C mission. This is the view from the crawler transporter, the tractor that moves the Shuttle assembly on its Mobile Launch Platform from the Vehicle Assembly Building.

lenger at an earlier date but it had then been decided that *Challenger* could retain the original Canadian-supplied arm for its initial flights. The change was now made as a direct result of the inflight failure of the previous system and the lack of time to troubleshoot the problem before the Solar Max mission, for which the full operational use of the RMS was essential.

As *Challenger* was prepared for its new task, activities at the VAB were centred on the other elements of the Shuttle 11 stack. On February 16 the twin SRBs were stacked on MLP-1 in High Bay 3, followed by the mating of the ET to the SRBs on February 28.

On March 14 *Challenger* was towed to the VAB and mated with the ET/SRB combination for final checks and tests before the move to the pad, which was accomplished five days later on March 19. Finally installed on Pad 39A, the vehicle spent the next 19 days undergoing full systems checks and preparations for an April 6 launch, carrying the LDEF-1 satellite and twin MMUs (the same units flown on the previous mission). All was set for a spectacular mission.

The crew participated in a dry Countdown Demonstration Test (CDT) at the Cape during March 20-21. During final launch countdown a multiplexer/demultiplexer on *Challenger* failed and was replaced without further incident.

Launch phase

At 08:57:59.999 EST on April 6 1984 NASA launched the 11th Shuttle mission, the second of 1984 and the fifth for *Challenger*. In order to conserve valuable OMS fuel for the rendezvous phase of the mission, it was decided to fly the trajectory as a 'direct ascent' profile, which meant burning the SSMEs for a few seconds longer to result in a 288 mile (463km) high orbit and a cut-off velocity of 26,021ft (7,931m) per second, which was 351ft (107m) per second faster than previous standard velocity limits. This increase of SSME burn duration resulted in the deletion of an OMS-1 burn and required only the OMS-2 (*sic*) burn to place the vehicle in the required orbit.

All aspects of the ascent profile were nominal, with both SRBs recovered despite the failure of one main parachute to open fully. The ET impacted within the planned Hawaii footprint. Despite the fact that the Shuttle reached the velocity required to reach the final orbital attitude, post-launch analysis was conducted into the reason why *Challenger* used all of the main margin fuel capacity plus a portion of the extra propellant carried for any unforeseen problems which might occur. The ascent never fell to minimum flight safety levels but did get closer than was desirable, resulting in only 5,200lb (2,359kg) of oxygen propellant left for SSME consumption at cut-off. It was thought that lower-than-predicted performance of the twin SRBs, the SSMEs or vehicle mass pre-flight calculation error contributed to a low performance ascent trajectory. The only other problem during ascent was with the gas generator valve module temperature on all three APUs, which recorded a short-duration temperature drop during ascent.

Post-flight analysis of the SRBs indicated near-perfect performance. However, the aft skirt shoe shim material on the south posts remained intact, while the north post shims were missing and eroded by flame impingement, a condition which had been observed on previous flights. Separation time of the SRBs was about 1.4 seconds earlier than predicted and chase plane video and photo coverage revealed that one of the main parachutes on the right-hand SRB failed to fill. All the parachutes were recovered and received post-flight examinattion: some had been damaged by SRB hot propellant debris.

The cut-off of the three main engines occurred at GET 511 seconds, compared with the pre-launch predicted time of 510 seconds. Now safely in orbit, *Challenger* opened its payload bay doors and headed for a space rendezvous with Solar Max.

Orbital activities

Initial activities once *Challenger* was safely on orbit were kept to a minimum on the first few days in order to rest the crew and allow them to adapt fully to the weightlessness of space before the hectic days ahead of them. On the first

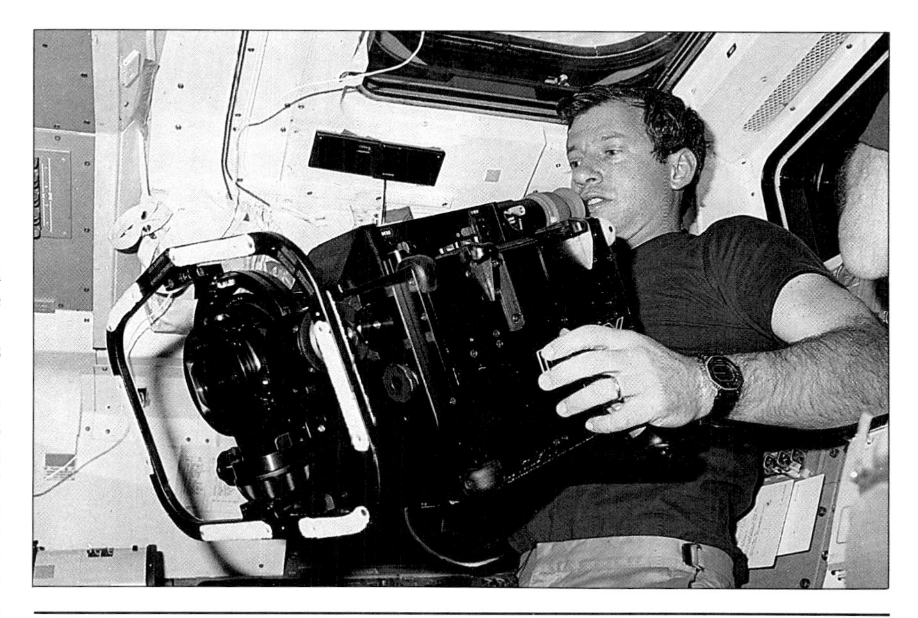

Right: Terry Hart, mission specialist on the 41-C flight, holds the 70lb (31.75kg) IMAX 65-mm camera on the orbiter's flight-deck. The high-resolution camera uses a 1,000ft (305m) film rolls with 3-minute running time. Roll changes were done in a black bag.

Manned Maneuvering Unit

When not in use the MMU rests in the Flight Support Station mounted in the payload bay.

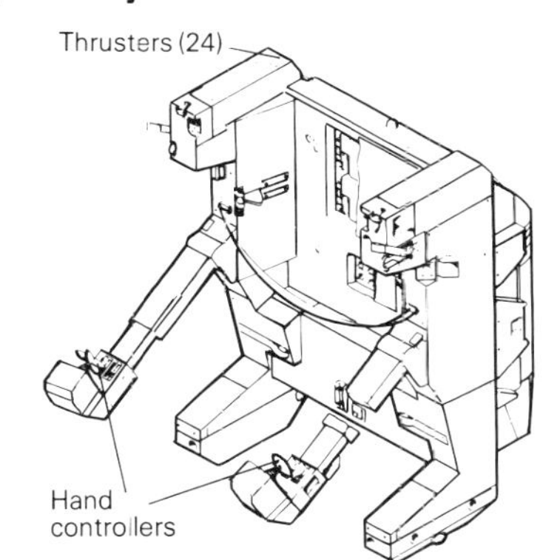

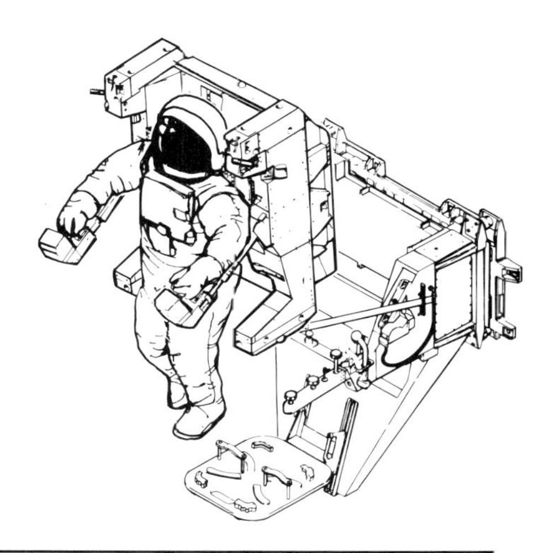

Right: At work in the payload bay, Van Hoften shows the neatness of the Extravehicular Mobility Unit spacesuit and its backpack Primary Life Support System.

flight day the systems of the RMS and LDEF payload were checked, and initial activities for the rendezvous manoeuvres which would position *Challenger* alongside Solar Max on Day 3 were carried out. The LDEF was released by the RMS on flight day 2 at GET 27 hours 21 minutes after several manoeuvres had been performed with the LDEF attached to gain extra data for RMS activities with heavy payloads, such as accomplished with the PFTA on Shuttle 8 in 1983. Once the orbiter was in the correct position, all movements were halted and allowed to damp out. The experiment-filled satellite was released to begin what at that time was planned as a 12-month orbital mission. But at the time of the *Challenger*'s tragedy in 1986 the LDEF was still circling the Earth, with the likelihood of extending that duration to probably five years.

By the third mission day preparations were well under way for the first of two EVAs to capture and repair the Solar Max satellite, now floating just outside the windows of *Challenger*, the successful result of almost three days of orbital dynamics and skilful flying by the *Challenger* crew. With the orbiter flying just 200ft (61m) from the ailing satellite, the EVA crew of Nelson and Van Hoften exited the airlock to begin their first EVA at GET 48 hours 20 minutes. With Van Hoften monitoring his progress, Nelson donned the starboard MMU, collected the TPAD docking retention system and slowly moved out to the Solar Max satellite. After matching the rotational rate of the solar observatory, the astronaut closed in to attempt several dockings with the TPAD system. However, the TPAD refused to fire its retention latches and capture the Solar Max's trunnion pin, much to the frustration of Nelson, who even tried grasping the solar wing of the satellite to slow its rotation in preparation for an attempted RMS grapple, but to no avail.

Left: Workaday life in space is foreshadowed by this shot of Nelson flying the starboard MMU towards the Solar Max satellite. This capture in fact failed because of technical problems with the TPAD system.

In fact this increased the instability of the satellite, and with MMU consumables running low Nelson was forced to return to *Challenger*. While the problem of capturing the satellite was investigated, the EVA crew re-entered *Challenger*. With time for the capture running out, ground controllers tried to point the satellite directly at the sun so that the onboard batteries could be powered up sufficiently to enable controllers to command the satellite to stop its spin and so allow the RMS to grapple the satellite. This work continued into the night of April 8-9, and while the crew slept, ground controllers at the Goddard Space Flight Center fought to halt the satellite's rotation, a result finally achieved in the early hours of April 9.

As the crew members awoke to the news that the satellite had stopped spinning, they faced a more important problem of low fuel supplies as a direct result of prolonged station keeping with the satellite after the failed EVA capture the previous day. Therefore the satellite was again commanded slowly to spin-up again allowing repeated grapple attempts without excessive orbiter manoeuvring as a way of conserving fuel, which was expected to fall to only 6% if *Challenger* attempted solo grapple manoeuvres. The result of so low a fuel margin also ruled out further attempts at an MMU flight to grapple the Solar Max, as the Shuttle would not have enough fuel left to attempt the rescue of the astronaut if the MMU failed. The fourth day saw the spin-up of the satellite which now had sufficient power in its batteries, while the crew rested before attempting the RMS grapple.

The next day Crippen gingerly manoeuvred *Challenger* towards Solar Max, conserving as much fuel as possible to allow a second approach if required. Air-to-ground commentary was kept to a minimum as all five crew members concentrated on the final approach manoeuvre and, as *Challenger* moved out of radio contact, all that ground control could do was sit and wait for the news of the capture attempt. As *Challenger* moved into range high above the Australian tracking station the news burst into Mission Control from Crippen: 'Okay, we've got it,' as the RMS finally lowered the satellite into the support structure in the payload bay. 'Outstanding,' came the congratulatory reply. Hart had grabbed the satellite at the first attempt and now it was safely locked in the payload bay awaiting repair.

Left: Nelson and Van Hoften work on the captured Solar Max in the payload bay. The two EVA astronauts are using the mobile foot restraint on the RMS arm for mobility. The repaired satellite was then redeployed into orbit by the RMS.

The following day the EVA crew of Nelson and Van Hoften again entered the payload bay of *Challenger*, now occupied by the Solar Max satellite at the far end. For the next 7 hours 18 minutes the crew worked in the bay, the majority of this time on the Solar Max satellite atop RMS foot restraints as the astronauts removed the modular attitude-control system of the satellite and replaced it with a new one. One hour 15 minutes later the men were busy replacing the main electronics box, which was difficult to remove as it was restrained by gold-coloured thermal covers and small screws not intended for inflight maintenance, then release electrical connections held by no less than 22 screws. The electrical wiring was retained on the new unit by screw-less plastic attachments.

With the repair successfully completed, the crew stowed away the tools and, as the satellite was prepared for release into space again, Van Hoften performed a limited test flight of the other MMU in the confines of the payload bay, not being allowed out into deep space as *Challenger*'s fuel was too low. Once the RMS had safely grappled the satellite again, the astronauts returned to the airlock to rejoin their colleagues in the final phase of the mission. On the following day, after all movement had ceased on the arm and the satellite had been checked, it was cast adrift in space to continue its important solar research work with a new breath of life.

The crew now concentrated on the completion of the onboard experiments, stowing gear and preparing the spacecraft for what was planned as the second KSC landing attempt.

Re-entry and landing

With the crew up and ready for landing at the Cape, the 'go' was given for closing the payload bay doors and performing the de-orbit burn for approach to KSC. Just 15 minutes before Crippen initiated that burn and committed descent, the wave-off for a KSC landing (because of low cloud cover) was relayed to the crew, who thus received a one-orbit bonus to their flight, already extended one day as a result of the late repair of Solar Max.

As Crippen brought *Challenger* home for his second and the orbiter's fifth time, he initiated eight of the 10 planned flight test maneouvres during the descent profile to Runway 17 at Edwards AFB. The 242-second OMS descent burn occurred during the 107th orbit, with the vehicle flying tail-first over the Indian Ocean, to provide a velocity reduction of 461.1ft (140.5m) per second. As *Challenger* landed at Edwards AFB at 05:38 PST, chief astronaut John Young, veteran of six spaceflights including two Shuttle missions, simulated a *Challenger* landing in the Gulfstream Shuttle Training Aircraft at the time the orbiter was supposed to have landed at the Cape. He encountered moderate rain and cloud during the approach, confirming the correct action in moving to an Edwards AFB landing.

Post-landing activities

After the crew exited at the end of a very eventful but highly successful mission, ground crews again prepared to configure the orbiter for the long haul back to the Cape for its next mission, even then under threat of cancellation. On the whole the *Challenger* had again stood up well to its fifth trip into space, with the crew completing all 25 pre-flight objectives with 100% success.

In all, *Challenger* logged 33 anomalies during its fifth trip into space. The most serious again occurred with the waste-collection system, though further difficulties were encountered with the Ku-band rendezvous radar and other EVA-related equipment including the TPAD system.

Post-flight analysis of the *Challenger*'s braking system revealed that all four main landing gear brakes had been damaged. Cracked beryllium rotors were found on both the right-hand inboard and left-hand inboard nos 3 and 4 rotors, and on the no. 4 rotor of the left-hand outboard brake. In addition carbon edges had been chipped, retainer washers were missing, drive clips had been bent, and all four brakes had suffered carbon surface debris on the outer two rotors. The same types of damage had been recorded on *Challenger*'s second mission (Shuttle 7) in June 1983. This time the brakes had been applied at 110kts (204km/h) ground speed, with deceleration by Crippen being varied from 12 to 6ft (3.66 to 1.83m) per second^2 along 2,142ft (653m) of braking distance in the 8,716ft (2,657m) rollout distance.

On April 17 *Challenger* was ferried from Edwards AFB to Kelly AFB, San Antonio, Texas, and following an overnight stay was then transported from Kelly to the KSC for the start of preparations for its sixth mission. At that time it was not all that clear what the mission designation would be.

Above: Van Hoften flying one of the Manned Maneuvering Units along *Challenger*'s payload bay. There can be few more impressive or beautiful backdrops than the sunlit Earth above the EVA astronaut.

Below: Nelson and Van Hoften (right, on the mobile foot restraint) change a faulty attitude control module on the Solar Max, in the process confirming the ability of men to work usefully in a space environment.

When *Challenger* arrived at KSC atop the Boeing 747 SCA on April 18, 1984 at the end of its fifth mission, it was not clear just which mission the orbiter would undertake next. It was originally planned that the vehicle would fly mission 41-E in July, but when that mission was cancelled earlier in the year *Challenger* was booked for 41-H (both of these were dedicated DoD missions). Mission 41-H was also tentatively booked for the second civilian TDRS satellite launch.

As the months of 1984 continued, so did the problems associated with clearing the IUS for further use. As a result of this the 41-H mission was cancelled. At the same time the August mission of 41-G had slipped to October, and it was decided to fly the mission with *Challenger* rather than *Columbia* as planned, because the latter was not yet available as it was undergoing systems upgrading at the Rockwell plant in California.

Mission 41-G proved to be the 13th of the programme and centred on a scientific research mission, observing the Earth in more detail than had been accomplished on any previous U.S. mission since Skylab 4 in 1973-74.

Launch preparations

Challenger was offloaded from the SCA on April 19 and towed to Bay 2 of the OPF for the preparations before its sixth mission. Processing for the 41-G mission took 69 working days in the OPF, and included the removal of the remaining 41-C payload and corrective action to the vehicle following that flight. On June 25 *Challenger*'s back-up GPC was removed and installed in *Discovery*, then on Pad 39A having suffered a launch abort situation at T-9 after failure of *Discovery*'s original computer during the countdown.

Whilst in the OPF, *Challenger* underwent engine changes which resulted in the exchange of No. 1 engine from No. 2109 to No. 2023 on July 20, followed by the No. 3 engine after the Shuttle 12 mission in September, when *Challenger*'s original engine (No. 2012) developed a fault in a hydraulic pump and needed to be replaced by the recently-flown *Discovery* engine. This second engine exchange was accomplished whilst the vehicle was on the pad.

On August 9, 1984 the payload for the 41-G mission was carefully lowered into the payload bay of the orbiter, and began a long series of equipment checks and compatability tests with the orbiter systems. Finally, at 08:00 on Saturday September 8, *Challenger* was towed, between rain showers, from the OPF to the VAB. Over the next five days it was mated to the ET and SRB stack and underwent a full combined systems checkout.

Awaiting the orbiter were the twin SRBs and ET, which had originally been stacked for the subsequently cancelled 41-F mission in August. The SRB stacking process had been started on June 6, and the ET was mated on June 19. Once the 41-F mission had been removed from the launch schedule, the assigned and stacked SRB/ET combination was reallocated to the 41-G mission. Stacking of the 13th Shuttle mission occurred on MLP-1 in High Bay 3 of the VAB.

On September 13, 1984 the Shuttle 13 combination slowly made its 3 mile (4.8km) trip to Pad 39A, where it spent the next 23 days until launch.

Launch phase

After one of the smoothest launch countdowns in the programme, the crew of *Challenger* entered the vehicle and occupied a record number of seats, a further addition in the turnaround cycle. The NASA crew had been selected in November 1983, and was supplemented early in 1984 by Marc Garneau, the first Canadian in space, and on June 13 by the Australian-born but naturalized US citizen and US Navy civilian oceanographer Paul Scully-Power. For the first time seven persons (five male and two female) would be launched in the same vehicle at the same time. In addition Sally Ride and Kathy Sullivan were the first pair of female astronauts on a crew, and Sullivan was assigned to become the first US female astronaut to perform EVA.

The launch of the Shuttle 13 mission occurred on time at 07:03 on October 5, 1984 in a spectacular pre-dawn lift-off into a twilight blue sky. The ascent profile of *Challenger*, heading over the north Atlantic to a 57° inclination orbit, was near perfect with SRB and ET separation and recovery/entry as predicted. The SSMEs performed without incident and, with perfect OMS-1 and OMS-2 burns, *Challenger* was kicked into Earth orbit for the sixth time in 18 months, an impressive record. Another record set was that the commander on this mission was making a fourth Shuttle flight (his third on *Challenger*). That Crippen had also been commander of the orbiter's previous flight was a notable achievement, made possible by the fact that NASA was using this veteran astronaut to determine the minimum time feasible between two flights to plan adequate training cycles between assignments for future crews.

Orbital activities

For the next eight days the seven crew members busied themselves with their packed and varied scientific programme, only briefly interrupted by minor hardware problems, none of which seriously hampered an otherwise highly successful flight which successfully accomplished all 14 detailed test objectives as well as a further 11 supplementary test objectives. The OSTA-3 experiments were completed fully, apart from the SIR-B radar experiment, which was only partially successful.

Shortly after launch the crew reported slight damage to the TPS blanket coverage, noting that a strip of insulation was missing from the right side of the SSME housing, and that a tile had been detached from the left OMS pod. This was thought to be the result of severe aerodynamic forces or high winds during the ascent, but did not present a serious or dangerous condition to the vehicle or crew. Another minor problem early in the flight was the failure of a small thruster, which was not a critical problem.

The deployment of the ERBE satellite by RMS was delayed by two orbits after the crew discovered that the satellite's solar panels would not deploy as programmed: the crew thus pointed the wings at the sun to 'defrost' the panels and so permit them to open normally, which they did after four attempts. High above California the RMS released the satellite (after a procedural error had also been corrected during the unplanned delay) at GET 11 hours 15 minutes. Throughout most of the mission difficulties with the Ku-band antenna and the SIR-B experiment had been experienced. These problems were tackled by the crew and ground control, and a solution was found in manoeuvring the orbiter and non-tracking antenna to fix on the TDRS satellite. The EVA was delayed in the flight plan to accommodate further data collection on the malfunctioning SIR-B equipment. The TDRS-A satellite suffered a loss of contact for 11 hours before finally being restored to working order, the result of a large cosmic storm, and this did not help the already troubled data-gathering task.

During the seventh flight day Leestma and Sullivan successfully completed a 3 hour 30 minute EVA in the payload bay of *Challenger*, the first by an American female astronaut. Though no MMUs were carried or satellites repaired, the two astronauts performed useful work in demonstrating satellite-refuelling techniques in hooking up dummy fuel transfer lines with which they continued working after entering *Challenger* at the end of the EVA. Satellite refuelling missions were then in the planning stages to extend the useful operational life of orbiting platforms whose attitude-control fuel had been used, thus rendering them inoperative. The initial target then planned for this type of EVA work was Landsat 4 in 1987 (72-A). The EVA crew also manually configured the Ku-band antenna and inspected the SIR-B antenna, which had had to be pushed shut by the RMS earlier in the mission. After Leestma performed a somersault in the

Right: Kathy Sullivan (left) and Sally Ride synchronize watches just before entering *Challenger* for the seven-person 41-G mission.

MISSION DATA CHALLENGER 6

Sequence: Shuttle 13
Designation: 41-G
OV-099 Mission: Six
Launch Date: October 5, 1984
Launch Time: 07:03:00.0 EDT
Launch Site: Pad 39A, Kennedy Space Center, Cape Canaveral, Florida, USA
Launch Weight: 4,499,000lb (2,040,712kg)
Maximum Altitude: 218 miles (351km)
Inclination: 57°
Orbits: 133
EVA Duration: EVA-1 3 hours 27 minutes
Mission Duration: 8 days 5 hours 23 minutes 33 seconds; travelled 3.04 million miles
Landing Date: October 13, 1984
Landing Time (main gear): 12:26:33 EDT
Landing Site: Runway 33, Kennedy Space Center, Florida, USA
Rollout Distance and Duration: 10,565ft (3,220m) & 59 seconds
Crew: (Commander) Captain Robert L. Crippen, USN, 47, NASA; (Pilot) Commander Jon A. McBride, USN, 41, NASA; (MS-1) Dr Sally K. Ride, 33, NASA; (MS-2) Dr Kathryn D. Sullivan, 33, NASA (EV-2); (MS-3) Lieutenant-Commander David C. Leestma, USN, 35, NASA (EV-1); (PS-1) Commander Marc Garneau, Canadian Navy, 35, NRC; (PS-2) Paul D. Scully-Power, USN, 40
Payloads: Remote Manipulator System; OSTA-3: Shuttle Imaging Radar B (SIR—B)/Large Format Camera/Measurement of Air Pollution from Satellites (MAPS)/Feature Identification and Location Experiment (FILE); Earth Radiation Budget Experiment: ERB Satellite (deployed Day 1, GET 11 hours 15 minutes 22 seconds)/ERB Non-Scanner and Scanner/Stratospheric Aerosol and Gas Experiment (SAGE-2); Canadian Experiment Programme (CANEX): NRC Space Vision System/Advanced Composite Materials Exposure/Measurements Using a Sunphotometer/Atmospheric Emission and Shuttle Glow Measurements/Space Adaptation Syndrome Experiment Studies; GAS Canisters (8); Radiation Monitoring Equipment (RME); Thermo-Luminescent Dosimeter (TLD); Orbital Refueling System

FLIGHT LOG CHALLENGER 6

1 (OCTOBER 5, 1984) **00:00:00** SRB ignition command (lift-off) **00:00:18.4** SSME throttledown to 92% thrust (No. 3) **00:00:26** SSME throttledown to 65% thrust (No. 3) **00:00:51** Maximum dynamic pressure (Max Q) **00:00:58** SSME throttleup to 100% thrust (No. 3) **00:02:04** SRB separation command **00:07:52** MPS throttledown for 3-g acceleration **00:08:50.8** MECO **00:09:08.4** ET separation **00:10:50.5** OMS-1 ignition **00:13:04** OMS-1 cut-off **00:13:57** APU deactivation (APU No. 3) **00:46:30** OMS-2 ignition **00:48:54** OMS-2 cut-off **11:15:22** ERBE satellite release by RMS
7 (OCTOBER 11, 1984) **148:35:00** Start first EVA **152:02:00** End EVA-1
8 (OCTOBER 12, 1984) **170:43:04** OPS-8 flight-control system checkout
9 (OCTOBER 13, 1984) **196:22:01** APU No. 2 activation **196:27:00** De-orbit manoeuvre ignition **196:29:22** De-orbit manoeuvre cut-off **196:39:09** APU Nos 1 and 3 activation **196:52:04** Entry interface (400,000ft, 121,920m) **197:09:00** End blackout **197:17:12** TAEM **197:23:33** Main landing gear contact **197:23:47** Nose landing gear contact **197:24:32** Wheel stop

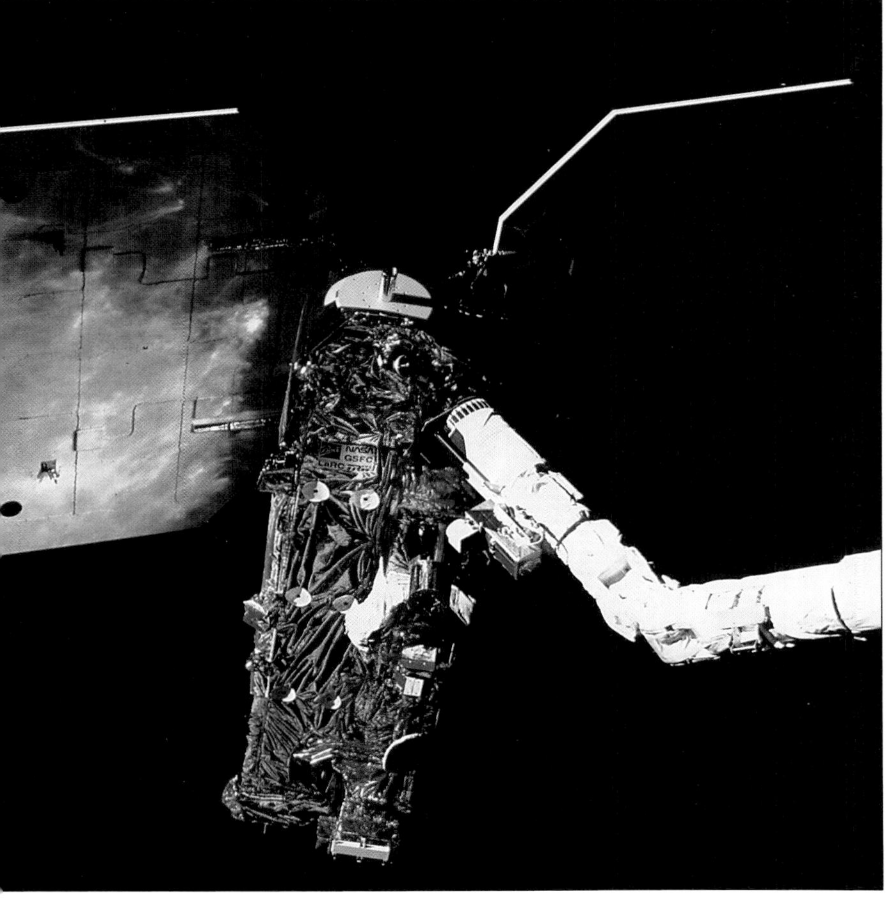

Left: The value of the RMS arm was confirmed during 41-G, when Sally Ride was able to warm and shake the arm-deployed Earth Radiation Budget Satellite to free its solar panels, which had failed to open properly.

Above: The RMS arm is used to secure the SIR-B's antenna, which troubled the crew throughout the on-orbit phase of the mission and delayed the EVA, which was in the event able to inspect the malfunctioning antenna.

bay to retrieve a loose airlock safety cover, the EVA personnel re-entered *Challenger*'s airlock to complete the EVA, which in the event proved to be the final EVA from that orbiter. *Challenger* had supported all the EVAs of the programme to date, including the first EVA in 1983, the first MMU flights the Solar Max repair EVAs, and this satellite refuelling demonstration EVA in 1984. A total of eight astronauts (seven male and one female) had accomplished six periods of EVA outside the vehicle.

Challenger was rapidly becoming known as the favourite orbiter, and again on this mission only minor problems dogged the flight. Apart from the problems with the Ku-band antenna and the SIR-B experiment, the other major malfunctions recorded in flight were two failed display electronic units; failure of a flash evaporator system; a failed CRT screen, which the crew repaired inflight; and clogging of the plumbing of the water spray boiler system by an ice-ball, sending the temperature inside the cabin to 35°C (95°F) and prompting Crippen to remark that it reminded him of 'a late August in Houston'. On a lighter but still important note, the toilet worked properly on this mission for the first time, which with seven crew members certainly was a welcome relief, and a press conference was interrupted by a Houston telephone operator getting patched in on the air-to-ground loop asking the callers to dial again if they were having difficulties! On the whole *Challenger* and its crew had a good mission with both the payload specialists (Garneau and Scully-Power) enthusiastically reporting significant progress with their experiments and observations in their weightless environment.

Re-entry and landing

The orbital track of *Challenger* dictated an unusual entry approach for the end of the mission. Unlike any previous manned spacecraft re-entry, *Challenger* had to leave a 57° inclination and land in Florida For Crippen this would be his third attempt at a KSC landing, and as always the weather at the landing site, this time in the form of Hurricane Josephine, threatened again to cancel his attempt. However, as the re-entry day of October 13 dawned the weather reports indicated perfect conditions for the landing, and Crippen was on his way to KSC at last.

The OMS de-orbit burn of 2 minutes 22 seconds slowed *Challenger*'s orbital velocity by 267.5ft (81.5m) per second, and was initiated over Perth in Western Australia as the spacecraft was completing its 133rd orbit. *Challenger* flew over the Alaskan coastline, turning to overfly Winnipeg in Canada at Mach 22 and 224,000ft (68,275m), and providing Crippen and McBride with spectacular views of the continental USA during their seven-minute traverse from north to south. As normal, the flight crew conducted several flight test manoeuvres as they brought the spacecraft in for the landing.

After completing a flight south over the Atlantic Crippen and McBride brought *Challenger* in for a final approach to the Shuttle Landing Facility, achieving main landing gear contact at 12:26 EDT after completing 133 orbits and 4,300,000 miles (6,919,990km) in 8 days 5 hours 23 minutes 33 seconds.

Post-landing activities

At last Crippen had completed his long overdue KSC landing and, as the *Challenger* slowed to wheelstop, engineers at KSC were planning to return the vehicle to the OPF to begin preparations for its next mission, then planned as 51-C in December, a dedicated DoD mission.

At that time the damage of the TPS tiles and blankets was known from inflight video and crew reports, but the extent of the damage and its effects on the programme (especially in the turnaround for *Challenger*'s next flight) were not fully appreciated as an elated crew exited the orbiter at the end of what was in fact *Challenger*'s last mission of 1984.

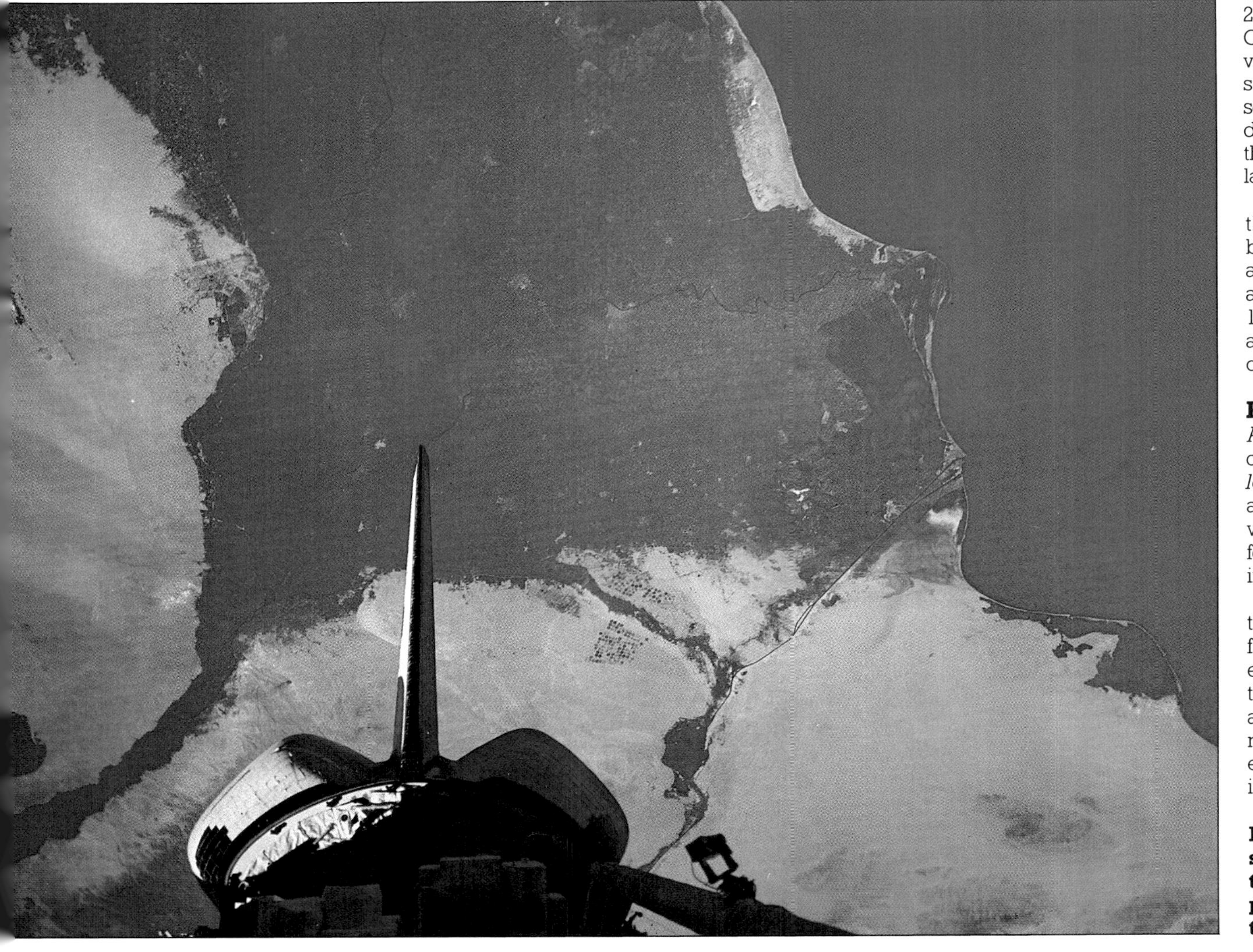

Left: A typical high-quality image shows Egypt and the Nile delta, with the Suez Canal above the port OMS pod and Cairo with the pyramids over the starboard OMS pod.

Above: Part of the ESA's Spacelab 3 Long Module is pictured against a backdrop of Lake Ontario and the Finger Lakes area of New York state.

Some 25 anomalies were tracked following the Shuttle 13 mission in October 1984, none so serious as the problem with the TPS which, combined with hardware problems, resulted in *Challenger* being grounded over six months. During that time the vehicle changed mission assignments three times, finally beginning its 1985 flight assignments with the first of an eventual three Spacelab missions planned for that year, all of which *Challenger* would carry.

51-E/B launch preparations

By October 5, 1984, *Challenger* was back in the OPF, where it underwent tile-damage examination. Inspection of several damaged areas revealed much softer RTV than designed. Originally thought to be a result of turnaround processing, a batch of RTV, was, in fact, found to be incorrectly labelled. The tile problem pushed *Challenger*'s next mission (51-C) into January 1985, forcing a reassignment to 51-E.

While the tile problem was being tackled, in another part of the KSC the payload and other components of the 51-E mission were being prepared. The TDRS-B and Anik C-1 satellites were undergoing systems processing before being loaded into the payload canister, transported to *Challenger* on the pad and installed in the payload bay. The SRBs for 51-E were stacked on top of MLP-2 on November 28, followed by attachment of the ET on January 9, 1985 in High Bay 1. Finally, on February 10 *Challenger* left Bay 1 of the OPF after just over four months and was towed to the VAB with about a dozen tile cavities remaining. The cargo was loaded in the VAB on February 11, and *Challenger* was mated to the ET/SRB combination on February 13. After five days in VAB the combination for 51-E was transported to Pad 39A on February 15 for final preparations for a March 4 launch.

A few days after rollout the launch again slipped to March 7 after the discovery of a battery problem with the TDRS, the delay being designed to allow technicians into the payload bay to exchange one of the satellite's three 24-cell batteries, which refused to charge.

During late February a far more serious problem loomed into the forefront of the mission's problems. In the early part of 1985 TDRS managers monitoring the TDRS-A satellite in orbit noted certain malfunctions, which were at first believed to be telemetry-oriented defects rather than hardware design problems. The problem centred on a timing error which could seriously threaten the launch of 51-E carrying the second TDRS. NASA was informed of the problem on February 26, and the malfunction was confirmed in tests on TDRS-A during February 27-28. On March 1, just six days before the launch of 51-E, the mission was scrubbed when it was decided that the launch of the second TDRS would have to be delayed until the cause of the timing switch problem had been cleared from the second and future satellites of the series.

It was also announced that a combination of payloads would fly the new mission 51-D in April aboard *Discovery*, and that *Challenger* would be remanifested with the Spacelab 3 payload it was already scheduled to fly after the 51-E mission. The second TDRS would now probably fly aboard 51-L later in that year. The effects of the constant delays in 51-E/D had a lasting effect on the launch schedule for 1985.

The 51-E payloads were removed on the pad, and on March 4 the *Challenger* stack was rolled back to the VAB High Bay 1 for demate and remanifest of payloads to 51-B/Spacelab 3. After spending 15 days on the pad, *Challenger* spent a further three days in the VAB before moving to the OPF for processing. The twin SRBs and ET remained stacked and atop the MLP awaiting the return of the orbiter for the 51-B mission.

Preparations for 51-B continued through 1984, with the arrival of various elements of the payload at the Cape. The Long Module flew on SL1 in December 1983 and after being fitted with SL3 equipment, was installed in *Challenger's* payload bay in OPF Bay 1, on March 27, 1985. By April 10, *Challenger* had been mated to the SRB/ET. Roll-out occured on April 15.

Launch phase

The countdown for SL 3 proceeded without major incident, and was cited as one of the smoothest in the programme to date. The animal payload was installed aboard *Challenger* about 24 hours before the launch to allow the animals to get accustomed to their new home for the next week. The final countdown progressed smoothly until T-4 minutes, when a failure of a front-end processor in the Launch Processing System caused a 138-second hold. The failure resulted in the LO facility liquid replenish valve and LO vent valve not closing automatically as planned. During the hold the valves were manually positioned, allowing the count to resume.

Lift-off occurred at 11:02:18 EDT on April 29, 1985 providing a spectacular sight for the crowds of spectators at the Cape, who included astronaut Don Lind's mother, witnessing her son's launch into space at the age of 54 and after a 19-year wait since selection to NASA as a potential Apollo astronaut in 1966.

Ascent profile flown by *Challenger* was nominal in all respects. The separation and recovery of the SRBs were as planned, as was the separation and reentry of the ET.

Overall performance of the SSMEs was perfect despite the failure of the No. 2 (2020) gaseous hydrogen pressurant-supply pressure at T+6. This had no effect on ascent performance. As *Challenger* streaked spacewards for the seventh time, a new record for an orbiter (taking over from *Columbia*), several ground problems were being investigated.

During propellant loading, a hydrogen leak had occurred at the Ground Umbilical Carrier Plate, recording a hydrogen concentration of 12,000 parts per million for a short time while the valve was open, though after cycling no further problem was recorded. During the LH swing arm retraction, the arm had missed the catch and hit hard enough to break the LH vent line, causing a small fire at the facility.

Challenger, meanwhile, was also recording small problems during the early stages of flight. At lift-off the right ET door 'open', motor B was lost, and, later when the ET feed doors were

MISSION DATA CHALLENGER 7

Sequence: Shuttle 17
Designation: 51-B (Spacelab 3)
OV-099 Mission: Seven
Launch Date: April 29, 1985
Launch Time: 11:02:18 EDT
Launch Site: Pad 39A, Kennedy Space Center, Cape Canaveral, Florida, USA
Launch Weight: 4,501,581lb (2,041,883kg)
Maximum Altitude: 281 miles (452km)
Inclination: 57°
Orbits: 108, landing during 109th
EVA Duration: None
Mission Duration: 7 days 0 hours 8 minutes 46 seconds; travelled 2.5 million miles
Landing Date: May 6, 1985
Landing Time (main gear): 09:12:03 PDT
Landing Site: Runway 17, Edwards Air Force Base, California, USA
Rollout Distance and Duration: 8,317ft (2,535m) & 47 seconds
Crew: (Commander) Colonel Robert F. Overmyer, USMC, 48, NASA (Gold Team Leader); (Pilot) Colonel Frederick D. Gregory, USAF, 44, NASA (Silver Team Leader/EV-1); (MS-1) Dr Don L. Lind, 54, NASA (Gold Team); (MS-2) Dr Norman E. Thagard, 41, NASA (Silver Team/EV-2); (MS-3) Dr William E. Thornton, 56, NASA (Gold Team); (PS-1) Dr Taylor G. Wang, 44, NASA JPL (Gold Team Fluids Expert); (PS-2) Dr Lodewijk van den Berg, 53, EG&G Corp (Silver Team Materials Science Expert)
Payload: Spacelab 3 (Long Module plus Special Support Pallet): 3 materials science experiments/4 life science experiments/2 fluid mechanics experiments/4 atmospheric and astronomical experiments; 2 GAS canisters holding: NUSAT Satellite (deployed Day 1, GET 4 hours 14 minutes 42 seconds)/GLOMR Satellite (failed to deploy & returned to Earth)

FLIGHT LOG CHALLENGER 7

1 (APRIL 29, 1985) **00:00:00** SRB ignition command (lift-off) **00:00:18.8** MPS throttledown to 94% (Engine No. 3) **00:00:27.5** MPS throttledown to 65% (Engine No. 3) **00:00:51** Max Q **00:01:00.6** MPS throttleup to 104% (Engine No. 3) **00:02:06** SRB separation command from GPC **00:07:32.6** MPS throttledown for 3-g acceleration (Engine No. 3) **00:07:33** 3 g acceleration **00:08:35** MECO **00:08:53** ET separation **00:10:35** OMS-1 ignition **00:12:49** OMS-1 cut-off **00:46:15** OMS-2 ignition **00:48:40** OMS-2 cut-off **04:14:42** NUSAT deployment
7 (MAY 5, 1985) **153:01:59** FCS checkout start (APU No. 2 start) **153:06:22** FCS checkout end (APU No. 2 shutdown)
8 (MAY 6, 1985) **166:57:33** APU No. 1 activation **167:02:30** De-orbit manoeuvre ignition **167:06:54** De-orbit manoeuvre cut-off **167:24:41** APU activation (APU Nos 2 & 3) **167:37:46** Entry interface **167:52:26** End blackout **168:02:24** TAEM **168:08:46** Main landing gear contact **168:08:58** Nose landing gear contact **168:09:45** Wheel stop

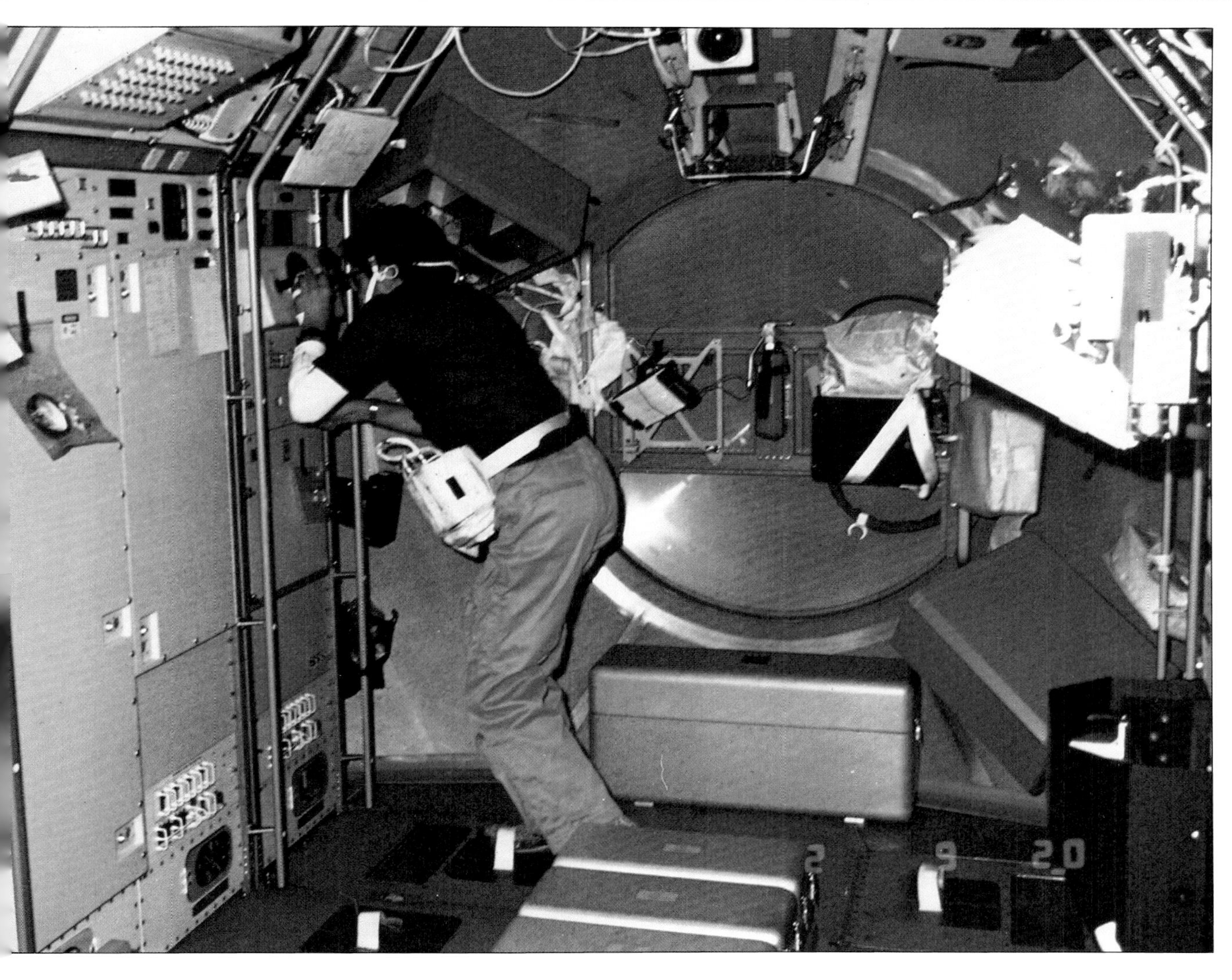

Above: Lodewijk van den Berg observes the growth of a mercuric iodide crystal in Spacelab 3's Vapor Crystal Growth System experiment.

closed motor B failed to operate, forcing motor A to close the door in single motor time.

After the normal two OMS burns *Challenger* was once again in orbit 190 miles (306km) above the Earth, inclined at 57°.

Orbital activities

Safely in orbit, the crew prepared for their heavy workload in the SL 3 module, by splitting into two (Gold and Silver) teams, one team powering up the SL and the other going to bed to begin a 24-hour cycle of SL operations for the duration of the mission.

Upon opening the Payload Bay Doors (PLBD) for the first time the crew reported a protrusion of TPS from the centre of the right OMS pod. After viewing this by TV, ground control confirmed that it was not a flight-safety issue. Deployment of the two small satellites was brought forward from Flight Day 6 to Flight Day 1 in order not to let the satellite batteries deplete in the cold of space. NUSAT was successfully deployed at GET 4 hours 14 minutes, but GLOMR could not be ejected due to a failure in the GAS canister door mechanism, forcing the return of the satellite to Earth for reassignment.

The remainder of the first day's activities centred on full activation of SL 3 systems and experiments, and for the next week the crew worked hard in securing as much data from these experiments as possible. The performance of SL 3 and the experiments was nominal in all but a few instances. Problems with the SL airlock in connection with the Very Wide Field Camera (as a result of a bent latch handle) prevented the full programme of activities with this experiment, which failed to reach its flight objectives. A pressure leak crippled the ATMOS experiment, but not before recording a wealth of information to make this one of the most successful SL 3 experiments. Initial problems with the Animal Holding Facility (AHF) and the adaptation of one of the monkeys to zero g were overcome to provide good results, though in the words of the crew the foodbits leaking into the crew quarters (at first wrongly reported as animal faeces) certainly needed further investigation before the AHF flew again. Wang's untiring efforts to repair his drop dynamics module proved one of the outstanding successes of the flight, and proved the usefulness of man-in-space, especially if that man who designed the equipment was on hand to repair it!

Several items of equipment failed to respond to commands, but as the crew expanded their experience of working in zero g so their performance in data gathering and equipment management increased to provide interesting and important research results.

As before *Challenger* stood up well to constant operations through its first 24-hour per day work cycle. Early in the flight one of the three APUs overheated and shut down, and after the problem had been traced to a faulty control system, ground control switched to a back up system which produced no further anomalies. During closure of the PLBDs no indication of A and B 'latched' configuration was shown for the port aft door latches, but the crew reported the door in the latched configuration, and all release and 'ready-to-latch' indications were received. Despite a preliminary plan for an EVA to close and check the doors manually, ground control decided to accept the reading as a fault in the indication system but decided to delete PTIs from the descent profile to reduce aerodynamic loading on the doors.

Early on Flight Day 8 all experimental activities were completed, and 5 hours before re-entry the SL was deactivated. With the closure of the payload bay doors and a 264-second OMS retrograde de-orbit burn, *Challenger* completed its seventh week in space and headed home towards California again.

Re-entry and landing

Following a re-entry ground track that allowed almost no re-entry communications, Overmyer and Gregory brought *Challenger* from near the Antarctic Circle northward over the Pacific, flying over Los Angeles at Mach 4 before finally achieving four hypersonic S-turns for energy management. *Challenger* was guided to a safe landing on Runway 17 at Edwards AFB, California. Overmyer did not suffer the brake and tyre problem Bobko had experienced on *Discovery* at the end of the previous mission, though when he tried to hold 10ft (3.05m) per second^2 of braking he felt the antiskid cycle noticeably and felt he could use only some 7ft (2.13m) per second^2.

Three hours after landing the animal payload was removed from the SL 3 module, the animals being sent back to KSC before distribution to researchers for post-flight analysis.

Challenger had lost about 20 tiles, and a panel of the FRSI to the rear of the right OMS had worked loose. Despite damage there appeared no serious effects to delay the next flight carrying the SL 2 all-pallet mission in July. It appeared on first inspections that the tile screed problem had not recurred. Brake damage was limited to three cracked rotors on the left main landing gear, and all tyres appeared undamaged. A total of 26 anomalies were logged against the 51-B mission, but to balance this the mission had chalked up an impressive amount of data collection from all but one of the 15 investigations in four scientific fields. The only major problem was with the VWFC, and this was attributable to the airlock and not the camera. Despite the usual inflight difficulties, the crew working in conjunction with the ground gathered over 250,000 million bits of data, enough material to fill 44,000 200-page books. In addition, 3 million frames of video pictures were obtained, as well as miles of audiotape and thousands of camera stills. Fifteen of the 17 detailed test objectives had been completed. With perhaps years of work ahead of them, the investigators of the scientific experiments were very happy with the SL 3 mission.

Post-landing activities

On May 10, 1985 *Challenger* (again on top of the SCA) left Edwards AFB for the first part of its trip back to KSC at the end of a mission. Arriving for an overnight stop at Kelly AFB, Texas, it left the next day arriving at KSC Florida later that same day. Later on May 11 it was transported to the OPF for mission turnaround for its eighth mission, again carrying a Spacelab payload.

Right: The crew of the most successful but little publicized 51-B mission leave *Challenger*. From bottom to top these are Robert Overmyer, Frederick Gregory, Norman Thagard, Lodewijk van den Berg, Taylor Wang, Don Lind and William Thornton.

Challenger 8, the 19th flight in the programme, carried the Spacelab 2 scientific payload in Earth orbit for one week. Unlike Spacelab 1 and Spacelab 3 which flew before it, the SL 2 mission comprised three pallets containing the scientific experiments, a special support structure holding a further experiment, and an unmanned igloo canister which provided a housing for Spacelab subsystems equipment. The control and operation of the instruments were achieved from the aft flight deck of the orbiter, the crew not entering the payload bay of *Challenger* at all during the mission.

The origins of SL 2, which encompassed a wide range of investigations in astronomy, physics and biology, lay with one of the earliest payloads assigned to the Shuttle programme in the mid 1970s. In fact one of the crew, astronaut Karl Henize, had worked on the payload since 1977. Several delays in the launch were experienced as a result of programme delays and hardware development difficulties (especially with the highly advanced Instrument Pointing System), and eventually with launch difficulties and flight schedule changes. When SL 2 did get off the ground, it provided the programme with the first abort-mode during the launch phase, and some of the best astronomical results from a manned spacecraft since the Skylab programme over 12 years before.

Launch preparations

After years of preparation and design, the Final Acceptance Review of Spacelab Flight Unit Configuration II (Spacelab 2) was completed on July 2, 1982 after the completion of the integration and test programme at ERNO in Bremen, West Germany. Equipment transport in two aircraft was completed on July 26 and July 29. Once arrived at KSC the West German-supplied items were inspected and stored before final preparations for SL 2, a mission then planned for November 1984. A Critical Design Review in August 1982 was completed successfully on the IPS, and NASA gave the go-ahead for production pending confirmation of performance for the 'man-disturbed mode' and a detailed analysis of the safety of the Payload Clamp Assembly. The three SL 2 pallets were located at the KSC Operations and Checkout Building, where during 1983 the pallets were equipped with the special support structures needed for attachment of SL 2 experiments.

After many delays and difficulties in qualifying the IPS in Europe, late in 1984 the equipment arrived at KSC, where after undergoing a further series of tests one atmospheric and three solar instruments were mounted on the IPS, which was later attached to the first pallet. Following some small problems with the IPS hardware, the integration of the SL 2 payload configuration continued. By the spring of 1985 the initial integration activities were completed with the Mission Sequence Testing, which proved compatibility of the experiments with each other and with simulated Spacelab support subsystems. In May 1985 the SL 2 integrated payload completed the Closed Loop Test where JSC's POCC operated, briefly, all commandable experiments in a combined test and integration programme with SL scientists and all SL 2 science crew members. (The SLS crew had been selected in stages in February and November 1983, and June 1984.) The SL 2 payload was then placed in the CITE stand (for verification of compatibility with the Shuttle) where duplication of orbiter mechanical and electrical systems was available.

While work continued on the SL 2 payload, other teams of engineers worked on *Challenger* to accept this SL 2 payload and to bring the vehicle to flight status for the eighth time. The orbiter was located in Bay 1 of the OPF for the turnaround process, and following the number of modifications for the SL 2 missions after removal of the Long Module of SL 3 the engineers prepared for the installation of the SL 2 payload.

Following borescope inspections of the three SSMEs (Nos 2023, 2020 and 2021) after their previous mission, engineers in June found several bent and pitted blades on the No. 2 (2020) engine's liquid oxygen pump. It was later discovered, when the pump was extracted, that a screw used to hold the turbine tip seal retainer had become loose and dropped into the blades, causing the damage.

On June 8, 1985 the SL 2 configuration carrying the experiments (and, because this was the first flight of the all-pallet configuration, the Verification Flight Test Instrument) was transferred to the OPF and lowered into the payload bay of *Challenger*. Once the attachment was complete, the payload/orbiter interface test was performed to check all Spacelab/Shuttle connections.

By now the vehicle was almost ready for the move to the VAB and the 3 mile (4.8km) trip to the launch pad. Stacking of the twin SRBs for *Challenger*'s eighth flight into space was begun on MLP-2 in High Bay 3 of the VAB during May 13, 1985 and was followed by mating of the ET to the SRBs on May 31. Carrying the SL 2 payload, *Challenger* was transferred to the VAB on June 24 and mated to the SRB/ET combination.

After verification of the stack, the vehicle was moved to Pad 39A on June 29, having spent 43 days in the OPF undergoing turnaround and 5 days in the VAB.

Right: Whereas Spacelab 3 had featured manned experiments, the Spacelab 2 configuration centred on remotely-controlled experiments.

51-F/Spacelab 2 Cargo Configuration

Infra-Red Telescope (IRT)
Vehicle Charging And Potential (VCAP) experiment
X-Ray Telescope (XRT)
Cosmic Ray Nuclei (CRN) experiment
Solar Optical Universal Polarimeter (SOUP)
Coronal Helium Abundance Spacelab Experiment (CHASE)
Igloo
Instrument Pointing System (IPS)
Plasma Diagnostics Package (PDP)
Solar Ultra-violet Spectral Irradiance Monitor (SUSIM)
Super-Fluid Helium Experiment (SFHE)
High-Resolution Telescope and Spectrograph (HRTS)

Launch phase and abort

As July 12 dawned it seemed at last that the SL 2 payload was going to get into space after years of planning and months of delays. With the crew strapped to their seats and the countdown clock ticking away to zero and lift off, all events proceeded smoothly towards the 16:30 EDT launch. However, as the SSMEs were ignited and the clock reached T-3 seconds the onboard computer automatically shut down the SSMEs just before ignition of the SRBs, which would have committed the vehicle to launch. Seconds after the SSME ignition command had been initiated the Shuttle's onboard computers automatically shut down the SSMEs when sensors recorded the failure of an actuator to close down in the hydrogen valve of SSME No. 2 Channel A system. Back-up systems routed the command through the B system but the Shuttle's sensitive redundancy systems, which must be fully operational at the moment of launch, recorded the failed system and immediately aborted the launch.

With the launch rescheduled for the end of July, the crew left the vehicle for a two-week wait while *Challenger* was again prepared for launch. The next 17 days were spent in replacing the engine valve and actuator with new components, and in completing component failure testing on the faulty units, which NASA stated was not a situation which threatened the safety of the crew but rather a slow-acting component communicating to a faster-operating computer.

The break until the second launch also allowed ground teams to repair a vacuum maintenance assembly pump, which was part of the superfluid helium experiment, and designed to ensure maximum data-gathering from the experiment. The second countdown progressed smoothly towards a July 29 launch date, with only two minor problems causing difficulties.

Ascent phase

Despite all the setbacks, the 19th Shuttle mission finally left the launch pad at 17:00 EST on July 29, 1985, and headed straight into trouble again! The initial ascent stage went well, with SRB separation achieved normally. At GET 3 minutes 30 seconds, however, the SSME flight controller received a warning light and data which recorded a failure in one of two temperature sensors in the centre (No. 1, 2023) engine's high-pressure engine pump and advised the flight director, who was informed that the problem was a sensor failure. Meanwhile *Challenger* was continuing its ascent, reaching the Negative Return Point at GET 3 minutes 58 seconds and the Abort-to-Orbit point at 5 minutes 12 seconds. Just over 30 seconds later, at GET 5 minutes 45 seconds, a loud warning alarm on the control console of *Challenger*'s flight deck sounded as Fullerton and Bridges noticed the engine status light shining red and the No. 1 engine chamber pressure reading falling rapidly to zero. They had a problem!

Upon checking data on the ground, the crew were instructed to 'Press to ATO' by CapCom astronaut Dick Richards: Fullerton turned the Abort Mode Selection switch on the control panel to ATO and depressed the nearby ABORT button. This operation sequenced the computers to configure for abort procedures and instructed the OMS system to dump 4,400lb (1,996kg) of fuel, which allowed the remaining SSME

MISSION DATA CHALLENGER 8

Sequence: Shuttle 19
Designation: 51-F (Spacelab 2)
OV-099 Mission: Eight
Launch Date: July 29, 1985
Launch Time: 17:00:00 EDT
Launch Site: Pad 39A, Kennedy Space Center, Cape Canaveral, Florida, USA
Launch Weight: 4,514,504lb (2,047,745kg)
Maximum Altitude: 170 miles (274km)
Inclination: 49.5°
Orbits: 125, landing during 126th
EVA Duration: None
Mission Duration: 7 days 22 hours 45 minutes 26 seconds; travelled 2.85 million miles
Landing Date: August 6, 1985
Landing Time (main gear): 12:45:26 PDT
Landing Site: Runway 23, Edwards AFB, California, USA
Rollout Distance and Duration: 8,569ft (2,612m) & 55 seconds
Crew: (Commander) Colonel Charles G. Fullerton, USAF, 48, NASA (Red/Blue Shift); (Pilot) Lieutenant-Colonel Roy D. Bridges, Jr, USAF, 42, NASA (Red Shift Leader); (MS-1) Dr F. Story Musgrave, 49, NASA (Blue Shift Leader/EV-1); (MS-2) Dr Karl G. Henize, 58, NASA (Red Shift); (MS-3) Dr Anthony W. England, 43, NASA (Blue Shift/EV-2); (PS-1) Dr Loren W. Acton, 49, Lockheed PAR Lab (Red Shift); (PS-2) Dr John-David F. Bartoe, 41, Naval Lab (Blue Shift)
Payload: Spacelab 2 (3 Pallets, Support Structure and Igloo): 3 solar physics experiments/1 astrophysics experiment/3 plasma physics experiments/2 high-energy astrophysics experiments/1 infra-red astronomy experiment/1 technology research experiment/2 life-sciences experiments/4 additional minor experiments Remote Manipulator System

FLIGHT LOG CHALLENGER 8

1 (JULY 29, 1985) **00:00:00** SRB ignition command from GPC (lift-off) **00:00:19.7** MPS throttledown to 97% (Engine No. 3) **00:00:29.9** MPS throttledown to 65% (Engine No. 3) **00:00:50** Max Q **00:00:55.9** MPS throttleup to 104% (Engine No. 3) **00:02:01** SRB separation command from GPC **00:05:43.4** SSME No. 1 (2023) cut-off **00:06:06** OMS dump ignition **00:07:52.4** OMS dump cut-off **00:09:42** MECO **00:10:00** ET separation **00:13:55** APU deactivation (No. 3) **00:33:00** OMS-2 ignition **00:35:02** OMS-2 cut-off **05:30:27** OMS-3 ignition **05:31:02.3** OMS-3 cut-off **06:22:18** OMS-4 ignition **06:23:03.1** OMS-4 cut-off **08:01:36.1** OMS-5 ignition **08:01:51.3** OMS-5 cut-off
9 (AUGUST 6, 1985) **189:38:06** APU No. 3 activation **189:43:00** De-orbit manoeuvre ignition **189:45:52** De-orbit manoeuvre cut-off **190:33:50** APU activation (No. 1) **190:01:29** APU activation (No. 2) **190:14:27** Entry interface **190:30:56** End blackout **190:39:10** TAEM **190:45:26** Main landing gear contact **190:45:36** Nose landing gear contact **190:46:21** Wheel stop

thrust to operate at a more efficient level. Only seconds after the first indication of trouble the OMS system ignited for 106 seconds: with the two remaining SSMEs firing correctly, this compensated for the lost engine and continued pushing *Challenger* towards orbit. The OMS burn added a further 12,000lb (5,443kg) of thrust, which combined with the lighter load to make it possible for the ET to re-enter over unpopulated areas.

On the ground, controllers saw the temperature-sensor reading fall on a second engine, which had been the start of the centre engine's problems, and a second sensor in the same engine also gave indications that it was about to quit. Flight Director Lacefield relayed to the crew instructions to inhibit the controls, which meant Fullerton flipping a switch to prevent cancelling the protective circuitry should the temperature rise. At GET 9 minutes 42 seconds the two remaining engines were shut down after burning for about 1 minute longer than normal: *Challenger* was travelling at 25,760ft (7,852m) per second, some 114ft (34.75m) per second slower than originally planned, resulting in a cut-off at 70.25 mile (113km) altitude.

ET separation occurred normally, the tank re-entering safely over Saudi Arabia, while the *Challenger* flight crew ignited the OMS engines again for an increase of veolocity of 194ft (59m) per second to produce an initial orbit of 164.7 by 124.4 miles (265 by 200km). With a little effort *Challenger* was again in Earth orbit for the eighth time, but for how long? The flight plan had called for an initial orbit of 122 by 162.4 miles (196.3 by 261.4km), and ground controllers soon calculated that the mission would be able to sustain orbital duration for the planned seven days, despite the lower orbital altitude which was later raised to 196.6 by 195.5 miles (316.4 by 314.6km) by three OMS burns on the first flight day.

During the routine post-launch pad inspection a piece of Spray-On Foam Insulation (SOFI) from the ET was found. Further inspection of the nearby beach areas revealed other pieces of SOFI from the ET. An on-orbit inspection of the tiles was then performed by the crew.

Orbital activities

Following the securing of *Challenger* in orbit, activities on the rest of Flight Day 1 centred on opening the payload bay doors, checking out the RMS activation of the SL 2 experiments, and deployment of the IPS. The crew worked in two shifts around the clock as on previous Spacelab missions.

From the science angle SL 2 recorded 80 to 85% success in pre-flight objectives from all 13 experiments despite problems that threatened several experiments. Early in the mission the IPS was not fully operable, and a solar telescope on the IPS failed after only minutes of operation. However, determined efforts by the flight crew and staff in the POCC successfully restored the operational capability of the IPS and solar telescope by adjusting software, and when the instruments resumed operation the mission was extended by 23 hours to obtain the data lost in the early stages of the flight.

The SOUP (Solar Optical Universal Polarimeter) experiment began its data-gathering activities late in the flight after an unexplained shutdown on the first day and an equally inexplicable start-up on the day before re-entry. The other instruments gathered a wide range of data from solar, atmospheric and plasma physics, infra-red astronomy, high-energy astrophysics, technology research and life sciences. One of the most publicized small experiments accomplished by the crew was an evaluation of carbonated drinks in zero g from specialized dispensers.

The PDP was released and recaptured after a period of free flight on Flight Day 3. This was followed by 6 hours of proximity operations with the free-flying PDP during Flight Day 4. Two flyaround operations were completed by the crew, who completed the PDP programme successfully and moved their full attention to solar and astronomical observations for the rest of the mission. The PDP had originally flown on Shuttle 3 (whose crew included Fullerton) in 1982 but was not released from the RMS.

During the mission *Challenger* itself operated normally, and despite a significant reduction in onboard propellants following the ATO situation, was able to support the PDP operation successfully. During the sixth day an inspection of the underside of the vehicle's TPS was achieved using the RMS, and showed no significant damage.

Re-entry and landing

On Flight Day 8 the crew powered down the SL 2 experiments and stowed unnecessary gear for the re-entry phase of the mission, which was scheduled for the following day. An APU No. 1 pressure anomaly had been recorded during ascent with the gearbox nitrogen pressure and gearbox lubrication oil outlet pressure, first increasing by 8lb/sq in (0.55 bar), then dropping to normal, and finally increasing again before being shut down with an off-scale high reading of over 30lb/sq in (2.07 bar) rather than the normal 20lb/sq in (1.38 bar) for the nitrogen pressure, and 90lb/sq in (6.21 bar) rather than the normal 60lb/sq in (4.14 bar) for the lubrication oil. During the descent APU No. 1 was started late, at about Mach 10, providing the most assurance of having three APUs for descent flight control and landing operations. During the descent APU No. 1's pressure recordings repeated those logged during ascent.

A 172-second OMS retrograde de-orbit manoeuvre was achieved by *Challenger*, which began a completely nominal entry profile to a landing at Edwards AFB, California. Eight of 10 PTIs were successfully accomplished, and after flying a 130° heading alignment circle, with Fullerton reporting some incorrect readings from his instruments, *Challenger* again touched terra firma at 12:45 PDT after a 7 day 22 hour mission, gently rolling down Runway 23 at Edwards to wheelstop.

Post-landing activities

Post-flight examination of *Challenger* revealed that the orbiter had stood up well to its latest trip in space, receiving only minor brake damage (a good sign) and minimal tile damage. Post-flight inspection revealed a total of 553 debris hits, of which 226 were greater than or equal to 1in (25.4mm) in diameter; the majority of the impact craters resulted from re-entry heating. This was the largest number of debris hits recorded by any mission, and a piece of SOFI was found lodged beneath the right-hand ET door. A review of the ET separation film revealed that several items of SOFI were missing from the intertank area.

With *Challenger* safely back on Earth again, plans were made to airlift the orbiter back to KSC for turnaround operations which would see its next mission flying the Spacelab D1 dedicated West German mission in October. The trip back to KSC was completed on August 12, when *Challenger* was again towed back into the OPF for removal of the SL 2 pallet payload before the installation once more of the Long Module for the SL D1 mission.

Above: Visible in the cluster of Spacelab 2 hardware in *Challenger*'s payload bay is the SOUP experiment and the Instrument Pointing System, as well as the RMS arm used on 51-F for the positioning of the Plasma Diagnostics Package.

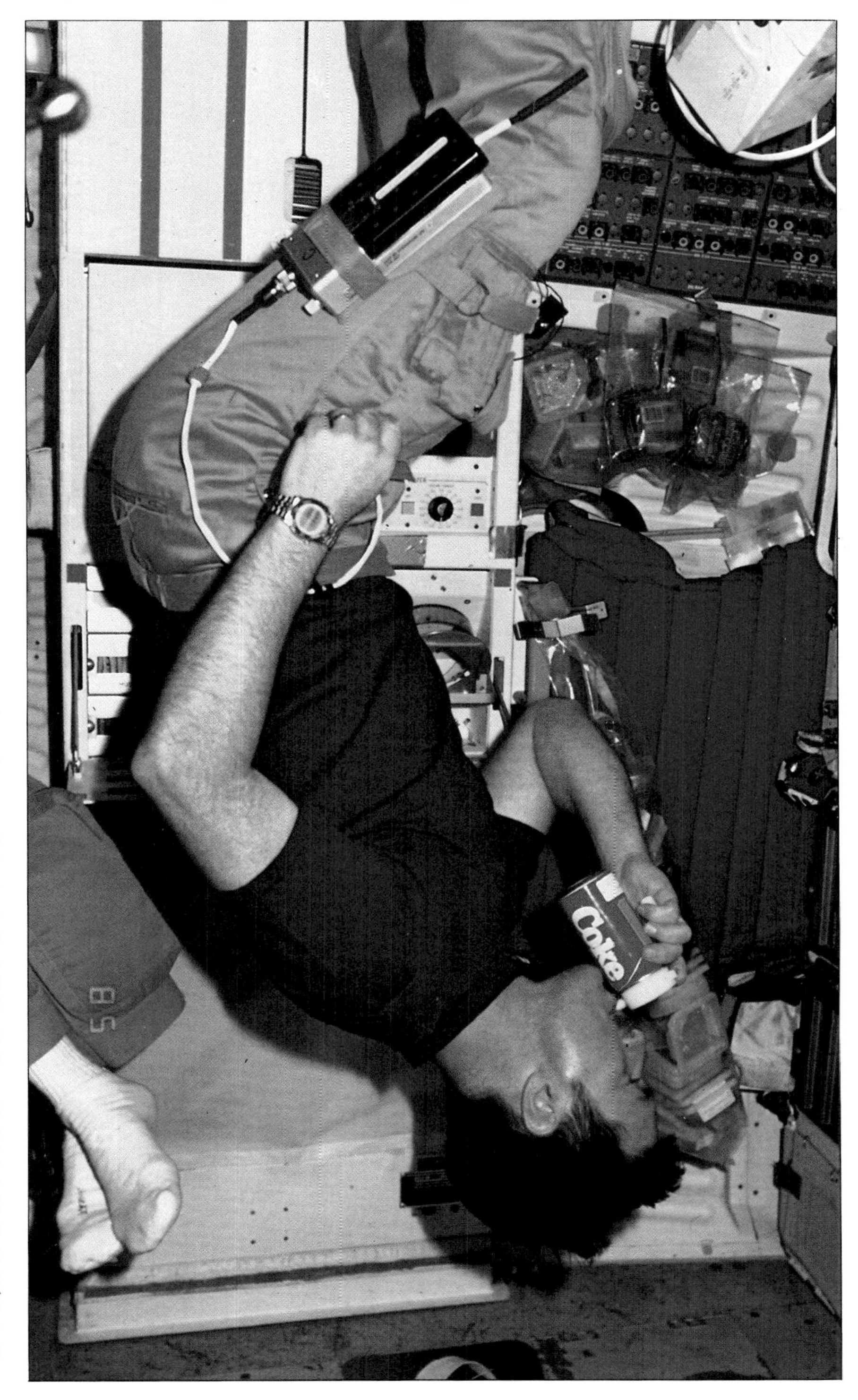

Below: Carbonated drinks were carried for the first time on 51-F and proved moderately popular. Such luxuries may have seemed irrelevant to the Shuttle programme, but will be important for morale on long-term space station missions.

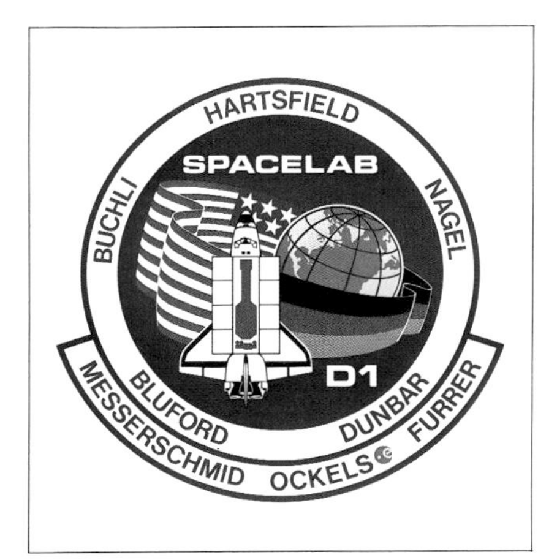

In a little over six months *Challenger* was sent into space for its third mission of 1985, again carrying a Spacelab payload, this time a dedicated Long Module West German mission called Spacelab D (Deutschland, or Germany) One, the first of a series of West German-sponsored Spacelab missions. By October 1985 a total of 21 successful Shuttle flights in four and a half years had pushed the Shuttle system into a reliable method of almost routine access to space, performing a wide variety of activities there and bringing the mission to a safe conclusion by regular land landings on either side of the USA. Several political and technical problems still plagued the programme, which was after all still in its early days, but as the Shuttle vehicles and the astronaut crews brought one spectacular mission to a close after another, the media lost interest in the missions, sometimes not even mentioning events in their news bulletins.

Launch preparations

As with other Spacelab payloads, the actual preparations of flight experiments and investigations began years before the actual mission. Indeed plans for a West German dedicated mission began at about the time of early Shuttle flights, around five years before actual launch. The scientific experiment racks and specialized equipment were developed and constructed in West Germany, the payload integration and checkout being performed at MBB/ERNO in Bremen, West Germany under the direction of the DFVLR. Spacelab D1 components were airlifted to the USA on April 30, 1985.

Challenger itself arrived back at KSC and was located in the OPF Bay 1 after the Shuttle 19 (51-F) Spacelab 2 mission by August 12, 1985. It was soon stripped of its SL 2 cargo and again fitted with equipment needed to support the Long Module configuration of SL D1, which was installed in the payload bay on September 18-20 following the installation of experiment racks in the module in the Operations and Checkout Building during the summer.

After inspection of *Challenger*'s three SSMEs, it was decided to fly the same configuration again, though minor repairs had first to be completed. The three engines had flown together on *Challenger* since the vehicle's sixth mission in October 1984 and, despite suffering a premature shutdown and an ATO situation on the previous flight, they were to power *Challenger* for a fourth time. Installation of the SL D1 Long Module and support structure was accompanied by installation of the GLOMR satellite GAS canister, which had failed to deploy during the Shuttle 17 (51-B) Spacelab 3 mission and had thus been reassigned to this mission. The most notable configuration change for SL D1 was the installation of a record eighth crew seat.

A total of 61 days was spent by *Challenger* in the OPF, during which time the vehicle received the Nose Wheel Steering Box and Actuator on October 7; after a full checkout this was cleared for operational checkout during the 61-A landing at Edwards AFB. The system was designed to reduce loads on the landing gear during rollout, an area of the flight profile which had generated a variety of problems for previous Shuttle missions, including burst tyres, damaged brakes and difficulty in holding the centreline during rollout. The success of this system it was hoped would see the resumption of KSC runway landings again.

As activities centred on preparing *Challenger* for the SL D1 payload, work in the VAB alongside the OPF again witnessed the erection of the other components for the Shuttle 22 mission. Located in High Bay 1 of the VAB, the SRBs for the mission were stacked atop MLP-1 from September 13, followed by ET attachment on September 23. The orbiter was attached to the combination on October 12, and for the next four days the system was checked both mechanically and electrically before movement to Pad 39A on October 16.

The movement lasted about 4 hours longer than usual when repairs had to be made after an electronic failure in the hydraulic levelling system of the huge crawler transporter; a small crack in the hydraulic line of the same system also had to be welded. The vehicle was about halfway along the 3 mile (4.8km) crawler way when the incident temporarily halted the journey to the launch pad.

Right: Caught by an airborne camera over Florida, 61-A begins to move down-range from the Kennedy Space Center after launch on October 30, 1985. The threat of a hurricane had raised fears of a launch scrub.

Following repairs, the crawler safely delivered *Challenger* to the pad and the system was secured hard down on Pad 39A by 20:15 on that same day.

A CDT was conducted on the pad during October 18, and included the participation of the eight-person crew. As the preparations continued towards the final countdown phase, only one problem loomed to delay the launch. During hypergolic loading on October 23, a secondary RCS fuel pressurization regulator failed to lock and forced NASA into a decision to forego a system whose repair would have meant the return of the vehicle to the VAB, and thus delayed the SL D1 launch by several weeks in an already tight launch schedule for 1985-86. NASA opted to remain on the pad and go ahead with the launch.

At 06:00 EST on October 28, 1985 the 43-hour countdown for the SL D1 mission was started. The countdown included planned hold time of three periods totalling 11 hours. In the event the holds were unnecessary, the countdown proving to be one of the smoothest and most uneventful in the whole programme.

Launch phase

Exactly on time at 12:00 EST on October 30, 1985 *Challenger* blasted away from Pad 39A to begin yet another week in space, carrying the SL D1 payload and a record crew of eight astronauts who were selected in stages in December 1982, and February and August 1984, and included citizens of Holland, West Germany and the USA.

All aspects of the ascent phase were nominal, the separation and recovery of the SRBs and separation and re-entry of the ET happening as predicted. Despite the fear of a launch scrub because of Hurricane Juan, which brought heavy rain and lightning to the Florida area some 24 hours before the launch, as *Challenger* rolled 120° after clearing the launch tower to head up to its 57° inclination orbit the vehicle passed through a clear sky apart from a few scattered clouds, giving ground onlookers an impressive view.

Challenger's Fuel Cell 1 condenser exit temperature cycled beyond the normal range of 145° to 160°F (63° to 71°C) throughout the launch and the rest of the mission. The cycle damped during descent, and temperature cycling returned to the normal control level during the flight. It was the first flight of this unit since being rebuilt and coming out of a one-year dry storage. Bench testing of the unit before installation in *Challenger* had not revealed the problem associated with the launch readings. The loss of the cell in flight did not hinder the operation of the Spacelab experiments or mission success.

Following the OMS-1 burn, the right-hand RCS fuel-tank pressure read 274lb/sq in (18.9 bar), an indication of the failure of a primary regulator in the open position. The flight crew closed the right RCS helium pressure A-Leg to prevent a possible overpressure condition, after which it was noted the fuel ullage pressure fell to 215lb/sq in (14.8 bar), indicating the failure of the B-Leg in the closed position. The crew then opened the A-Leg to repressurize the system, allowing the pressure to rise to 290lb/sq in (20 bar).

Following the second OMS burn the crew entered orbit and opened the cargo bay doors, exposing the SL module to the vacuum conditions of space.

Orbital activities

After successful emplacement of *Challenger* in orbit, the crew configured the vehicle for a week in space and began the activation of the SL D1 module some 3 hours after orbital insertion. The activation was completed about 5 hours after launch with the transfer of payload control from NASA's JSC Houston complex to the West German Space Operations Centre at Oberpfaffenhofen, a DFVLR facility near Munich. Control of

MISSION DATA CHALLENGER 9

Sequence: Shuttle 22
Designation: 61-A (Spacelab D1)
OV-099 Mission: Nine
Launch Date: October 30, 1985
Launch Time: 12:00 EST
Launch Site: Pad 39A, Kennedy Space Center, Cape Canaveral, Florida, USA
Launch Weight: 4,504,741lb (2,043,316kg)
Maximum Altitude: 200 miles (322km)
Inclination: 57°
Orbits: 111, landing during 112th
EVA Duration: None
Mission Duration: 7 days 0 hours 44 minutes 51 seconds; travelled 2.5 million miles
Landing Date: November 6, 1985
Landing Time (main gear): 9:44:51 PST
Landing Site: Runway 17, Edwards AFB, California, USA
Rollout Distance and Duration: 8,400ft (2,560m) & 48 seconds
Crew: (Commander) Colonel Henry W. Hartsfield, Jr, USAF, 51, NASA (not assigned shift); (Pilot) Lieutenant-Colonel Steven R. Nagel, USAF, 39, NASA (Blue Shift Leader/EV-1); (MS-1) Dr Bonnie J. Dunbar, 36, NASA (Blue Shift); (MS-2) Colonel James F. Buchli, USMC, 40, NASA (Red Shift Leader/EV-2); (MS-3) Colonel Guion S. Bluford, Jr, USAF, 41, NASA (Red Shift); (PS-1) Dr Ernst W. Messerschmid, 40, DFVLR (Red Shift); (PS-2) Dr Reinhard Furrer, 44, DFVLR (Blue Shift); (PS-3) Dr Wubbo J. Ockels, 39, ESA (not assigned shift)
Payload: Spacelab D1 (Long Module): 17 fluid physics experiments/31 solidification experiments/17 biological experiments/5 medical experiments/6 spacetime interaction experiments; GLOMR Satellite in GAS container (deployed Day 1, GET 12 hours 34 minutes); Special Pallet holding NAVEX experiments and Materials Experiments Assembly; RHS

FLIGHT LOG CHALLENGER 9

1 (OCTOBER 30, 1985) **00:00:00** SRB ignition command from GPC (lift-off) **00:00:18.5** MPS throttledown to 89% thrust (Engine No. 3) **00:00:27.1** MPS throttledown to 65% thrust (Engine No. 3) **00:00:50** Max Q **00:00:59.9** MPS throttleup to 104% thrust (Engine No. 3) **00:02:05** SRB separation command **00:08:28.5** MPS throttledown for 3-g acceleration (Engine No. 3) **00:08:36** MECO **00:08:54** ET separation **00:10:35** OMS-1 ignition **00:12:37** OMS-1 cut-off **00:18:53** APU deactivation (No. 3) **00:44:44** OMS-2 ignition **00:46:56** OMS-2 cut-off
7 (NOVEMBER 5, 1985) **144:31:03** FCS checkout (APU No. 1 activation) **144:35:12** APU No. 1 deactivation
8 (NOVEMBER 6, 1985) **167:35:31** APU No. 2 activation **167:40:30** De-orbit manoeuvre ignition **167:43:21** De-orbit maneouvre cut-off **168:00:25** APU No. 1 activation **168:00:26** APU No. 3 activation **168:13:32** Entry interface (400,000ft, 121,920m) **168:31:33** End blackout **168:38:26** TAEM **168:44:51** Main landing gear contact **168:44:59** Nose landing gear contact **168:45:50** Wheel stop

Challenger remained at JSC. The crew now split into the familiar two-shift system.

During the week-long mission 73 of the 76 experiments were successfully activated. However, the furnace in the materials science double rack for the MEDEA experiments malfunctioned. During the second day power usage was about 1.5kW below preflight predictions and, following a successful inflight repair of the MEDEA furnace, the processing of samples was initiated. Despite the desire for a one-day mission extension to recover the time lost on the experiment, *Challenger's* power levels could not be reduced enough to support a further day in orbit, so the orbiter had to come home on the pre-arranged day. A compromise was made, however, so that simultaneous materials processing and vestibular sled experiments could be undertaken to make up the lost time.

One of the most significant events during the mission was the lack of media reporting of the flight, a reflection of the 'routine' nature of the mission. The GLOMR satellite was successfully deployed from *Challenger* at 00:34 EST on October 31, finally being spring-ejected after failure on the SL 3 mission over 5 months earlier. Several difficulties were experienced by the crew in communications with the ground during the first 24 hours in space, but the situation improved after Flight Day 2. Several TV shots showed the crew hard at work in various parts of the vehicle throughout the mission, their dedicated efforts in repairing several pieces of malfunctioning hardware being rewarded with continued improvements in data downlink and flight data-collection during the course of the mission.

One of the more important aspects of the flight was the capacity of the crew of eight to handle the cramped living conditions and establish a routine of shift exchange, which had direct applications to future Spacelab missions and the planned Space Station era with multi-person crews operating more complex shift cycles and duty tasks. With a multinational crew English was the official language, though lapses into German and Dutch were sometimes heard on the air-to-ground loop.

Despite orientation problems by some of the crew, the eight members got along quite well, this giving useful experience on future international science missions. During the flight Ockels tried out his self-designed ESA sleeping bag, which removed the sensation of 'falling' during sleep periods by pressing inflated tubes inside the bag against the occupant to provide the impression of a surface against the body.

The flight of SL D1 was an outstanding success in terms of experiment return and operational experience, clearly pointing the way for the then planned German SL D2 mission of 1988 and the 1989 Japanese SL mission.

Re-entry and landing

Deactivation of the SL configuration for re-entry was completed during the final 24 hours in space, and with the 171-second de-orbit burn *Challenger* headed for the Edwards AFB landing site. Re-entry was nominal in all respects, and Hartsfield completed four roll reversals before landing after a 207° Heading Alignment Circle had been accomplished. *Challenger* landed on the lakebed Runway 17 at Edwards AFB in California, and rolled to a standstill 8,304ft (2,531m) down the runway. The orbiter had accomplished all the DTOs assigned to it, while seven further special test condition DTOs were also completed successfully or to a very high degree. Data were also collected on a further seven secondary DTOs.

An important event of the SL D1 landing was the nose wheel steering test, during which Hartsfield successfully moved the orbiter 20 to 30ft (6.1 to 9.1m) to the left of the runway centreline, then shifted the rolling vehicle to the right for several seconds before returning it to the centre for wheelstop.

Above: Bonnie Dunbar (foreground) and Ernst Messerschmid work inside the Spacelab D1 Long Module, which was fitted with its experiment racks at the Kennedy Space Center during the summer of 1985.

Post-landing activities

Following wheelstop, preparations were made for the return of the vehicle to Florida. Initial inspection of the brakes and tyres revealed no damage to the brakes. Initial post-flight examination of the faulty fuel cell reproduced the in-flight readings, and resulted in the removal and replacement of the cell before *Challenger's* next mission.

Challenger had now logged a record nine missions in 2 years 7 months, and examination of the landing images of *Challenger* during 61-A clearly show that the orbiter had begun to show the effects of weathering and constant use.

During November 6 *Challenger* was rolled to the mate/demate device to be attached to the waiting SCA for the trip to Florida. The orbiter twice broke through the crust of the dry lakebed of the Edwards pathway which the USAF had requested NASA to use in an effort to minimize Shuttle operation impact on the continual flying activity programme at the famous test flight centre.

The first incident was easily solved by reversing the vehicle out of the trench in which it had stuck, but the second involved 4 hours of work by about 30 technicians and engineers to free *Challenger's* landing gear from furrows about 12 to 18in (0.3 to 0.45m) deep.

Following the release of the vehicle, *Challenger* was mated to the top of the 747 for the long trip back to KSC, arriving on November 11 for preparation for its historic 10th and tragic last launch from Complex 39. No one could have foreseen that the 61-A mission would be the last mission from which *Challenger* would return safely: it had logged three in 1983, three in 1984 (all with EVAs), and three Spacelab missions in 1985. The year 1986 was expected to see no less than five trips into space by *Challenger*, carrying a variety of payloads.

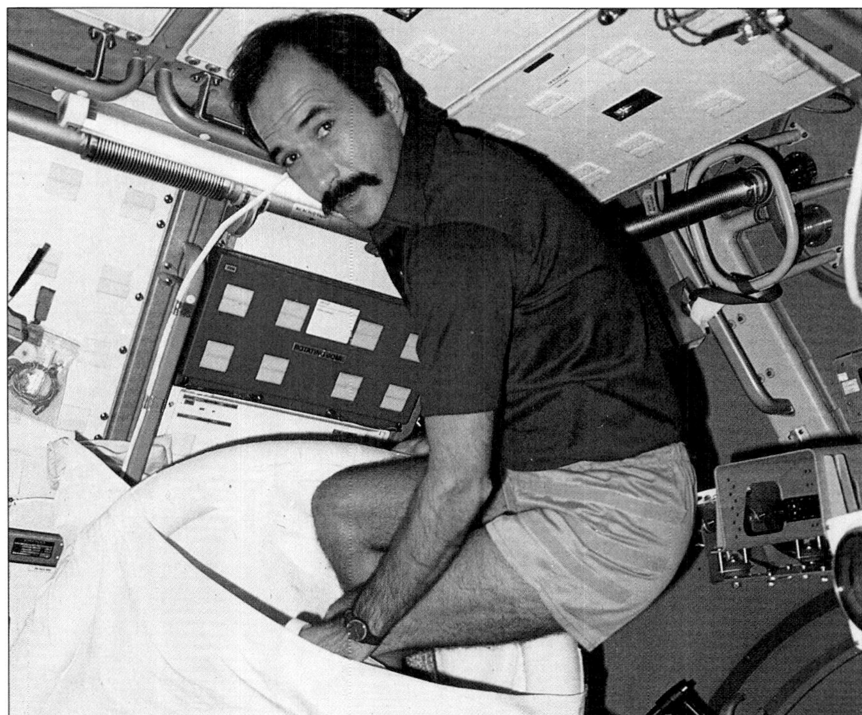

Above: A key figure in the scientific crew for Spacelab D1 was the Dutchman Wubbo Ockels, who used the flight to test the special sleeping bag he had designed for the ESA.

Below: The crew of the 61-A mission disembark at Edwards AFB from a *Challenger* that was beginning to show distinct signs of 'weathering' from its nine sorties into space.

The idea that spaceflight was for everyone received a significant boost on August 27, 1984 when President Reagan announced that the first private citizen to fly in space would be a US teacher as part of the Space Flight Participant Program designed to open Shuttle opportunities to a wider segment of private citizens with the purpose of communicating the experience and activities of the mission to the general public by educational and public information means. Throughout the rest of 1984 and the first half of 1985, the search for the Teacher-In-Space finalist was held across the USA.

Meanwhile, in a less public announcement the names of five NASA astronauts for a mission designated 51-L were announced by the agency on January 27, 1985, one year and one day before the eventual launch. Commander Scobee, a former USAF test pilot, had flown the X-24B lifting body before coming to NASA in 1978 and flying as pilot on *Challenger*'s fifth mission (Shuttle 11, or 41-C) in April 1984: pilot Smith, a Vietnam veteran, joined NASA in 1980 and was on his first mission; and the three mission specialists, who had all flown before, were from the 1978 astronaut class with Scobee. Resnik, the second US woman in space, had flown on the maiden launch of *Discovery* (Shuttle 12, or 41-D) in August-September 1984, Onizuka had also flown on *Discovery* during a military mission in January 1985 (Shuttle 15, or 51-C) and McNair had flown on *Challenger*'s fourth mission (Shuttle 10, or 41-B) in February 1984. The training would last almost 12 months, and include some payload and launch date adjustments.

On July 19, 1985 Sharon Christa McAuliffe was announced as the winner for the coveted Teacher-In-Space flight seat after examination of over 10,000 applications. She was assigned as a payload specialist to 51-L, and the crew was increased to seven on October 25, 1985 when a Hughes company payload specialist selected in 1984 for a Shuttle flight was assigned to the 51-L team. Greg Jarvis had been named to 51-D but was bumped by Congressman Jake Garn; he then lost his seat on 51-G, then again on 51-I when that mission was assigned the hazardous task of repairing the faulty Leasat satellite. He was again bumped, this time from the 61-C mission, by another politician, Congressman Bill Nelson. At last Jarvis was to get his long-awaited flight after months of bad luck.

Training for the 51-L mission progressed in various stages throughout 1985, and by December the crew members were ready for the mission, which was fated for a late January launch. The original plans had called for the 51-L mission to fly in July 1985, carrying the third TDRS satellite and the EOS-1 system. It was then reassigned to a November 1985 launch, still with the TDRS but also slated for the deployment of a retrieved satellite from Shuttle 14 (51-A). Crew and payloads changed, and by the summer of 1985 *Challenger* was assigned the mission flying TDRS-B and the Spartan-Halley free-flying satellite and the Teacher-In-Space project.

For the 51-L launch NASA used only two new units in the 22 units which made up the twin SRBs: the other 20 elements had been used a total of 29 times during ground tests or on previous missions. The first segments reached KSC by rail on October 11, 1985 and the last on November 4. The segments for 51-L were designated Booster Integration Set BI026.

Stacking for the left-hand SRB began on October 28, and that for the right-hand booster on December 4 atop MLP-2 in the VAB's High Bay 1. This was followed by the attachment of the ET for the mission on December 10, 1985.

Challenger had arrived back at KSC and was in the OPF Bay 1 by November 11, and was soon stripped of its Spacelab D1 payload and received the attachment fittings for the TDRS/IUS payload and the Spartan-Halley free-flying platform. Changes to the orbiter centred on the reconfiguration of the mid-deck to carry three astronauts rather than the four of the previous mission. Several elements from other orbiters were used to supply *Challenger* with the necessary equipment she needed to fly her tenth mission. The spares shop was not as well equipped as it might have been, and fortunately other orbiters were not too close to their launch schedules to prevent them being cannibalized for spares.

Challenger was moved to the VAB on December 10 after spending 35 days in the OPF. Following attachment to the SRB/ET combination, the vehicle was rolled out to the launch pad after only 6 days in the VAB, on December 16, 1985. *Challenger* would sit on Pad 39B for the next 37 days until that fateful January launch. Pad 39B was being used for the first time in the Shuttle programme, all other flights having used the nearby Pad 39A, which was occupied by the *Columbia* vehicle during the early part of January 1986 in preparation for Shuttle 24 (61-C). Pad 39B had been built in the 1960s for the Apollo programme, and had been used only five times previously: in May 1969 (for the Apollo 10 mission), in May, July and November 1973 (for the three manned Skylab missions) and in July 1975 (for the launch of the US ASTP crew to the historic rendezvous and docking with the Soviet Soyuz spacecraft). The opening of the second revamped Apollo pad for Shuttle operations would provide a bonus for the long Shuttle processing and launch cycles at the Cape.

Launch aborts

Launch was originally set for January 22, 1986, but was postponed several times before Shuttle 25 finally left the pad. On December 23, 1985 the launch date was delayed to January 23, 1986 in order to complete the requirements for a final simulation schedule, causing a slip of the 61-C launch from just before Christmas until the New Year. Difficulties in getting 61-C airborne resulted in further slips in the launch date of 51-L: it was announced on January 22 that the mission had been postponed to January 24 and then to January 25 in order to meet requirements resulting from the constant delays in launching 61-C, which was carrying equipment on *Columbia* that was also to be used on *Challenger* for 51-L.

The January 25 launch was also slipped one day to allow adequate work to be completed following the launch of 61-C on January 12, 1986, after no less than seven attempts, and to accommodate the Casablanca Transatlantic Landing Abort Mode (TAL) option. During the evening of January 25 a launch management conference reviewed the weather patterns for the January 26 attempt in the KSC area and contingency landing sites around the world. Reports were received that unacceptable weather was forecast throughout the January 26 window, and the launch count down for that date was terminated.

The January 27 attempt progressed closer to launch, and the fuelling of the huge ET was begun at 00:30 EST with all countdown activities proceeding smoothly. The members of the flight crew had been awakened at 05:07 and were strapped in their seats by 07:56. Just 1 hour 14 minutes later, however, the closeout ground crew reported a problem securing the side hatch handle. It took almost 80 minutes to solve the hatch handle problem, but by that time the winds at the Shuttle Landing Facility had seriously exceeded the crosswind level for a Return To Launch Site (RTLS) abort mode, and at 12:35 the launch attempt for the day was abandoned, being reset for January 28. The crew left the vehicle, disappointed but looking forward to the next day's attempt.

January 28

During the night of January 27-28 the temperature around the Cape dropped to well below freezing, and this prompted the management to review the pos-

MISSION DATA CHALLENGER 10

Sequence: Shuttle 25
Designation: 51-L
OV-099 Mission: Ten
Launch Date: January 28, 1986
Launch Time: 11:38:00 EDT
Launch Site: Pad 39B, Kennedy Space Center, Cape Canaveral, Florida, USA
Launch Weight: 4,529,122lb (2,054,375kg)
Maximum Altitude: 46,000ft (14,020m) but planned as 177 miles (285km)
Inclination: planned 28.45°
Orbits: None (planned 97)
EVA Duration: none planned
Mission Duration: vehicle exploded 73 seconds after launch (planned duration 6 days 0 hours 34 minutes)
Landing Date: planned February 3, 1986
Landing Time: planned 12:12 EDT
Landing Site: planned Shuttle Landing Facility, KSC, Florida, USA
Crew: (Commander) Major Francis R. Scobee, USAF, (Ret), 47, NASA; (Pilot) Commander Michael J. Smith, USN, 40, NASA; (MS-1) Dr Judith A. Resnik, 40, NASA; (MS-2) Colonel Ellison S. Onizuka, USAF, 39, NASA (EV-1); (MS-3) Dr Ronald E. McNair, 35, NASA (EV-2); (PS-1) Mrs S. Christa C. McAuliffe, 37, Teacher-In-Space participant; (PS-2) Gregory B. Jarvis, 41, Hughes
Payload: Remote Manipulator System: TDRS-B/Inertial Upper Stage/Airborne Support Equipment; Spartan-Halley Free Flyer/MPESS; Mid-deck Experiments: CHAMP, FDE, RME, TISP, PPE and three SSIP experiments

FLIGHT LOG **CHALLENGER 10**

1 (JANUARY 28, 1986) **00:00:00** SRB ignition command from GPC (lift-off) **00:00:04.3** MPS throttleup to 104% **00:00:07.7** Roll manoeuvre initiated **00:00:19.8** MPS throttledown to 94% **00:00:21.1** Roll manoeuvre completed **00:00:35.3** MPS throttledown to 65% **00:00:51.8** MPS throttleup to 104% **00:00:59.0** Max Q **00:01:13.6** *Challenger* explodes

Left: A training session for the 51-L mission at the Johnson Space Center in Texas shows (from left to right) back-up payload specialist Barbara Morgan, payload specialist Christa McAuliffe, payload specialist Gregory Jarvis and mission specialist Ronald McNair. Behind them is the airlock.

sible effects of the cold on the launch planned the next day. Following a review of the weather, which was forecast as clear but very cold, the decisions to fuel the ET and proceed with the launch were made, as no critical impact on the launch from the extreme cold was predicted.

Ice inspection teams were sent to the pad during the night to investigate several concerns raised by the launch team on the accumulation of ice in the area of the Pad 39B complex. On the results of these teams' investigations the decision to proceed was confirmed. A problem with a fire detector in the ground liquid hydrogen storage tank was repaired at the cost of 150 minutes in the countdown, but by using part of a planned hold the delay was reduced to only 60 minutes.

By the scheduled wake-up time of 06:18 the crew members were already up and preparing for breakfast. At 07:30 the Casablanca alternate abort site was declared a 'no-go' area, though this had no impact on the launch decision. With an extra hour available to them, the seven members of the crew took a leisurely breakfast, obtained a weather status check and suited up in the familiar blue flight coveralls ready for the trip to *Challenger*. It was at the weather briefing that ice on the pad was mentioned, but the effect of this extreme low temperature on the Shuttle vehicle was at no time discussed with the crew. They were also not informed of the concern by several SRB engineers about the problems of the O-rings in several previous flights, or of the conversations between Morton Thiokol, Marshall Spaceflight Center and KSC on the option of delaying the mission until the temperature had increased to a more acceptable level.

Above: *Challenger* sits on the pad at LC 39B before the fateful 51-L launch. The northernmost complex at the Kennedy Space Center, LC 39B was being used for the first time in the Shuttle programme as the usual LC 39A was occupied by *Columbia* for the 61-C mission which launched on January 12.

By 08:03 the crew had arrived at the foot of Pad 39B, and were strapped in their seats aboard *Challenger* 33 minutes later. On *Challenger*'s flight deck were Scobee in the left-hand seat and Smith in the right-hand seat, and between them to the rear were Resnik (acting as flight engineer) and Onizuka; on the mid-deck sat McNair, McAuliffe and Jarvis. With their backs to the ground, the flight crew of Scobee and Smith were helped by Resnik in ploughing through the routine pre-flight checklist. The other four sat and waited.

After two further ice inspection teams had reviewed the condition of the pad, the decision to proceed for launch was made during the planned hold 9 minutes before ignition.

Launch

At precisely 11:38:00.010 EST on January 28, 1986 *Challenger* slowly left the launch pad of Complex 39B to begin its 10th and final mission. As the vehicle rose into the clear blue sky no indication was visible that disaster was only a minute or so away. The watching crowds cheered as America's first Teacher-In-Space was finally on her way. On the ground engineers scanned their computer screens for signs of problems but all seemed normal, and as Max Q was reached and passed the command for throttleup was given to Scobee, who acknowledged the call. Then suddenly there was a flash, and *Challenger* and her seven crew members disappeared in a ball of fire. The flight of Challenger 10 had ended barely one and a quarter minutes after it had begun. On the ground the impact of what had happened hit home, and as debris from the vehicle dropped from the sky into the Atlantic Ocean there began the search for an answer to the question of how the pride of the USA's space fleet had been lost.

Below: Whatever the deficiencies of the SRB design, it needed adverse climatic conditions to bring these to the fore in the 51-L disaster. Here the left-hand SRB and *Challenger*'s belly are framed against an ice-covered gantry structure.

Right: Seen leaving the Operations and Checkout Building are the 51-L crew, namely (from front to back) Dick Scobee, Judith Resnik, Ronald McNair, Michael Smith, Christa McAuliffe, Ellison Onizuka and Gregory Jarvis.

Left: At 6.678 seconds after lift-off an automatic camera records a telltale puff of grey smoke erupting from the region of the right-hand SRB's aft field joint, revealing an O-ring failure.

Using the official Presidential Commission Report into the accident, supported by NASA photographs, videos and audio recording of the accident, a full account of the final flight of *Challenger* is reconstructed below.

At 6.6 seconds before the launch of *Challenger*, the three SSMEs were ignited in sequence and built up in thrust whilst the vehicle was still attached to the launch pad. At lift-off the twin SRBs were ignited and the vehicle released to begin its upward motion. At 0:678 seconds into the mission ground-based automatic photographic data revealed a distinct puff of grey smoke jetting from the vicinity of the right-hand SRB's aft field joint. The exact location of the smoke was not immediately apparent, but subsequent computer graphic reconstruction of other film of the area at launch indicates that the plume originated from the aft field joint in the 270° to 310° sector at a point facing the virtually full ET. As *Challenger* rose from the pad a further eight puffs of smoke were registered by other cameras through the 2.5 second mark. As the smoke blackened and eventually disappeared into the exhaust plumes of the SSMEs and SRBs, the crew had no indication of the chain of events that had begun and already sealed their fate less than 70 seconds later.

Analysis of the smoke emissions following the disaster indicated a fault in the SRB O-ring sealing mechanism: the grease, sealing compounds and rubber O-rings had been burned and evaporated by extremely hot propellant gases from within the SRB casing. As *Challenger* climbed into the blue Florida sky all indications from the air-to-ground commentary indicated a normal ascent, with the crew dutifully reporting the ascent profile and acknowledging calls from the ground CapCom. To the ground onlookers it appeared just another normal and very routine ascent of the Shuttle.

After 37 seconds of flight *Challenger* entered a region of high-altitude windshear conditions, which lasted until 64 seconds of flight. Sensing severe fluctuations to the flight path caused by these winds, the onboard guidance, navigation and control subsystem noted the deviations and stress imposed on the ascending vehicle, and ordered the thrust vector control system of the SRBs to compensate for the higher loads through which the combination was flying. Though these loads were the highest yet recorded during a Shuttle ascent, they were by no means critical, and remained well within the design limits of the combination. The wind shear nevertheless forced the steering system to be more active on this flight than on any previous mission.

As *Challenger*'s engines were throttled to 104%, the orbiter completed the required roll and at that stage throttled down to 94%.

As *Challenger* climbed, all seemed normal to the crowds of onlookers, though to some experienced Shuttle followers the SRB plume seemed to pulsate visibly and seemed less powerful than normal. No unusual comments were made during the brief exchanges between the vehicle and the ground. However, four of the seven had experienced a Shuttle launch before and two of them (Scobee and McNair) had flown *Challenger* on their first missions in 1984. Scobee was an accomplished test pilot and flightdeck-experienced *Challenger* astronaut, and it may have occurred to him that perhaps this launch was different. Maybe he put it down to the age of the vehicle or maybe not, but his expertise and previous Shuttle experience must have made him aware of the different 'feel' of this ride.

At GET 45 seconds three bright flashes were observed by tracking cameras, and later diagnosed as reflections of the SSME exhaust on the OMS pods, an event which had been observed on previous missions. *Challenger* now throttled down its engines, passed through Max Q, and received the command to throttle the engines again to 104%, a call acknowledged by the crew.

It was shortly after this that, according to enhanced video of the ascent, the first small flickers of flame appeared. The SRBs were increasing their thrust after passing Max Q when, around the aft field joint on the right-hand SRB and at about 305° on the booster circumference, fire became apparent. The time was 58.788 seconds into the mission, and the final sequence to disaster had begun. Less than a second later the flame increased to a size not requiring photo enhancement for visibility, and at the same time pressure levels in the left- and right-hand SRBs were noticeably different, with pressure in the right chamber dropping and so confirming the increasing leak from the field joint.

The disaster

As *Challenger* continued upwards, the slipstream of the vehicle cutting through the atmosphere directed the escaping flame plume rearwards and around the structures attaching the ET to the SRBs. As the flame grew in intensity, *Challenger*'s onboard automatic control system compensated for the forces generated by the plume, the left-hand SRB thrust-vector control being activated to balance the yaw caused by the leaking right-hand SRB.

At 64.660 seconds evidence of the first breach in the ET was recorded: the SRB plume had inevitably worn away the skin of the ET, and a sharp increase in the plume's change of shape and colour indicated that the flame was mixing with hydrogen leaking from the ET. Telemetry data confirmed the breach, and just 45 milliseconds later a bright sustained glow appeared under *Challenger*'s belly and between the orbiter and the ET.

At about 72 seconds into the flight a rapid sequence of events began the flight's final moments after a variety of control-system actions tried to fight against the growing forces of the pending disaster.

At 72.20 seconds the lower strut supporting the SRB to the ET either broke or was pulled away from its mountings on the weakened hydrogen tank, allowing the right-hand SRB to rotate around the forward upper attachment point, a fact confirmed by yaw and pitch rate dif-

Left: At 59.25 seconds after lift-off the camera records a well defined and intense plume of flame on the side and towards the base of the right-hand SRB. Catastrophe is seconds away.

ferences recorded from both boosters. At 73.124 seconds video tracking cameras recorded a large circumferential white vapour pattern developing from the lower dome of the ET, the beginning of the massive structural failure of the hydrogen tank which ended with the entire aft dome section dropping away. With this event about 2,800,000lb (1,270,059kg) of forward thrust was imparted to the vehicle as large amounts of liquid hydrogen were released from the crumbling tank, pushing the structure into the intertank area of the ET. At the same time the right-hand SRB impacted the ET intertank structure and the lower part of the oxygen tank in the forward part of the ET. Evidence of the failure of these structures occurred at GET 73.137 seconds as white vapour was recorded around the intertank structure. The flames suddenly tracked around the circumference of the lower ET and shot dramatically up the side of the ET towards the oxygen tank along the feed pipes running up the side of the ET.

Within only milliseconds of these events, the explosive burning of liquid hydrogen and liquid oxygen combined into an eruption of massive proportions, engulfing *Challenger* and its crew as they travelled at Mach 1.92 at an altitude of 46,000ft (14,020m) above the Atlantic Ocean. As the vehicle emerged from the ball of fire its onboard hypergolic fuel load exploded in the nose of the craft, as recorded in the reddish-brown colours of the edge of the main fireball. As a result of extreme aerodynamic stresses on the vehicle's structure, *Challenger* broke up into several large pieces as wreckage was thrown out of the fireball. Film analysis recorded the MPS/tail section (still burning residual fuel), one of the wings, and the forward fuselage trailing a mass of umbilical lines pulled from the payload bay.

On the ground onlookers were at first awed by the impression of what they thought was the spectacular separation of the SRBs as planned. Then the harsh reality of the tragic events hit them. Families, friends, colleagues and school children watching across America witnessed the complete and utter destruction of the orbiter, and the loss of seven astronauts including the country's most famous teacher, who would never become the first school teacher in space after all.

Right: Moments after the mid-air explosion of *Challenger*'s liquid propellants, a detached SRB climbs out of the huge fireball with its fuel still burning fiercely.

As components of *Challenger* and the wreckage of the ET and SRBs, which had been destroyed by the range safety officer after they appeared to be heading for land impact, fell into the Atlantic, an immediate search and rescue operation was mounted in the remote possibility of finding survivors.

It was subsequently revealed that the crew, or at least some of them, had survived the initial explosion and break-up of the vehicle, the flight crew activating some of the personal air-breathing systems behind their seats as *Challenger's* separated crew module dropped like a stone towards the ocean. It was revealed that the crew probably were fully aware of the pending explosion in the last few milliseconds of the mission as the warning lights flashed on the flight deck in front of their eyes and bright flashes blinded them through the orbiter windows. The last recorded commentary from the crew was from pilot Smith, who uttered 'Uh-oh', followed by Scobee activating his communication 'speak' switch before all downlink from the doomed vehicle was lost. The extreme rates of descent and g-forces imparted to the cabin as it fell and spun meant that despite probably being alive the crew were far from conscious as the cabin fell and eventually hit the water at 1,997mph (3,214km/h).

Challenger exploded 20 miles (32km) off Florida at an altitude of almost 9 miles (14.5km), the force of the explosion producing a forward momentum which pushed debris a further 11 miles (17.7km) higher and shredding it into featherweight pieces, which fell for 60 minutes after the explosion and hampered the recovery forces.

As the crowds left KSC, shocked and stunned by what they had just witnessed, a full-scale search for wreckage was begun and President Reagan, in the Oval Room of the White House preparing his afternoon State of the Union Address, was informed of the disaster. The president immediately cancelled his plans for the day.

As search and rescue teams began the long, painstaking recovery of debris from the ocean and beaches around the Cape, a process which lasted about six months, President Reagan addressed the nation on coast-to-coast TV, mourning the crew, admiring their dedication in the exploration of space, and also promising that the Shuttle programme would continue and that the sacrifice would not be forgotten or in vain.

Below: Flight Directors Jay Greene and Alan Briscoe look on aghast at JSC as telemetry begins to confirm the visual record of disaster.

Three days after the loss, the memorial service for the Challenger Seven (as they were now called) was held in NASA's Johnson Space Flight Center, where tributes to the brave crew were heard. On February 3 the president announced the names of 13 members of a Presidential Commission set up to investigate the cause of the accident and to make recommendations which would allow the resumption of the programme with safeguards so that such a tragedy would not again occur. The commission worked from February 6 until presenting its report on June 6, 1986. During this time it investigated not only the *Challenger* accident but also several other areas of concern. The very core of NASA was under close scrutiny: it was 19 years since the tragic loss of the three Apollo 1 crew in a pad fire at the Cape, and NASA was once more in the spotlight, though not for the reasons it would have liked. The very future of the agency, the Shuttle and US manned spaceflight rested on the results of the commission and the effective implementation of its recommendations.

During the term of the commission the wreckage of *Challenger* was brought ashore and, some six weeks after hitting the ocean, the crew module of *Challenger* was recovered. The bodies of the seven astronauts were removed examined and buried with full honours. The families grieved and threatened to sue NASA and the contractors for their loss. All Shuttle flights were cancelled, and assigned crews stood down while the investigations continued.

The Inquiry

Following the shock of the 51-L catastrophe, the urgent response of the President, NASA and the people of the USA was to discover what had gone wrong. A Presidential Commission of Inquiry was set up under the chairmanship of William Rogers, and so began an exhaustive analysis of all available evidence. Suspicions focussed on the performance of the Solid Rocket Boosters, and more specifically on the aft field joint of the right hand SRB. A failure of its O-ring seals in the sub-zero temperatures to which the Shuttle stack was exposed on Pad 39B during the preparations for launch seems to have led to unavoidable tragedy.

On February 6, 1986 just nine days after the loss of *Challenger* and its crew of seven, the 13 members of the Presidential Commission, assigned by President Reagan to investigate the tragic loss and its causes, were sworn in and immediately began their work. This resulted after four months in the publication of five volumes of results and recommendations covering not only the 51-L accident and the events leading to the loss of the vehicle, but also investigations into areas of NASA management structures, inter-department communications, pressures on the launch schedule, problems with the Shuttle brakes and planned landings at Kennedy, future payloads and, eventually, the whole direction of the Shuttle programme and involvement of the astronauts in decision-making processes.

The members of the commission were: Chairman William P. Rogers (former Secretary of State for President Nixon, an Attorney General under President Eisenhower, and a leading law attorney); Vice Chairman Neil A. Armstrong (former NASA astronaut who flew Gemini 8 and Apollo 11, was the first man on the moon, became Professor of Aeronautical Engineering at the University of Cincinnati, then Chairman of Computing Technologies for Aviation Inc, and a member of National Commission on Space); David C. Acheson (former Senior Vice President and General Counsel of ComSat Corp, and a partner in the law firm Drinker, Biddle & Reath); Dr Eugene E. Covert (educator and engineer); Dr Richard P. Feynman (physicist); Robert B. Hotz (editor and publisher); Major General Donald J. Kutyna, USAF (Director of Space Systems and Command, Control and Communications); Dr Sally K. Ride (NASA astronaut, who flew on *Challenger* twice on Missions 7 and 13, and had become the first US woman in space); Robert W. Rummel (space expert and aerospace engineer); Joseph F. Sutter (aerospace engineer); Dr Arthur B. C. Walker Jr (astronomer); Dr Albert D. Wheelon (physicist); and Brigadier General Charles Yeager (a retired USAF officer, former experimental test pilot, member of the National Commission on Space, former X-1 pilot and first person to break the 'sound barrier'). In addition, Dr Alton G. Keel Jr served as Executive Director of the Commission, being detailed from his position in the Executive Office of the President, Office of Management and Budget.

Following a complete review of all available data reports and records to which they had access, and instigating a number of tests and investigations, the commission reported: '. . . the loss of the Space Shuttle Challenger was caused by a failure in the joint between the two lower segments of the right Solid Rocket Motor. The specific failure was the destruction of the seals that are intended to prevent hot gases from leaking through the joint during the propellant burn of the rocket motor . . . The evidence assembled by the Commission indicates that no other element of the Space Shuttle system contributed to this failure . . .'

Pinpointing the failure

The commission's task to discover the cause for the loss of *Challenger* was helped by the availability of detailed telemetric and photographic data, and analysis of debris recovered from the ocean. From early releases of photographic evidence and preliminary examination of the recovered debris it soon became evident that the problem which triggered the chain of events leading to the explosion of the vehicle after 73 seconds of flight originated from the SRB right-hand element.

It was soon ruled that there was no evidence to support the suggestion of sabotage at the launch pad, during launch processing or the launch itself.

Examination of the recovered ET debris indicated that none of the range safety elements had been activated, while examination of the construction history, testing and data analysis combined with results of tests on recovered debris to rule out a premature detonation of the ET by the range safety devices, structural flaws which would have contributed to the failure or any serious damage at lift off, higher than designed loads, or overheating of onboard propellants. Examination of debris revealed burn marks both before and after the ET broke up. The only recorded overheating could be timed to the moment when the SRB plume impinged the surface of the tank in the final moments of ascent. In summary the commission found no evidence that supported the theory that the ET caused or contributed to the cause of the accident.

The recovery of the three SSMEs was achieved on February 23 off the coast of Florida in 80ft (24m) of water. All elements were recovered in close proximity, and all were found to have suffered from water impact or water-attributable deterioration. All three engines had evidence of burn marks as a result of an oxygen-rich shutdown, indicating that the loss of hydrogen led to the initiation of SSME shutdown. Comparison with data from other launches and with the previous performance of engines 2020 2021 and 2023 (all of which had flown on several missions before 51-L) provided comparable data, indicating

Below: Members of the Presidential Commission examine an SRB segment at KSC; next to Chairman William Rogers (pointing) is Sally Ride.

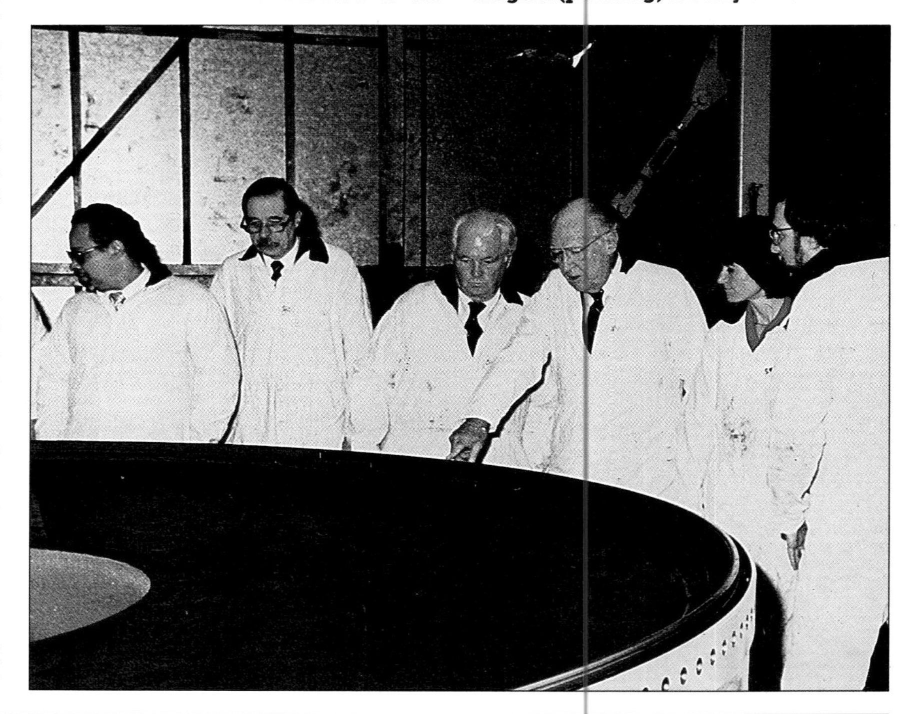

The Joint That Failed

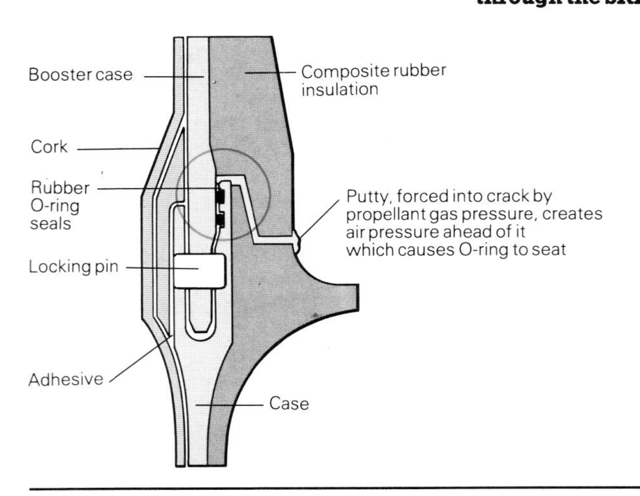

Below: A detail of the O-ring seals that were meant to prevent gases escaping through the SRB joint.

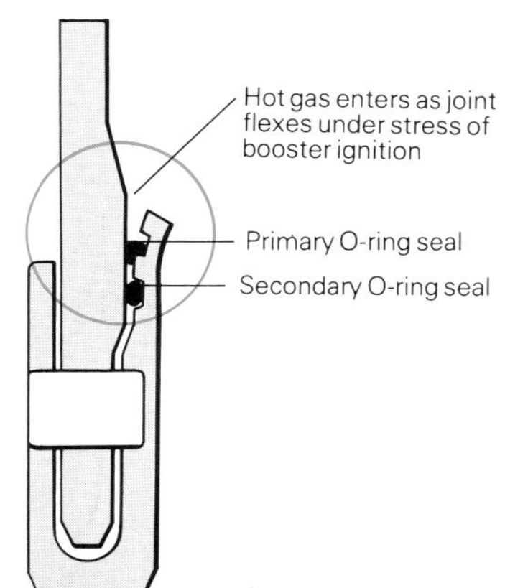

Possible Fixes

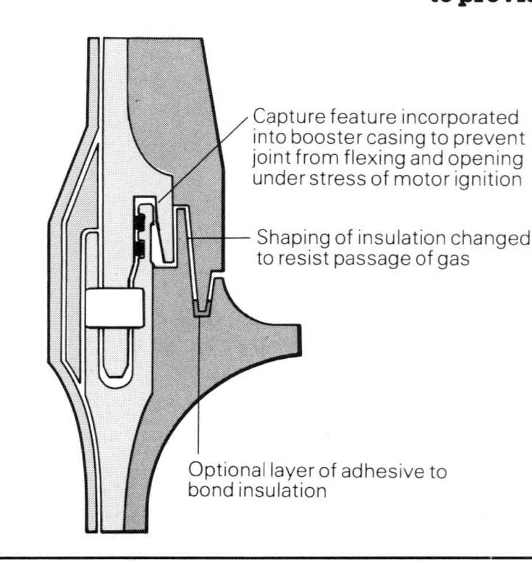

Below: Two alternatives, proposed by NASA in 1986, for fixing the SRB joint to provide secure seals.

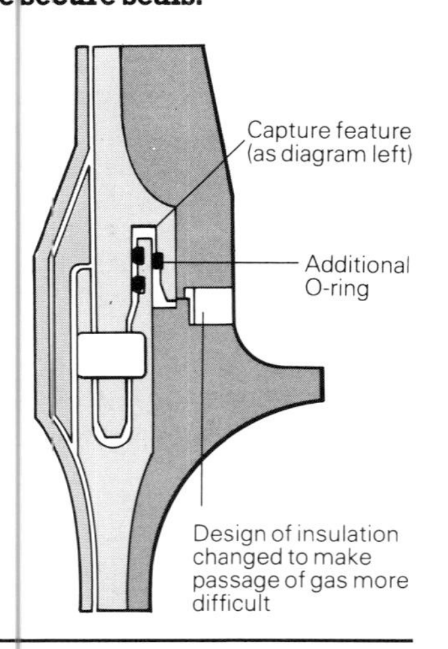

Left: Milliseconds before disaster, a tracking camera catches a flash of flame between the orbiter and external tank; such evidence was vital to the official inquiry.

Right: Part of the left-hand SRB 210ft (64m) down on the ocean bed east of KSC. It was photographed by Deep Drone, a remotely-controlled US Navy submersible.

that the operation of the SSMEs had been normal, and that the engines had shut down in a predicted manner in view of the circumstances (loss of pressure and fuel supply). The commission concluded that *Challenger*'s SSMEs did not contribute to the accident.

Analysis of recorded elements of *Challenger* itself also indicated that the vehicle had not suffered serious onboard failure before the explosions which led to the structural disintegration of the vehicle at high speeds. About 30 per cent of *Challenger* was recovered in the weeks following the disaster, including the three SSMEs, the forward fuselage (including the crew module), the right inboard and outboard elevons, a large portion of the right wing, a lower portion of the vertical stabilizer, three rudder speed brake panels, and portions from both the left- and right-hand mid-fuselage side walls.

Evidence from all elements of *Challenger* which were recovered indicated that the break-up had been the result of overload forces imparted by the explosion, subsequent higher-than-designed aerodynamic flight through the atmosphere, and high-velocity water impact. There was no evidence of internal burn damage or exposure to explosive forces, but there was evidence that supported the data indicating that the right-hand SRB had struck the outboard end of *Challenger*'s right wing and elevon, and that the right side of the vehicle had been sprayed by hot gases spilled from the leaking SRB field joint. The crew module wreckage was eventually found on an area of seabed measuring 20 by 80ft (6.1 by 24.4m), and all around it were portions of the forward fuselage outer shell. Examination of the module, which was found resting on the ocean bed with its left side downwards, showed no evidence of internal explosion, heat or fire damage: the module was shattered, but it seems that the forward fuselage shell and crew module had remained intact until water impact, which occurred on the left side of the structure. Examination of all preflight data, inflight data, photographic evidence and subsequent analysis of recovered debris indicated nominal performance of all orbiter components and associated subsystems throughout the 73 seconds of powered flight, and the commission reported that *Challenger* and associated orbiter equipment were not the cause of the accident.

Evidence about payload interfaces and the payload itself (especially the IUS upper stage) was examined closely by the commission in order to determine if an onboard explosion had occurred to trigger the chain of events which ultimately destroyed the vehicle, or if the payload had shifted in the payload bay causing a dramatic change in the centre of gravity of the vehicle. The evidence supported neither of these theories, however, inflight data recording nominal operations up to the time of data loss, and recovered debris indicating that the payload suffered severe damage only from the explosion and break-up of the vehicle, and the subsequent impact in the Atlantic Ocean. Once again the commission concluded that the payload and support equipment had neither contributed to nor caused the accident.

The final element to receive investigation by the commission was the SRB motors, which were tracked by ground cameras throughout the boosted phase of the mission and which provided the evidence of the probable cause of the accident.

The SRBs' construction history, previous use and the launch loads on this and previous missions were all examined, as were possible structure overloads, premature ignition of range safety devices, and aerodynamic forces during ascent. All these were found not to be contributory causes to the accident, and were thus eliminated from the inquiry. Indeed, seconds after the explosion the twin SRBs were seen arcing away from the ball of flame and still appeared, in initial film, to be burning normally until destroyed by the range safety officer 110 seconds after launch, when it appeared they were heading for a land impact. As it turned out this was not the case. Elements from both boosters were recovered from the ocean and examined for damage or malfunction.

The right-hand SRB

As the commission continued its investigation, and as evidence was gathered and examined, several items were assessed as improbable causes of the accident and therefore eliminated from further consideration. The area of major focus thus came to centre on the right-hand Solid Rocket Motor, and as a result four areas were identified for detailed analysis to determine their part in the tragic accident.

Evaluation of the structural loads experienced by the right SRB during launch and the boosted phase of the mission were reproduced using test models and evaluated to see if these loads exceeded design limitations. In addition, all previous Shuttle launch data were examined and compared with those of 51-L. The results indicated that the loads encountered by the SRB were well within the design limits for the booster, in both this and previous flights in the programme. Wind shear was investigated and found to be higher than expected for this mission, but still inside design limitations. The commission found that the loads were well below design limits and did not contribute to the cause of the accident.

Analysis of the Case Membrane, the 0.5in (12.7mm) thick steel wall of the rocket between the joints, was also undertaken. However, subsequent analysis of the recovered sections of the SRB, and of flight photographic data also led the commission to report: '. . . assessments of the sections do not support a failure that started in the membrane and progressed slowly to the joint; or one that started in the membrane and grew rapidly the length of the Solid Rocket Motor Segment. . .'

The examination of the SRB propellant by the commission also indicated that the propellant used on this flight (TP-H1148) was most unlikely to have produced anomalies and thus to have contributed to the 51-L accident.

The tragedy of 51-L was fortunate in the fact that the whole event was recorded on several still and motion cameras, and this permitted an accurate interpreting of exactly what went wrong. Had a failure occurred on orbit or during re-entry, where photographic evidence is never available, the task of determining the cause of the tragedy and thus preventing a reoccurrence would have been much harder. But as the seven astronauts died in the eyes of all the world, those same pictures would help future crews fly a safer and more reliable Shuttle system.

Above: The US Coast Guard Cutter *Dallas* offloads part of orbiter *Challenger*'s forward structure at Cape Canaveral. Its break-up was thought to be caused by aerodynamic loads rather than explosive stress.

Below: Terry Armentrout, Director of Reconstruction and Evaluation, briefs newsmen on the analysis of recovered wreckage; behind him are the nozzles of two of the Space Shuttle Main Engines.

Left: The very first Solid Rocket Booster motor segments for STS-1 being offloaded in High Bay 4 of the VAB in September 1979. No-one then realised that the design of the motor joints was fatally flawed.

O-ring failure

Enhanced examination of photographic evidence and computer-graphic positioning eventually determined that the flame originated from the right SRB at about the 305-degree circumferential position. In addition, lift-off photographs by automatic cameras around the LC-39B pad showed black smoke jetting from the same general location. Early in the investigation this area was the location of primary analysis and inspection, and after elements of the SRB debris from the right-hand unit had been recovered, detailed examination revealed large holes extending from 291 degrees to 318 degrees. Several probable causes were then considered.

During the stacking process of the SRBs, four segments are stacked to form the Solid Rocket Motor element. The joints between these segments are called Field Joints, which are sealed by two rubber O-rings of 0.280in ±0.005 to 0.003in (7.11mm ±0.127 to 0.076mm) diameter and installed during assembly. Static compression during stacking is dictated by the width of the gap and concentricity of the segment. In addition zinc chromate putty is applied to the composite rubber (NBR) insulation face before assembly to provide an insulation barrier and so prevent direct contact between the combustion gases and the O-rings. The system was also designed so that the displacement of the putty drives the compressed air into the O-rings: this is called Pressure Actuation of the O-Ring Seal, and occurs very early during SRB ignition as pressure loads on the tang and clevis elements of the SRB segments increase. It was known that if the pressure actuation was delayed the clevis/tang gap would open enough to allow exhaust gases to pass onto the O-rings and thus damage or destroy the seals. Two O-rings were fitted to help delay the inevitable burn-through of the exhaust gases if this did occur.

Investigation of this action revealed several areas which would seriously inhibit the correct functioning of the O-ring design: damage to the joints or seals because of manufacturing tolerances; out-of-round factors resulting from mishandling or the effects of reuse; opening of the tang/clevis gap as a consequence of motor pressure or other loads; static O-ring compression; joint temperature which affected the O-ring response under dynamic conditions (resiliency) or hardening; joint temperature as it related to ice formation from water intrusion in the joint; and putty effect on O-ring pressure actuation timing or O-ring erosion.

Subsequent investigations in these areas were conducted, and the results indicated that the problem occurred in several of these areas, namely out-of-round segments; possible tang/clevis gap tolerance distortion; launch temperature, which affected the putty and O-ring characteristics; and reuse of flight hardware.

Analysis of recovered wreckage

Apart from items of debris retrieved from the surface of the ocean and those washed up on the beaches along the Florida coastline around KSC, several larger items were discovered at depths of between 100 and 1,200ft (30 and 366m).

As parts of *Challenger* were recovered, it became apparent that the original markings were retained and no signs of thermal damage were apparent. However, scorched and blackened paint was found on the right rudder speed brake panel and elevon, and on the aft right sides of fuselage panels. Evidence that the right SRB had struck the underside of the right wing was seen in some indentation on the TPS system.

Substantial debris was recovered from the ET which, in combination with the photographic data, revealed that flame from the right-hand SRB had encircled the ET. This had caused the ET's aft dome to break free. The large increase of thrust thus created severely buckled the intertank region, which was recovered from the ocean. Further analysis of the intertank revealed that the right side of the structure showed signs of crushing.

However, significant elements of debris from the twin SRBs were retrieved from the ocean by the search teams. Analysis of recovered SRB debris and detailed reconstruction of the area around the P12 strut confirmed the evidence of a large hole around the 307-degree circumferential position approximately 27in (68.6cm) in circumference. All around the hole was evidence of hot gas erosion that had bevelled surrounding areas of insulation and the steel case materials. The area of the aft centre segment around the O-ring showed signs of erosion and burning. In addition severe discoloration of the surrounding areas and flows of molten metal were evident in the recovered debris.

Left: Wreckage of *Challenger* laid out in the Logistics Facility at KSC for analysis. As is apparent, there is little sign of scorching or thermal damage to the orbiter's exterior or national insignia and markings.

Findings

When the final report was published by the Presidential Commission on June 6, 1986, a total of 16 items was listed as the result of 16 weeks of work across America. In clearing several areas of investigation from the probable cause of the Shuttle 51-L loss the commission reported: 'A combustion leak through the right Solid Rocket Motor aft field joint initiated at, or shortly after ignition eventually weakened and/or penetrated the External Tank initiating vehicle structural breakup and the loss of the Space Shuttle Challenger during STS Mission 51-L.'

In addition the commission noted that though the assembly of SRB components followed approved procedures there were several areas where water contamination, out-of-round segments, severe temperatures at the launch site during the night before launch, and the resiliency of O-rings in a cold state all contributed to the 51-L tragedy.

Conclusion

'IN VIEW OF THE FINDINGS, THE COMMISSION CONCLUDED THAT THE CAUSE OF THE CHALLENGER ACCIDENT WAS THE FAILURE OF THE PRESSURE SEAL IN THE AFT FIELD JOINT OF THE RIGHT SOLID ROCKET MOTOR. The failure was due to a faulty design unacceptably sensitive to a number of factors. These factors were the effects of temperature, physical dimensions, the character of materials, the effects of reusability, processing, and reaction to dynamic loading.'

Restarting the programme

As the Presidential Commission published its finding, so the work of getting Shuttle back into space resumed. Over the remaining months of 1986 NASA aimed for a launch date for Shuttle 26, initially scheduled for the summer of 1987 but eventually moved to a more realistic date of the first quarter of 1988.

During the investigation into the cause and events of the January 28 accident, the revelation of serious administrative and procedural errors rocked NASA to its core and seriously threatened the agency and the very future of American manned space exploration. For months the continued viability of Shuttle as a satellite carrier was in doubt, and expendable launch vehicles were revived and gained a new lease of life as the future of Shuttle was examined. In a new role Shuttle would fly only eight or ten missions per year, possibly expanding to 16. Most satellites would be flown on expendable launch vehicles, and only security-related, domestic and Shuttle-designed satellites would be carried by future orbiters. The Space Shuttle would become a test bed for Space Station and micro-gravity research programmes, and it would continue to construct and support the Space Station, but its days as a reliable sole deployer of US and foreign satellites by NASA were over.

The commission revealed that the pressure to launch was always high, as was the pressure of astronaut training. Communications between contractors to launch/flight personnel were minimal, to say the least, as evidenced by Morton Thiokol employees' urgent but totally ignored pressures to delay the launch of 51-L until the weather improved and the

Right: A piece of the aft centre segment tang joint of the right hand SRB is offloaded from a recovery ship. The large burned-out area in the region of the field joint is clearly visible at the bottom right.

freezing temperatures declined. Evidence that O-rings had been a problem for several years surfaced to general knowledge: the SRBs of previous flights, notably Shuttle 8, had shown clear evidence of O-ring damage and near burn-through.

Astronauts voiced concern that they had not been told of the O-ring problem. The old days of astronaut involvement in the development of hardware were long gone, but the notion was soon revived upon recommendations from the commission, several astronauts or former astronauts receiving key assignments in influential posts in Washington the Cape and JSC. Astronaut training cycles were reviewed and the plans for carrying passengers delayed, through McAuliffe's back-up teacher Barbara Morgan and the journalist-in-space finalists were promised seats on Shuttle missions. Payload specialists across the USA and in the UK, Italy, France, West Germany, India, Australia, Japan, the Philippines and Canada were stood down.

Science missions were cut from the programme, the Centaur liquid-fuelled upper stage was deleted from further Shuttle manifests, and the need to land on concrete runways at weather-plagued KSC, an on-going problem, was also questioned. Payloads were removed and reassigned to expendable launch vehicles, and all Shuttles were grounded, even from flying on the 747 in case another vehicle should be lost and the fleet reduced to two. Methods of crew escape were also studied, one idea being a 'tractor rocket' system to pull astronauts clear of the orbiter

Shuttle after *Challenger*

As NASA and the USA looked seriously into the Shuttle programme, the old question of a new orbiter resurfaced, the new vehicle now being urgently promoted as *Challenger*'s replacement. Supporters of the programme urged a four-orbiter programme needed to sustain even the new modest flight manifest, which was now mostly of DoD or Space Station-related missions. Opponents supported research and development into the next-generation Shuttle vehicles, pointing out that the current design was over 15 years old. A 'mixed fleet' policy comprising Shuttle orbiters operating alongside complementary Expendable Launch Vehicles (ELVs) also had its advocates.

On August 15, 1986 President Reagan finally gave NASA the go-ahead to order a sixth orbiter from Rockwell, though he did not detail exactly how the money to build the vehicle would be found, indicating only that it would come from existing programmes within NASA and not from extra funding. This is a feat which NASA will be hard pressed to achieve with an already tight budget and stretched-out programme. The new orbiter is expected to begin flight operations in 1993, seven years after the loss of the vehicle it replaces.

As the late months of 1986 proceeded the decision to proceed with the redesigned SRM was finally given. Several static tests had been completed on SRBs both to reproduce the *Challenger* mishap (which was successfully demonstrated) and so gather more information on what exactly happened on that fateful January day, and to test several new designs of field joints. The best type of field joint was expected to be selected early in 1987. A series of SRB firings is planned before the next Shuttle leaves the launch pad.

The new launch date for Shuttle 26 from Pad 39B was announced as February 18, 1988, with the *Discovery* making the flight to carry TDRS-C into orbit. The crew for the flight was announced on January 9, 1987 as Rick Hauck (commander), Richard Covey (pilot), and John Lounge, George Nelson and David Hilmers (mission specialists). Part of the preparations to support this and later flights was the October 8, 1986 rollout of *Atlantis* to Pad 39B for seven weeks of tests, and also the evaluation of solutions to several questions raised while *Challenger* was on that same pad 10 months earlier in a period of high winds and freezing weather.

Meanwhile on October 3, 1986 NASA announced plans for the disposition of the *Challenger* debris following the completion of wreckage analysis. It was announced that the recovered debris would be placed in long-term storage at Cape Canaveral Air Force Station in Florida, the USAF transferring the deactivated Minuteman facilities at Complexes 31 and 32 at CCAFS. The facilities included two underground silos of about 31,000cu ft (877.2m^3) storage space and several equipment and support buildings. Following the preparation of the facilities in the autumn of 1986 the installation of *Challenger* debris began early in 1987, concluding NASA's primary activities connected with analysis and the disposition of all recovered hardware. As selected components complete longer testing programmes they too are to be transferred to the silos.

Once the approximately 215,000lb (97,525kg) of debris recovered have been installed in the silos, huge concrete covers are to be placed over the tubes to provide a weathertight seal for the stored debris.

It was also announced that the hangar at Dulles Airport destined to hold the orbiter *Enterprise* on display would be named after *Challenger*.

On Wednesday January 28, 1987, exactly one year after the disaster, several thousand workers at JSC, Houston, observed a 73-second silence outside the centre, as a US flag was lowered to half-mast at 10.38 CDT.

In Memoriam

'The future is not free: the story of all human progress is one of struggle against all odds. We learned again that this America, which Abraham Lincoln called the last, best hope of man on Earth, was built on heroism and noble sacrifice. It was built by men and women like our seven star voyagers, who answered a call beyond duty, who gave more than was expected or required and who gave it little thought of worldly reward.' So said President Reagan during the 51-L Memorial Service held at NASA JSC Space Center on January 31, 1986.

Right: The *Challenger* 7: (back row, left to right) Ellison Onizuka, Christa McAuliffe, Greg Jarvis, Judy Resnik; (front row, left to right) Mike Smith, Dick Scobee and Ron McNair.

The Astronauts

During its 33-month long operational life, a total of 51 different people flew aboard the orbiter *Challenger*. They ranged in experience from dedicated NASA career astronauts, such as Robert Crippen, who piloted the very first Space Shuttle flight in 1981 and commanded *Challenger* on three separate missions, to the Payload Specialists, scientists who were assigned to a specific mission to undertake experiments related to the payload. *Challenger* was also notable for taking the first US woman into space – Sally Ride.

Between April 1983 and January 1986 a total of 51 people were launched aboard the *Challenger* orbiter at least once. Of these 46 were male and five female. Seven of them (six males and one female) flew the vehicle twice, and one male flew *Challenger* a record three times. On its 10 missions *Challenger* carried a total complement of 60 astronauts from the Kennedy Space Center.

Forty astronauts (36 male and four female) were serving NASA career astronauts and 11 (10 male and one female) were of PS categories. The PS crew members each flew only a single mission, the multiple flights being accomplished by the career NASA astronauts. Of the PSs four (including the female) were natural US citizens. There were a further three who were naturalized US citizens (one each from Australia, China and the Netherlands) and four who were foreign citizens (one each from Canada and the Netherlands, and two from West Germany).

Of the NASA astronaut crew members 15 were from NASA Astronaut Selections before 1970 (four from 1966, four from 1967 and seven from 1969, the last being the whole group selection for that year). Of these, two from the 1967 selection flew *Challenger* twice, and one from the 1969 selection flew three times. From 1966 two flew as commanders and two as MSs; from 1967 all flew as MSs (including those on their second flight). Of the 1969 group one flew as an MS the others as commanders (including the astronaut who flew three times). EVA was performed by three from these groups, one from each selection. The 1966 astronaut who performed EVA also flew the MMU.

Of the remaining 25 NASA astronauts, all were selected in the Shuttle selections from 1978 (21 from 1978 and four from 1980). Of the 21 selected in 1978 (18 males and three females), one was oriental and three black (all male). Of this group seven were in the pilot (including one black) and the rest in MS categories (including the females, oriental and two blacks). Of this group five flew *Challenger* twice (four males, including two blacks, and one female). All flew their first and second *Challenger* missions as selected, except one pilot who flew his second *Challenger* mission as commander. Other MSs served as MS-1, MS-2 or MS-3 on their second flights. A total of four (three male and one female) performed EVA from *Challenger*. The three males also flew the MMUs during their EVA periods.

A total of three males and one female from the second Shuttle selection in 1980 flew on *Challenger*. Two served as pilots and two (including the female) as MSs. One of the MSs performed EVA during his flight.

Of the 51 persons who flew *Challenger*, two males had pre-Shuttle space experience (one on Skylab and the other on Apollo-Soyuz), and one had also flown on *Columbia* before flying *Challenger*. Of the 51, nine (eight males and one female) had flown Shuttle flights on their first missions before flying their first on *Challenger* (four on *Columbia*, three on *Discovery* and one male who had flown both *Columbia* and *Discovery* before flying *Challenger*). In addition eight (all male) flew other Shuttle vehicles after flying on *Challenger* (two on *Columbia*, four on *Discovery*, one on *Atlantis*, and one who flew both *Discovery* and *Atlantis*). Finally, two *Challenger* pilots had also experienced landing *Enterprise* in 1977 before both undertook *Columbia* and then *Challenger* missions.

Seven astronauts flying *Challenger* (five NASA astronauts and two PSs) representing a cross-section of US culture (male and female/black, white and oriental/pilot, scientist, engineer and teacher) gave all they could for the space programme, namely their lives. As those seven, known as the *Challenger* 7, were lost in a ball of fire and debris, memories of the other 44 pioneers who flew *Challenger* and survived were recalled. Below is a complete listing of brief biographical notes on all 51 *Challenger* astronauts. Tables summarizing the achievements of the 51 are also presented for reference on pages 62-3.

ACTON, Loren Wilbur (Payload Specialist *Challenger* 8)
Civilian, born March 7, 1936 at Lewiston, Montana. He earned a BS degree in Physics from Montana State University (1959) and a PhD degree in Solar Physics from the University of Colorado, Boulder (1965). His experience includes work on solar physics and high-energy astrophysics on several NASA projects. He served as Research Scientist, then Senior Staff Scientist with Lockheed Space and Missile Company, Palo Alto Research Laboratory, Palo Alto, California before selection for astronaut training as one of four Spacelab 2 Payload Specialist candidates on August 9, 1978. He trained for the mission over the next seven years, being named PS-1 (Red Shift) for Spacelab 2 on June 8, 1984. A co-principal investigator for an instrument on the Solar Maximum spacecraft, he was also co-investigator for the Spacelab 2 Solar Magnetic Field and Velocity Measurement experiment. Flew as PS-1 on Shuttle 19 (51-F), the eighth *Challenger* mission carrying Spacelab 2 (July 29 to August 6, 1985). Following Shuttle 19 he returned to the Space Science Laboratory at Palo Alto to continue evaluation of Spacelab 2 results and research into the Sun and other celestial objects. Subsequently involved in foreign astronomical programmes.

BARTOE, John David (Payload Specialist *Challenger* 8)
Civilian, born November 17, 1944 at Abingdon, Pennsylvania. He received a BS degree in Physics from Lehigh University (1966), an MS degree in Physics from Georgetown University (1974) and a PhD also in Physics from Georgetown (1976). Before his spaceflight he had undertaken solar research at the Naval Research Laboratory, Washington DC, for almost 20 years. Bartoe has carried out a range of solar ultraviolet studies with sounding rockets, satellites and instruments flown on Apollo and Skylab manned missions. A supervisory astrophysicist, he was co-investigator on the solar ultraviolet High-Resolution Telescope and Spectrograph (HRTS) experiment and the Solar Ultraviolet Spectral Irradiance Monitor (SUSIM) experiment, both flown on Spacelab 2. Named Spacelab 2 Payload Specialist candidate on August 9, 1978, he was selected as PS-2 (Blue Shift) for the Spacelab 2 mission on June 8, 1984. He served as PS-2 during the eighth flight of *Challenger*, designated Shuttle 19 (51-F), carrying Spacelab 2 (July 29 to August 6, 1985). Returned to NLR.

BLUFORD, Guion Stewart, Jr (Mission Specialist *Challenger* 3 and Mission Specialist *Challenger* 9)
Colonel, USAF, born November 22, 1942 at Philadelphia, Pennsylvania. He received his BS degree in Aerospace Engineering from Pennsylvania State University (1964), an MS degree with distinction in Aeronautical Engineering (1974) and his PhD (1977) in Aeronautical Engineering, both from the Air Force Institute of Technology. He entered the USAF in 1964 and received pilot training, gaining his wings in January 1965. Following combat training he served in the Vietnam War. He then served as a T-38A instructor pilot, standardization/evaluation officer and assistant flight commander before attending Squadron Officer's School and the USAF Institute of Technology. From 1974 to selection by NASA he served at the Air Force Flight Dynamics Laboratory, Wright Patterson AFB, as a staff development officer, also serving in a variety of posts in the laboratory branch. Selected to NASA on January 16, 1978 (Group 8) as one of the first Shuttle candidate intake, he was designated Mission Specialist. Following a 12-month training programme (July 1978 to August 1979) he was assigned Shuttle support duties which included work with the RMS, Spacelab 3 experiments, Shuttle systems, the Shuttle Avionics Integration Laboratories (SAIL), the FSL Laboratory as well as a variety of other assignments within the Astronaut Office. On April 24, 1982 he was named MS-2 for Shuttle 8 (flown between August 30 and September 5, 1983 as *Challenger*'s third mission), and was also the first black American in space. On February 14, 1984 he was named MS-3 (Red Shift) for the Spacelab D1 mission (October 30 to November 6, 1985). He reached a total of 13 days 1 hour 53 minutes 31 seconds aboard *Challenger*, and logged a total of 219 orbits. Active NASA astronaut.

BOBKO, Karol Joseph (Pilot *Challenger* 1)
Colonel, USAF, born December 23, 1937 at New York, New York. He earned his BS degree from the USAF Academy (1959), and an MS degree in Aerospace Engineering from the University of Southern California, Los Angeles (1970). He entered USAF Academy's first class in 1954, graduating in 1959. He gained navigator rating, flight training, and gunnery training by 1960; between 1960 and 1965 flew F-100s then F-105s before entering the USAF Aerospace Research Pilots' School in late 1965, graduating in the spring of 1966. He was selected for the USAF Manned Orbiting Laboratory Programme (MOL) on June 17, 1966 (Group 2) as one of five astronaut trainees. He transferred to NASA when MOL was cancelled in August 1969 (Group 7) and worked on support assignments for Skylab including the Skylab Medical Experiment Altitude Test, the 1972 medical baseline Skylab simulation experiment for 56 days, and the Apollo-Soyuz Test Project (ASTP), in which he served as CapCom-Houston during the July 1975 mission. He supported early Shuttle development and served alternatively as CapCom and prime T-38 chase pilot during *Enterprise* Approach and Landing Test (ALT) programme in 1977; worked on the *Columbia* test and checkout group (lead astronaut) at KSC, Florida (1979-81); was named pilot for Shuttle 6 on March 2, 1982; and flew on Shuttle 6 (31-B) as pilot on April 4-9, 1983. Following his Shuttle flight in *Challenger*, he went on to fly *Discovery* (Shuttle 16 or 51-D) in April 1985 as commander, and on the maiden flight of *Atlantis* (Shuttle 21 or 51-J) in October 1985, again as commander. Active NASA astronaut.

BRAND, Vance DeVoe (Commander *Challenger* 4)
Civilian, born May 9, 1931 at St Vrain Valley, Longmont, Colorado. He earned his BS degree in Business from the University of Colorado (1953), a BS degree in Aeronautical Engineering from the University of Colorado (1960) and an MS degree in Business Administration from the University of California, Los Angeles (1964). He served in the USMC (1953-1957), initially on a ground job with no intention to fly, then as a jet pilot including a 15-month tour in Japan. He attended the University of Colorado (1957-1960), then worked for Lockheed Aircraft Corporation as a flight test engineer and later test pilot. He was selected by NASA April 4, 1966 (Group 5), one of 19 applicants. Following basic training he served on support assignment in the Apollo programme (including Apollo CSM development group, thermal vacuum testing of the prototype Apollo CM; crew member CSM simulation test in vacuum chamber in 1968; Support Crew/CapCom for Apollo 8; Support Crew/CapCom for Apollo 13; back-up CMP Apollo 15 and CapCom; and original CMP for cancelled Apollo 18), support assignments in Skylab (back-up commander for Skylab 3 and 4; commander for unflown Skylab Rescue Crew; and original commander for planned Skylab 5 mission). He trained for joint US-Soviet Apollo-Soyuz Test Project (1972-75) and flew as CMP Apollo 18 (ASTP) in July 1975, the last ballistic-type US spaceflight. He was assigned to early Shuttle development; named commander of the fourth OFT on March 16, 1978; and subsequently reassigned as commander of Shuttle 5, the first operational mission, in 1981. He flew as commander of Shuttle 5 (31-A) in November 1982, this being the fifth flight of *Columbia* and the first operational mission of the programme. He was named commander for Shuttle 11 (41-B) on February 4, 1983, flying this fourth flight of *Challenger* on February 3-11, 1984. At the present time still an active NASA astronaut.

BRANDENSTEIN, Daniel Charles (Pilot *Challenger* 3)
Captain, USN, born January 17, 1943 at Watertown, Wisconsin. He earned a BS degree in Maths and Physics from the University of Wisconsin, River Falls, Wisconsin (1965), and entered active duty in the USN in September 1965. He received flight training and was designated a naval aviator in May 1967. After combat training he served in the Vietnam conflict between 1968 and 1970, completing two deployments and 192 combat missions. He served as a USN test pilot from 1970 to 1975, and from 1975 to selection by NASA he flew A-6 Intruders for two USN squadrons. Selected by NASA in January 1978 (Group 8), he completed his one-year training programme in August 1979, and was designated pilot astronaut. He served as support crew for Shuttles 1 and 2, serving as Ascent CapCom for both missions in 1981. He was named pilot for Shuttle 8 on April 24, 1982 and flew Shuttle 8 (31-D or Challenger 3), August 30 and September 5, 1983. Active.

BRIDGES, Roy Dunbard, Jr (Pilot *Challenger* 8)
Colonel, USAF, born July 19, 1943 at Atlanta, Georgia. He received a BS degree in Engineering

CHALLENGER FLIGHT CREW ASSIGNMENTS: MISSIONS 1 TO 10

Mission	Commander	Pilot	MS-1	MS-2	MS-3	PS-1	PS-2	PS-3
Sh06/Ch01	Weitz (5)	Bobko (7)	Musgrave (6)	Peterson (7)	–	–	–	–
Sh07/Ch02	Crippen (7)	Hauck (8)	Fabian (8)	Ride (8)	Thornton (6)	–	–	–
Sh08/Ch03	Truly (7)	Brandenstein (8)	Gardner (8)	Bluford (8)	Thagard (8)	–	–	–
Sh10/Ch04	Brand (5)	Gibson (8)	Stewart (8)	McCandless (5)	McNair (8)	–	–	–
Sh11/Ch05	Crippen (7)	Scobee (8)	Hart (8)	Nelson (8)	Van Hoften (8)	–	–	–
Sh13/Ch06	Crippen (7)	McBride (8)	Ride (8)	Sullivan (8)	Leestma (9)	Garneau	Scully-Power	–
Sh17/Ch07	Overmyer (7)	Gregory (8)	Lind (5)	Thagard (8)	Thornton (6)	Wang	Van Den Berg	–
Sh19/Ch08	Fullerton (7)	Bridges (9)	Musgrave (6)	Henize (6)	England (6)	Acton	Bartoe	–
Sh22/Ch09	Hartsfield (7)	Nagel (8)	Dunbar (9)	Buchli (8)	Bluford (8)	Messerschmid	Furrer	Ockels
Sh25/Ch10	Scobee (8)	Smith (9)	Resnik (8)	Onizuka (8)	McNair (8)	McAuliffe	Jarvis	–

Note: ( ) identifies NASA Group selection number (NASA astronauts only).

Left: Man in space: mission 41-B astronaut Robert L. Stewart floats above *Challenger*'s payload bay during his second period of MMU-powered EVA.

Science from the USAF Academy (1965) and an MS degree in Astronautics from Purdue University (1966). He was a student at the USAF Academy (1961-65) and at Purdue University through 1966. He underwent flight training in 1966-67, and subsequently completed 226 combat missions in the Vietnam conflict in the late 1960s. Following an assignment as instructor pilot at a US air base, he was a USAF test pilot student in 1970-71 and subsequently served as a test pilot at Edwards AFB until 1975. Following assignment to the Air Command and Staff College in 1975, he was assigned to the Department of the Chief of Staff for Research and Development, USAF HQ, Washington DC. At the time of selection for astronaut training he was assigned to the USAF Flight Test Center as Special Projects Officer, Edwards AFB California. Selected by NASA in May 1980 (Group 9), he completed training as a potential Shuttle pilot astronaut one year later. From 1981 to 1984 he completed Shuttle support assignments (including Entry CapCom for Shuttles 5 and 6, and Ascent CapCom for Shuttle 7), and in October 1984 it was announced that he would replace astronaut Griggs on Shuttle 51-F/Spacelab 2 since Griggs was also assigned to Shuttle 51-E and the close sequencing of the two missions would not allow Griggs to complete the required Spacelab 2 pilot training after the 51-E mission. He flew as pilot on Shuttle 19 (51-F/Spacelab 2, Red Shift). 1986 reassigned as Cdr 6510th USAF Test Wing.

BUCHLI, James Frederick (Mission Specialist *Challenger* 9)
Colonel, USMC, born June 20, 1945 at New Rockford, South Dakota. He received a BS degree in Aeronautical Engineering from the USN Academy (1967) and an MS degree in Aeronautical Engineering Systems from the University of West Florida (1975). He graduated the USN Academy in 1967 and entered the USMC, completing basic infantry training in the following year; he completed a one-year tour of duty in Vietnam in 1969 and subsequently completed flight training in 1970; from 1970 to 1973 was assigned to several USMC fighter attack squadrons in Hawaii, Japan and Thailand. He completed his advanced degree studies between 1973 and 1975 at the University of West Florida, subsequently receiving a two-year assignment to a USMC fighter attack squadron at Beaufort, South Carolina. From 1977 until selection for astronaut training by NASA, he was a test pilot student at the USN Test Pilot School, Patuxent River, Maryland. Selected by NASA in January 1978 (Group 8), he completed training in August 1979 for assignment as an MS for future Shuttle crews. He served as Support Crew/CapCom for Shuttles 1 and 2 in 1981, and was named MS for Shuttle 10 (the first dedicated DoD mission) on October 11, 1982. The mission was eventually flown as Shuttle 15 (51-C or Discovery 3) in January 1985. He had been named to the Engle crew in November 1983, was reassigned to the Hartsfield crew on August 3, 1984 and flew as MS-2 (EV-2 on Red Shift) on the Shuttle 22 (61-A) Spacelab D1 flight, *Challenger*'s ninth mission between October 30 and November 6, 1985. Active NASA astronaut.

CRIPPEN, Robert Laurel (Commander *Challenger* 2, Commander *Challenger* 5 and Commander *Challenger* 6)
Captain, USN, born September 11, 1937 at Beaumont, Texas. He received a BS degree in Aerospace Engineering from University of Texas (1960). He enlisted in USN on June 8, 1960 and subsequently completed flight training (December 1961) before serving in a variety of naval assignments up to November 1964, when he became a student at the Aerospace Research Pilots' School, Edwards AFB, California. Following graduation from the course he served as a flight instructor pilot at the school until joining the USAF Manned Orbiting Laboratory (MOL) programme. Selected on June 17, 1966 as one of five Group 2 MOL candidates, he trained for the MOL programme from October 1966 to June 1969, when the programme was terminated. He transferred to NASA (Group 7) in August 1969, and immediately began support assignments for the Skylab programme. He accomplished a variety of support assignments within the Skylab programme over the next 4½ years, including a crew member for the Skylab Medical Experiment Altitude Test (SMEAT), 1972, as well as Support Crew/CapCom for all three manned Skylab missions (1973-74). Selected as a member of the US astronaut group for the joint US-Soviet manned spaceflight, the Apollo-Soyuz Test Project (ASTP) in January 1973, he worked on the programme through to July 1975 as a member of the US Astronaut Support Crew and served as CapCom during the mission. Late in 1975 he began support work on the Shuttle development programme, being named pilot for the first manned flight in March 1978. He served as pilot of Shuttle 1 (STS-1) in April 1981, the first mission of the programme flying *Columbia*. On April 20, 1982 he was named commander for Shuttle 7 (31-C) flown on June 18-24, 1982. On February 22, 1983 he was named commander of Shuttle 13 (41-C), eventually flown as the 11th mission of the programme. Shuttle 11 was the fifth flight of *Challenger* (April 6-13, 1984). He became the first US astronaut to be named to a mission before flying his next. In November 1983 (after Shuttle 7 but before Shuttle 11) he was assigned to a record fourth Shuttle mission, 41-G in 1984. It was stated that he was the study subject for determining the optimum period of training needed by an astronaut between missions. Shuttle 13 (41-G) was the sixth flight of *Challenger* and was flown on October 5-13, 1984. Shortly after this mission he was named as commander of Shuttle 62-A, the first flight from Vandenberg AFB, California which was scheduled for 1985 but then delayed into 1986. He was training for this mission aboard *Discovery* when *Challenger* was lost above KSC in 1986. He has also held a variety of administrative posts during his astronaut career, including Deputy Director of Flight Crew Operations and Chief of the Ascent/Entry Group in the Astronaut Office. He has logged a total of 21 days 7 hours 27 minutes 37 seconds and over 316 orbits on the three missions flown on *Challenger*. Active.

DUNBAR, Bonnie Jeanne (Mission Specialist *Challenger* 9)
Civilian, born March 3, 1949 at Sunnyside Washington. She gained her BS degree in Ceramic Engineering from the University of Washington (1971), her MS in Ceramic Engineering from Washington University (1975), and her PhD in Biomedical Engineering from the University of Houston (1983). Following graduation from the University of Washington in 1971 she worked for two years as a systems analyst at Boeing Computer Services. From 1973 to 1976 she studied for her Masters degree at the University of Washington under a NASA research grant, and between May and August 1976 was a guest researcher at Harwell Laboratories, Oxford, England. From 1976 to 1978 she worked for Rockwell International Space Division as a senior research engineer, working on the development and processes for the manufacture of the Shuttle TPS. During her years at Rockwell she also represented the company as a member of Dr Kraft Ehricke's evaluation committee on space industrialization concepts. In 1978 she joined NASA as a payloads officer/flight controller at the Johnson Spaceflight Center, Texas. She served as guidance and navigation officer/flight controller for the Skylab re-entry mission in 1979, and was subsequently designated project officer/payload officer for the integration of several Shuttle payloads. Selected for astronaut training in May 1980, she completed the training course in May 1981 and was designated MS for future crew assignment. She completed a variety of Shuttle support assignments between 1981 and 1984, including work in the Shuttle Avionics Integration Laboratories (SAIL), verification of

Above: (l to r) Ride, Crippen, Hauck, Thagard and Fabian during *Challenger*'s second mission, STS-7.

Shuttle software, technical monitoring of TPS and crew equipment, and Shuttle 9 Support Crew. On February 14, 1984 she was named as MS for Shuttle 51-K/Spacelab D1, the West German Spacelab mission planned for a September 1985 launch. By August 3 the mission had been redesignated 61-A, flying on *Columbia*. Shuttle 22 (61-A)/Spacelab D1 in fact became the ninth mission for *Challenger*, 1985. Active.

ENGLAND, Anthony Wayne (Mission Specialist *Challenger* 8)
Civilian, born May 15, 1942 at Indianapolis, Indiana. He earned a BS degree in Geology and Physics from MIT (1965), an MS degree in Geology and Physics, also from MIT (1967) and a PhD in Geophysics – Earth and Planetary Sciences at MIT (1970). Between 1964 and 1967 as a graduate fellow of MIT he performed heatflow measurements throughout the southwestern USA, participated in a magnetic study in Montana, Oklahoma and New Mexico, performed radar soundings in Alaska and airborne geothermal research in Alaska and Washington state, and completed two trips to Antarctica. Selected by NASA in August 1967 (Group 6), he provided support work in the Apollo and Skylab programmes through to 1972, including ground control duties during Apollo 13 (1970) and Support Crew/CapCom for Apollo 16 (1972). He resigned from NASA on August 14, 1972 to join the US Geological Survey because of 'lack of flight prospects' at that time. Between 1972 and 1979 he worked on the Skylab geological programme and the Apollo 17 Surface Electrical Properties Experiment (SEPE), and held several academic positions. Seven years after leaving, on June 3, 1979 he returned to NASA as a senior MS in the operations and missions development group of the Astronaut Office. On February 22, 1983 he was named MS-3 (EV-2 on Blue Shift) for the STS-24/Spacelab 2 mission. In September 1983 STS-24 was redesignated 51-F. Shuttle 19 (51-F)/Spacelab 2, the eighth flight of *Challenger*. Active.

FABIAN, John McCreary (Mission Specialist *Challenger* 2)
Colonel, USAF, born January 28, 1939 at Goosecreek, Texas. He earned a BS degree in Mechanical Engineering from Washington State University (1962), an MS degree in Aerospace Engineering from the USAF Institute of Technology (1964) and a PhD in Aeronautics and Astronautics from the University of Washington (1974). He entered the USAF in 1962 and, after graduating from the USAF Institute of Technology in 1964, served two years with the Aeronautical Engineer Service, Engineering Division, Kelly AFB, Texas, before completing pilot training at Williams AFB, Texas. From 1968 to 1973 he served as a KC-135 pilot, completing a tour in the Vietnam conflict and flying 90 combat missions. After finishing graduate work for his PhD in 1974 he served for four years as Assistant Professor of Aeronautics at the USAF Academy, Colorado, until selection by NASA in January 1978 (Group 8) for astronaut training. He completed the 12-month training course in August 1979 and completed a number of Shuttle support/development assignments, including work as a member of the RMS Core Group specializing in areas of USAF arm work for DoD payloads. On April 20, 1982 he was named MS-1 (EV-1) for Shuttle 7 (31-C) flown on June 18-24, 1983. Following his only *Challenger* flight, in June 1985 he flew on Shuttle 18 (51-G), the fifth flight of *Discovery*, and was in training for a flight on *Atlantis* for 61-G in May 1986 when he announced his resignation from NASA in October 1985 to return to the USAF. Member of the Presidential Commission for the 51-L investigation.

FULLERTON, Charles Gordon (Commander *Challenger* 8)
Colonel, USAF, born October 11, 1936 at Rochester, New York. He received a BS degree in Mechanical Engineering from the California Institute of Technology (1957) and an MS degree from CalTech (1958). Following work as a mechanical design engineer for Hughes Aircraft Company, Culver City, California in 1958 he entered active duty with the USAF, after flight training serving as a B-47 jet bomber pilot with the Strategic Air Command in Arizona from 1960 to 1964. He attended the Aerospace Research Pilots' School at Edwards AFB, and served as a Bomber Operations test pilot in the Aeronautical Systems Division at Wright-Patterson AFB before selection to the USAF MOL programme on June 17, 1966 (Group 2). Following cancellation of MOL in 1969, in August he transferred to NASA (Group 7), and began support work on Apollo/Skylab programmes. He was Support Crew/CapCom for Apollo 14, CapCom for Apollo 15, CapCom for Apollo 16 and Support Crew/CapCom for Apollo 17 before transferring to the Shuttle Branch of the Astronaut Office in early 1973, working on recovery, controls and displays. In February 1976 was named as an ALT crew member flying *Enterprise* through a series of landing test flights in 1977. Assigned to the Shuttle OFT programme in March 1978, he flew as pilot of Shuttle 3 (STS-3/OFT-3) in March 1982, the third flight of *Columbia*. He was named commander for Shuttle 51-F/Spacelab 2 in November 1983, flown as Shuttle 19 (51-F)/Spacelab 2 between July 29 and August 6, 1985. Resigned 1986. Test Pilot, Edwards AFB.

Below: (l to r) Brandenstein, Truly, Thornton, Bluford and Gardner with commemorative postal cover during *Challenger* 3, STS-8.

Below: (l to r, red) Acton, Bridges and Henize; (l to r, blue) Bartoe, Musgrave and England; plus Fullerton, *Challenger* 8 (51F).

FURRER, Reinhard (Payload Specialist *Challenger* 9)
Civilian, born November 25, 1940 at Worgl, Germany. He studied physics at the Universities of Kiel and Berlin, and received a diploma and doctorate of philosophy in physics. His experience includes assistant professor of physics, visiting scientist at the University of Chicago and Argonne National Laboratory, and practical research in atomic physics, solid-state physics, chemical physics, and photophysics and biophysics. In addition he has taught experimental physics, supervised undergraduate and graduate students, and presented a public lecture series at the University of Chicago. Named on December 17, 1982 as prime PS for Spacelab D1, a dedicated West German science mission, he flew Shuttle 22 (61-A)/Spacelab D1 (PS-2, Blue Shift). Returned to DFVLR, West Germany.

GARDNER, Dale Allan (Mission Specialist *Challenger* 3)
Commander, USN, born November 8, 1948 at Fairmont, Minnesota. He received a BS degree in Engineering Physics from the University of Illinois (1970), entered the USN in July 1970, received flight training, and was designated a naval aviator on May 5, 1971. He served at Naval Air Test Center, Patuxent River, Maryland (1971-73) assigned to the Weapons Systems Test Division. From 1973 to 1976 he was with Fighter Squadron 1 (flying F-14As), participating in two Western Pacific cruises aboard USS *Enterprise*. From December 1976 until assignment at NASA, he served in the operational test and evaluation of fighter aircraft with the Air Test & Evaluation Squadron. Selected by NASA in January 1978 (Group 8), he completed MS training in August 1979 and was allocated to Shuttle assignments, including support duties for the STS-4 mission in 1982. He was named MS-1 (EV-2) for Shuttle 8 on April 24, 1982, flown as Shuttle 8 (31-D) or Challenger 3 between August 30 and September 5, 1983. Following this mission he flew as MS on Shuttle 14 (51-A) performing two EVAs and flying the MMU, and was in training for the first launch (62-A) of the Shuttle from Vandenberg AFB, California, when *Challenger* was lost. Reassigned October 1986, USN Space Command.

GARNEAU, Mark (Payload Specialist *Challenger* 6)
Commander, Canadian navy, born February 23, 1949 at Quebec City, Quebec, Canada. He received a BS in Engineering Physics from the Royal Military College of Kingston (1970), and a PhD in Electrical Engineering from Imperial College of Science and Technology, London, UK (1973). He is a career naval officer, serving as Combat Systems Engineer, HMCS *Algonquin* (1974-76); instructor in naval weapons systems at the Canadian Forces Fleet School, Halifax (1976-77); designer of simulators for use in training weapons officers in the use of missile systems aboard 'Tribal' class destroyers; project engineer in naval weapons systems, Ottawa (1977-80); and transferring back to Halifax with the Naval Engineering Unit (1980-82) for troubleshooting and system trials on ship-fitted equipment. He attended the Canadian Armed Forces Command and Staff College, Toronto (1982-83). Promoted commander and transferred to Ottawa, he then became design authority for all Canadian naval communications and electronic warfare equipment and systems. Named one of six Canadian astronauts on December 5, 1983, he flew as PS-1 on Shuttle 13 (41-G), the sixth flight of *Challenger* on October 5-13, 1984. Garneau had been selected for his mission only two months after astronaut selection! Returned NRC.

GIBSON, Robert Lee (Pilot *Challenger* 3)
Commander, USN, born October 30, 1946 at Cooperstown, New York. He received a BS degree in Aeronautical Engineering from California Polytechnic State University (1969) and entered active duty with the USN after graduation. Following flight training he was designated a naval aviator in April 1972. He served with Fighter Squadrons 111 and 1 aboard USS *Coral Sea* and USS *Enterprise* between April 1972 and September 1975, flying 56 combat missions in South-East Asia. Following assignment as an F-14A instructor pilot, he completed the USN test pilot course in June 1977 and, until selection by NASA, served as a naval test pilot assigned Naval Air Test Center's Strike Aircraft Test Directorate, evaluating the F-14A aircraft. Selected by NASA in January 1978 (Group 8, pilot category), he completed the 12-month training programme in August 1979 and was assigned to Shuttle development duties. In 1980 he completed T-38/SR-71 intercept and tracking flights in tests of T-38/Shuttle landing approaches for the first orbital missions; he was then assigned to the Shuttle Avionics Integration Laboratories (SAIL) and flew as Chase 1 pilot (T-38) during the Shuttle 2 landing in November 1981. He was named pilot for Shuttle 11 on February 4, 1983, the mission being flown as Shuttle 10 (41-B), *Challenger's* fourth mission, on February 3-11, 1984. Following this mission Gibson was promoted to commander and flew Shuttle 24 (61-C), the seventh flight of *Columbia* and last successful Shuttle mission before the *Challenger* tragedy in January 1986. Active.

GREGORY, Frederick Drew (Pilot *Challenger* 6)
Colonel, USAF, born January 7, 1941 at Washington, DC. He earned a BS degree from the USAF Academy (1964) and an MS degree in Information Systems from George Washington University (1977). He entered pilot training in the USAF following graduation from the USAF Academy in 1964 and emerged as a helicopter pilot in 1965. Between 1965 and 1968 he served as a USAF helicopter pilot, including a tour in Vietnam as a rescue crew commander. From 1969 to 1971 he cross-trained to fixed-wing aircraft and entered the USN Test Pilot School, completing the rotary- and as much of the fixed-wing study courses as time permitted. Between 1971 and 1977 he served as a research/engineering test pilot for the USAF at Wright-Patterson AFB, Ohio, and for NASA at the Langley Research Center, Virginia. Before selection as a pilot astronaut candidate by NASA in January 1978 (Group 8), Gregory was a staff member at the Armed Forces College, Norfolk, Virginia. He completed the astronaut training programme in August 1979 and was assigned to Shuttle support duties, completing a number of technical assignments whilst in the Astronaut Office. On February 22, 1983 was named pilot (Silver Team leader and EV-1) for Shuttle 18 (51-B)/Spacelab 3, flown between April 29 and May 6, 1985. In October 1986 he was named chief of the Operational Safety Branch, NASA HQ. Active.

HART, Terry Jonathan (Mission Specialist *Challenger* 5)
Civilian, born October 27, 1946 at Pittsburgh, Pennsylvania. He gained a BS degree in Mechanical Engineering from Lehigh University (1968), an MS degree in Mechanical Engineering from MIT (1969) and an MS degree in Electrical Engineering from Rutgers University (1978). He worked for Bell Telephone Laboratories as a member of the technical staff from 1968 to 1978, being responsible for a variety of electrical power equipment items used in the Bell system, and is holder of two patents. He also served in the USAF Reserve from 1969 and continues in the Air National Guard as an F-106 pilot. Selected to NASA in January 1978 (Group 8) he completed MS training in August 1979 and was assigned to Shuttle support work including service as a member of the astronaut support team for Shuttles 1, 2, 3 and 7, and CapCom for Shuttles 2, 3 and 7. He was named MS-1 for STS-13 (redesignated 41-C). The mission was flown as Shuttle 11 (41-C). Resigned 1984. Returned to Bell Laboratories.

HARTSFIELD, Henry Warren, Jr (Commander *Challenger* 9)
Colonel, USAF (Ret), born November 21, 1933 at Birmingham, Alabama. He received a BS degree in Physics from Auburn University, Auburn, Alabama (1954) and an MS degree in Engineering Science from the University of Tennessee (1971). He entered active duty with the USAF following graduation from Auburn in 1955, and completed a variety of USAF assignments, including a tour in West Germany, over the next 10 years. He graduated from the Aerospace Research Pilots' School in May 1966 and was selected for the MOL programme on June 17, 1966 (Group 2), transferring to NASA in August 1969 (Group 7) when MOL was cancelled. He was a member of the Apollo 16 support crew and served as CapCom during the April 1972 lunar mission; thereafter he was part of the Support Crew/CapCom for all three Skylab missions (1973-74) and worked on Shuttle development, was CapCom for Shuttle 1 in April 1981 and served as back-up pilot for Shuttle 2 (November 1981) and Shuttle 3 (March 1982) before flying as pilot for Shuttle 4 (last OFT) aboard *Columbia* in June and July 1982. Following this mission he flew Shuttle 12 (41-D) as commander of *Discovery's* maiden flight in August and September 1984. On August 3, 1984 he was named commander of Shuttle 22 (61-A)/Spacelab D1, the first planned eight-person launch and dedicated West German science mission. Active.

HAUCK, Frederick Hamilton (Pilot *Challenger* 2)
Captain, USN, born April 11, 1941 at Long Beach, California. He earned a BS degree in Physics from Tufts University (1962) and an MS degree in Nuclear Engineering from MIT (1966). Commissioned in the USN upon graduation from Tufts University in 1962, he completed a 20-month tour as a communications officer aboard USS *Warrington* (1962-64) and then continued his academic studies (1964-66) including studying maths and physics at the USN Postgraduate School, studied Russian at the Defence Language Institute, studied under the USN Advanced Science Programme and finally attended MIT. He completed a two-year pilot training course (1968) and, following replacement pilot training, he was assigned Attack Squadron 35 and completed a number of duties over the 1968-70 period, including a tour aboard USS *Coral Sea* in the Vietnam conflict. He completed USN test pilot training in 1971 and served as test pilot for automatic carrier landing systems in a variety of aircraft attached to the Naval Air Test Center's Carrier Suitability Branch up to 1974; completed a tour aboard USS *Enterprise* as Operations Officer; participated in air operations combat support for the evacuation of South Vietnam in 1975; and served in Attack Squadrons 128 and 145 before joining NASA as one of 35 Group 8 Shuttle candidates in January 1978. He completed astronaut training for pilot assignments in August 1979 and served as CapCom for Shuttles 1 and 2; served as Head of the Ascent/Entry Development Group STS programme; and on April 20, 1982 was selected as pilot for Shuttle 7. This was flown as Shuttle 7 (31-C), the second mission of *Challenger*, on June 18-24, 1983. Following his flight on *Challenger* he continued his astronaut assignments, flying as commander of Shuttle 14 (51-A). Active. Commander Shuttle 26.

HENIZE, Karl Gordon (Mission Specialist *Challenger* 8)
Civilian, born October 17, 1926 at Cincinnati, Ohio. He earned a BA in Maths from the University of Virginia (1947), an MA in Astronomy from the University of Virginia (1948) and a PhD in Astronomy from the University of Michigan (1954). He served in USN Reserve on active duty from July 1944 to June 1947, and participated in the Naval Research Reserve from 1952 to 1967, retiring as a lieutenant commander USNR. He was observer for the University of Michigan Observatory Station, Lamont-Hussey Observatory, Bloemfontein, South Africa (1948-51); studied at University of Michigan (1951-54); was a post-doctoral fellow at Mt Wilson Observatory, Pasadena California (1954-56); was Senior Astronomer at the Smithsonian Astrophysical Observatory (1956-59); was Associate Professor of Northwestern University's Department of Astronomy (1959-60); was a guest observer at Mt Stromlo Observatory, Canberra, Australia (1961-62); was Assistant Professor of Astronomy in the Northwestern University's Department of Astronomy (1963); was Professor of Astronomy at Northwestern University (1964-67); briefed astronaut crews on his Gemini astronomical experiment (S-013); was Professor on Leave from Northwestern University (1967-72) and Professor on Leave from University of Texas, Austin (1972 to date). He was selected for NASA in August 1967 (Group 6) and completed training in 1969 before being allocated to the Support Crew/CapCom for Apollo 15 in 1970-71 and Skylab Support/CapCom (1971-74). He was assigned to Shuttle development duties-payloads (1974-83), served on several study groups and working groups. Participated in several airborne Spacelab simulations (November 1973, October 1974 and May 1977), and worked on the Spacelab 2 science payload (1977-85). Named Mission Specialist for Spacelab 2 on February 22, 1983, he flew Shuttle 19 (51-F)/Spacelab 2 as MS-2 (Red Team), the eighth flight of *Challenger*, between July 29 and August 6, 1985. At 58, he was the oldest person to fly in space after waiting almost 18 years since selection for his first flight! April 1986, reassigned JSC Science Branch, senior scientist.

JARVIS, Greg (Payload Specialist *Challenger* 10)
Civilian, born August 24, 1944 at MoHawk, New York, USA and died January 28, 1986 as a result of the explosion of *Challenger*, KSC, Florida. He earned a BS degree in Electrical Engineering from the State University, New York (1967), and an MS degree in Electrical Engineering from Northeastern University Boston (1969). He worked for a MS degree in Management at the West Coast University, Los Angeles, California in 1973, and had worked for the USAF (honorably discharged with rank of captain) on attachment to the Space Division, El Segundo, for work on military communications satellites before joining the Hughes Aircraft Corporation in 1973. He then worked on the Marisat programme (1973-76) as Assistant Communications Subsystems Engineer and as Spacecraft Manager for Marisat 3, being responsible for the integration and testing of the Marisat satellites during the construction phase. From 1976 to 1978 he continued with the Marisat programme but in a new role, working with a USAF new-generation repeater to provide communications between strategic aircraft and their command elements. From 1978 to 1984 he worked with the Leasat programme with assignments on the concept of the programme, before becoming subsystems integration engineer, bus subsystem engineering manager, assistant spacecraft subsystems engineering manager, and Leasat 1 and 2 cradle manager (responsible for integration of the Leasat 1 and 2 with the cradle and combined systems testing). He was described as Project Manager and Systems Engineer upon selection by Hughes as one of four PS candidates for Shuttle missions in 1984. He was selected for the 51-D mission in 1985, reassigned to 51-I, 51-G, 61-C and finally assigned as PS-1 to 51-L set for a January 1986 launch. Shuttle 25 (51-L) *Challenger* 10 was launched on January 28, 1986 and exploded 73 seconds after leaving the pad, resulting in the loss of the seven crew members.

LEESTMA, David Cornell (Mission Specialist *Challenger* 6)
Commander, USN, born May 6, 1949 at Muskegon, Michigan. He gained a BS degree in Aeronautical Engineering from the USN Academy (1971) and an MS degree in Aeronautical Engineering from the USN Postgraduate School (1972). He graduated 1st in his class from the USN Academy in 1971 and served as 1st Lt afloat in USS *Hepburn* (1971-72). He received flight training (1972-73) and pilot wings (October 1973) before being assigned to Fighter Squadron 124 (October 1973 to June 1974), initially training on F-14A Tomcats. From June 1974 to 1977 he was assigned to Fighter Squadron 32 and completed three overseas deployments in the Mediterranean and North Atlantic aboard USS *John F. Kennedy*. He then became Operational Test Director, Air Test and Evaluation Squadron 4, NAS Point Mugu, California (1977-80). Selected as one of 19 Group 9 NASA astronauts in May 1980, he completed the 12-month MS training course in May 1981 and was selected for 41-G in November 1983. He flew the Shuttle 13 (41-G) mission on October 5-13, 1984. He also completed an EVA of 3 hours 27 minutes during the mission. Active astronaut.

LIND, Don Leslie (Mission Specialist *Challenger* 7)
Civilian, born May 18, 1930 at Midvale, Utah. He gained a BS degree in Physics from the University of Utah (1953) and a PhD in High Energy Physics from the University of California, Berkeley (1964). He completed five years of active duty USN (1954-60), during which he finished flight training (September 1955) and was assigned to Fighter Squadron 143 for a tour aboard USS *Hancock* (September 1955 to September 1957) before being transferred to the USN Reserve (September 1957). He then worked at the Lawrence Radiation Laboratory, Berkeley, California (October 1957 to 1960). He was a student at the University of Berkeley (1960-64) and a Space Physicist, NASA Goddard Space Flight Center, before being selected with NASA Group 5 on April 4, 1966. He was assigned to Apollo support roles including development work on the Apollo LM,

Below: (l to r, back) Scully-Power, Crippen and Garneau; (l to r, front) McBride, Ride, Sullivan and Leetsma, the crew of *Challenger* 6 (41-G).

Above: (clockwise from lower left) McNair, Gibson, Brand, Stewart and McCandless pictured during *Challenger* 4 (41B).

lunar surface simulations (1968-69), CapCom for Apollos 11 and 12, Skylab, back-up pilot for Skylabs 3 and 4, pilot for Skylab Rescue Crew (unflown) and original pilot for Skylab 5 (not flown). He took leave of absence in 1975-76 to attend the University of Alaska and complete his post-doctoral studies. He then worked on Shuttle support (early OFT/payload work), and on February 22, 1983 he was named MS-1 for the Spacelab 3 life science mission and co-investigator of one of the Spacelab 3 experiments. He thus flew as MS-1 (Gold Team) on the Shuttle 17 (51-B)/Spacelab 3 mission. Resigned. Currently Professor of Physics, Utah State University.

McAULIFFE, Sharon Christa (Teacher-In-Space Participant *Challenger* 10)
Civilian, born September 2, 1948 at Boston, Massachusetts, and died January 28, 1986 as a result of the mid-air explosion of Shuttle 25 (51-L) *Challenger* 10 during launch phase. She gained a BA degree from Framingham State College and a Masters degree in Education from Bowie State College. She had taught English and American history since 1970, and until selection into the NASA Teacher in Space Project had taught economics, law and American history, as well as a course she had developed (The American Woman) to students of the 10th through 12th grades. On August 27, 1984 President Reagan announced that a teacher would be chosen as the first US Private Citizen in Space. The applications ran from December 1, 1984 to February 1, 1985 and resulted in 114 nominees. A review of the group was accomplished in June 1985 and on July 1 McAuliffe was announced as one of 10 finalists in the programme; finally, on July 19 she was named primary candidate for the 51-L Teacher in Space Project. Flying Shuttle 25 (51-L) *Challenger* 10 she was launched on January 28, 1986 and died as the vehicle exploded in mid-air and the crew compartment fell into the sea.

McBRIDE, Jon Andrew (Pilot *Challenger* 6)
Commander, USN, born August 14, 1943 at Charleston, West Virginia. He gained a BS degree in Aeronautical Engineering from the USN Postgraduate School (1971). He received flight training, and was designated naval aviator in 1965. Between 1966 and 1978, he completed a variety of USN assignments including a posting to Fighter Squadron 101 for Phantom II training, three years as a fighter pilot and division officer with Fighter Squadron 41, several tours with Fighter Squadrons 11 and 103 on deployments to South-East Asia, attendance at the USAF Test Pilot School, service with Air Test and Development Squadron 4 as maintenance officer and Sidewinder projects officer, and pilot of the USN *Spirit of 76* Bicentennial-painted Phantom in various air shows between 1976 and 1978. He was selected to NASA in January 1978 (Group 8) and completed pilot training in August 1979. He completed T-38/SR-71 intercept/tracking flights early in 1981, and was lead chase pilot (Chase 1) for the landing of Shuttle 1 in April 1981. He worked in the Shuttle Avionics Integration Laboratories on software verification; was named pilot for 41-G in November 1983 and flew Shuttle 13 (41-G) on October 5-13, 1984. Active astronaut.

McCANDLESS II, Bruce (Mission Specialist *Challenger* 4)
Captain, USN, born June 8, 1937 at Boston, Massachusetts. He received a BS degree in Naval Sciences from the USN Academy (1958) and an MS degree in Electrical Engineering from Stanford University (1965). He joined the USN in June 1954, and after graduation from the USN Academy at Annapolis received flight training, being designated a naval aviator in March 1960. Thereafter he served in Attack Squadron 43 and Fighter Squadron 102 with tours aboard USS *Forrestal* and USS *Enterprise*, the latter during the Cuban blockade. He completed MS degree work before joining NASA as one of 19 Group 5 astronauts in April 1966. He was then a member of the technical support team within the Astronaut Office for the development and testing of the Apollo LM, CapCom for Apollo 10, CapCom for Apollo 11 and Support Crew/CapCom for Apollo 14. He worked on Skylab, was back-up pilot for Skylab 2, worked on Skylab EVA and trained on Shuttle EVA equipment and procedures (especially development of the MMU). On February 3, 1983 he was named MS-3/EV-1 for Shuttle 11 (redesignated 41-B) in the event flown as Shuttle 10 (41-B) on February 3-11, 1984, the fourth flight of *Challenger*. McCandless was the first person to perform a planned untethered free flight flying the MMU unit. Active astronaut.

McNAIR, Ronald Erwin (Mission Specialist *Challenger* 4 and Mission Specialist *Challenger* 10)
Civilian, born October 21, 1950 at Lake City, South Carolina, and died January 28, 1986 as a result of the mid-air explosion of *Challenger* above KSC, Florida. He gained a BS degree in Physics from North Carolina A&T State University (1971), a PhD in Physics from MIT (1976), an Honorary PhD of Laws from North Carolina A&T State University (1978) and an Honorary PhD of Science from Morris College (1980). Between 1971 and 1976 he performed some of the earliest development of chemical and high-pressure lasers. In 1975 his studies continued in the Ecole d'Ete Theorique de Physique, Les Houches, France, and from 1976 to 1978 he was a member of Technical Staff (Physicist), Optical Physics Department, Hughes Research Laboratories, Malibu, California, his work including the use of lasers for satellite-to-satellite communications. He was selected by NASA in January 1978 and, after completion of training in August 1979, he was assigned to Shuttle development duties including support crew for Shuttle 3. Named MS-3 for STS-11 on February 3, 1982, he flew this mission, redesignated Shuttle 10 (41-B) on February 3-11, 1984. Following this mission he continued work towards a second flight which was announced on January 29, 1985, almost one year to the day before the fateful launch date. Launched as MS-3 on Shuttle 25 (51-L) on January 28, 1986, the tenth flight of *Challenger*, he was killed following the mid-air explosion of the vehicle shortly after leaving the pad.

MESSERSCHMID, Ernst (Payload Specialist *Challenger* 9)
Civilian, born May 21, 1945 at Reutlingen, Germany. He received a diploma of physics (1972) and a doctorate in physics (1976), studying at the universities of Tübingen and Bonn. He was a visiting scientist and fellow at CERN, Geneva (1970-75) and a lecturer and research associate at the Freiberg University and the Brookhaven National Laboratory, New York, USA (1975-76). From 1978 to 1982 he was employed at the Institute of Communications Technology, DFVLR, at Oberpfaffenhofen, conducting research in spaceborne communications. He has also designed (1977) the beam optics for PETRA electron storage rings at DESY (Hamburg). He was named one of two West German PS candidates for the German Spacelab D1 mission on 17 December 1982, and trained for the mission in Germany and the USA for the next three years. Launched as Shuttle 22 (61-A)/Spacelab D1, the mission was flown between October 30 and November 6, 1985. Returned to DFVLR.

MUSGRAVE, Franklin Story (Mission Specialist *Challenger* 1 and Mission Specialist *Challenger* 8)
Civilian, born August 19, 1935 at Boston Massachusetts. He gained a BS degree in Mathematics and Statistics from Syracuse University (1958), a Master of Business Administration in Operational Analysis and Computer Programming from University of California, Los Angeles (1959), a BA in Chemistry from Marietta College (1960), an MD Medicine from Columbia University (1964) and an MS in Physiology and Biophysics from the University of Kentucky (1966). He served in the USMC, where he trained as an aviation electrician, instrument technician and aircraft crew chief, and completed tours aboard the USS *Wasp* in the Far East. A highly experienced jet pilot, parachutist and flying instructor, he has worked as a mathematician and operations analyst for the Eastman Kodak Co. (1958), served a surgical internship at the University of Kentucky Medical Center (1964-65), and continued there as a USAF post-doctoral fellow (1965-66) working on aerospace medicine and as a National Heart Institute post-doctoral fellow (1966-67) teaching and conducting research in cardiovascular and exercise physiology. Selected by NASA in August 1967, he completed training in 1969 and worked on Skylab design and development assignments, was back-up science pilot for Skylab 2, and CapCom for Skylabs 3 and 4. He served as an MS for the first and second Spacelab simulations (1974), and was involved in design and development of all Shuttle EVA equipment including the suit, EMU and MMU. He also served as a test and verification pilot in the Shuttle Avionics Integration Laboratories, and was named MS-1/EV-1 for Shuttle 6 on March 2, 1982, flying this first *Challenger* mission on April 4-9, 1983. Musgrave also completed a 4 hour 17 minute EVA in the payload bay of the orbiter, the first of the programme. Following the flight he continued training and was named MS-1/3rd pilot/EV-1 (Blue Shift commander) for Spacelab 2 in November 1983. This flew as Shuttle 19 (51-F)/Spacelab 2, *Challenger's* eighth mission between July 29 and August 6, 1985. Active astronaut.

NAGEL, Steven Ray (Pilot *Challenger* 9)
Lieutenant Colonel, USAF, born October 27, 1946 at Canton, Illinois. He gained a BS degree in Aeronautical and Astronautical Engineering from the University of Illinois (1969) and an MS degree in Mechanical Engineering from California State University (1978). He began active service with USAF in 1969 and completed pilot training; following checkout training in the F-100 he served as an F-100 pilot with the 68th Tactical Fighter Squadron, England AFB (October 1970 to July 1971), as a T-28 instructor for the Royal Laotian Air Force in Thailand (August 1971 to October 1972) and an A-7D instructor pilot and flight examiner (October 1972 to January 1975). He was then a student at the USAF Test Pilot School, Edwards AFB, California (February-December 1975) and a USAF test pilot with the 6512th Test Squadron at Edwards AFB on a variety of projects (January 1976 to July 1978), and was selected to NASA in January 1978 (Group 8, Pilot Category). He completed training in August 1979 and was assigned to Shuttle support duties, namely chase T-38 pilot for Shuttle 1, and Support Crew/CapCom for Shuttles 2 and 3. He was selected as MS-1 to Brandenstein's crew in November 1983, on the mission that eventually flew as Shuttle 18 (51-G), the fifth flight of *Discovery* in June 1985. At the same time that Nagel prepared for his 51-G assignment he trained for a second spaceflight (for which he had been named on February 14, 1984) as pilot of the Spacelab D1 West German mission, flown as Shuttle 22 (61-A)/Spacelab D1. Active.

NELSON, George Driver (Mission Specialist *Challenger* 5)
Civilian, born July 13, 1950 at Charles City, Iowa. He gained a BS degree in Physics from Harvey Mudd College (1972), an MS degree in Astronomy from the University of Washington (1974) and a PhD in Astronomy, also from the University of Washington (1977). He completed a variety of astronomical research assignments between 1972 and 1978, including tours at Sacramento Peak Solar Observatory, Sunspot in New Mexico, the Astronomical Institute at Utrecht in the Netherlands, and the University of Göttingen in West Germany, and was a post-doctoral research associate at the Joint Institute for Laboratory Astrophysics in Boulder, Colorado when selected for NASA in January 1978. He completed training in August 1979 and was assigned Shuttle development duties as an MS, including underwater EVA simulation tests with the mock-up Space Telescope (1979), a 14-hour MMU/EMU test (1980), Shuttle 1 support and Chase 1 Photo/Observer, CapCom for Shuttles 3 and 4, and a Scientific Equipment Operator flying high-altitude NASA RB-57F earth resources aircraft. He was named MS-3/EV-1 for Shuttle 13 (redesignated 41-C) on February 22, 1983. The mission was flown as Shuttle 13 (41-C), the fifth flight of *Challenger*. In addition he was the fifth person to perform an EVA from *Challenger*, logging two periods of EVA during the mission (2 hours 57 minutes and 6 hours 16 minutes) totalling 9 hours 13 minutes. He also completed a 42 minute flight on an MMU. Following his *Challenger* mission, Nelson flew as MS on Shuttle 24 (61-C), the seventh flight of *Columbia* and the last successful mission before the *Challenger's* loss. Training as MS Mission 26.

OCKELS, Wubbo J. (Payload Specialist *Challenger* 9)
Civilian, born March 28, 1946 at Almelo, the Netherlands. He received his Doctorate in Physics and Mathematics from the University of Groningen (1973) and undertook experimental investigations at the Nuclear Physics Accelerator Institute in Groningen (1973-78) before being selected by ESA in 1977 as one of four PS candidates for Spacelab 1; he was officially named as Spacelab 1 finalist on June 2, 1978 and selected as back-up PS for the Spacelab 1 mission (flown in late 1983) on September 20, 1982. He trained with NASA Group 9 selection (May 1980 to May 1981), and qualified as ESA MS available for non-ESA Shuttle flights. He was named PS-3 for Spacelab D1 on February 14, 1984 and flew on mission as Shuttle 22 (61-A)/Spacelab D1 October 29 and November 6, 1985. Returned ESA.

ONIZUKA, Ellison Shoji (Mission Specialist *Challenger* 25)
Lieutenant Colonel, USAF, born June 24, 1946 at Kealakekua, Hawaii, and died January 28, 1986 following the mid-air explosion of *Challenger* above KSC, Florida. He gained a BS degree in Aerospace Engineering from the University of Colorado (1969) and an MS degree in Aerospace Engineering, also from the University of Colorado (1969). He entered active duty in the USAF in January 1970 and served as an aerospace flight test engineer, participating in the flight test programmes and systems safety engineering for several aircraft at Sacramento Air Logistics Center, California. Between August 1974 and July 1975 he attended the USAF Test Pilot School and following graduation was assigned to the USAF Flight Test Center at Edwards AFB until selection to NASA in 1978, serving as a member of the USAF staff at the Test Pilot School as squadron flight test engineer, and later as chief of the emergency support section training resources branch. He was involved in instruction of courses and management of all flight-test modifications to several support fleet aircraft used at the school. Selected by NASA in January 1978, he completed training in August 1979 and was assigned to the support crew for Shuttle 1 through to April 1981; he then worked on the launch support crew for Shuttle 2 and was named MS-1 for Shuttle 10 (planned for a December 1983 launch) on October 11, 1982. Several cancellations and reassignments of the first dedicated DoD mission resulted in Onizuka flying as MS-1 on Shuttle 15 (51-C), the third flight of *Discovery*, in January 1985. Shortly after completing his first spaceflight he was named as MS-2/EV-1 for Shuttle 51-L on January 29, 1985. Launched as Shuttle 25 (51-L) on January 28, 1986, the vehicle exploded 73 seconds after launch.

Below: (l to r, back) Hartsfield, Dunbar, Buchli and Furrer; (l to r, front) Messerschmid, Ockels, Nagel and Bluford, *Challenger* 9 (61A).

Above: (top to bottom) Bobko, Peterson, Musgrave and Weitz leave the orbiter at Edwards AFB after *Challenger*'s successful first flight.

OVERMYER, Robert Franklyn (Commander *Challenger* 7)
Colonel, USMC (Ret), born July 14, 1936 at Lorain, Ohio. He gained a BS degree in Physics from Baldwin-Wallace College, Beria, Ohio (1958) and an MS degree in Aeronautics from the USN Postgraduate School, Monterey, California (1964). He enlisted in the USMC during February 1957, and joined the regular service in 1960. He received flight training and, after a variety of assignments, graduated from the USAF Aerospace Research Pilots' School at Edwards AFB, California. He was selected as one of five Group 2 MOL astronauts on June 17, 1966, and transferred to NASA (Group 7) in August 1969 after cancellation of MOL. He then participated in engineering development duties in the Skylab project office, was in the Support Crew/CapCom for Apollo 17 (December 1972), and became a member of the US Support Crew for the joint US-Soviet ASTP docking mission, serving as US CapCom in the Soviet flight control centre at Moscow during the July 1975 mission. He was assigned to the support crew for Shuttle ALT programme and served alternately as ALT chase pilot and CapCom (1977). He was then assigned to the Shuttle OFT Group, became Deputy Orbiter Manager responsible for the preparation of *Columbia* for Shuttle 1 at KSC (1979-80), flew as pilot of Shuttle 5 in November 1982 (the fifth flight of *Columbia* and the first operational flight of the programme), was named commander for Spacelab 3 on February 22, 1983. He thus flew as commander of Shuttle 17 (51-B)/Spacelab 3 (Gold Team leader) between April 30 and May 6, 1985. Retired, 1986.

PETERSON, Donald Herod (Mission Specialist *Challenger* 1)
Colonel, USAF (Ret), born October 22, 1933 at Winona, Mississippi. He gained a BS degree from the US Military Academy, West Point, New York (1955) and an MS degree in Nuclear Engineering from the USAF Institute of Technology, Wright-Patterson AFB, Ohio (1962). Following graduation from the USAF Academy in 1955 he completed a variety of USAF assignments, including four years as a flight instructor and military training officer, three years as a nuclear systems analyst in the USAF Systems Command, a student period at the Aerospace Research Pilots' School and one year as a fighter pilot with Tactical Air Command, this last including three months of combat weapons training. He was selected for MOL on June 30, 1967 (Group 3), and transferred to NASA in August 1969 upon the cancellation of the MOL programme. He then worked on Apollo support assignments, including Support Crew/CapCom for Apollo 16 (1972), and was assigned to Shuttle development duties (1972-81). He retired from the USAF in 1980, and was named MS-2 (EV-2) for Shuttle 6 on March 2, 1982, flying *Challenger*'s first mission on April 4-9, 1983. Resigned, 1984.

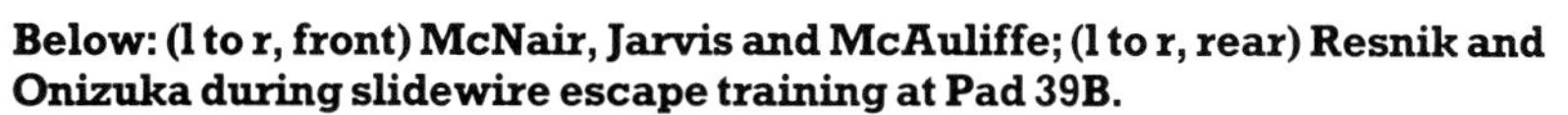

Below: (l to r, front) McNair, Jarvis and McAuliffe; (l to r, rear) Resnik and Onizuka during slidewire escape training at Pad 39B.

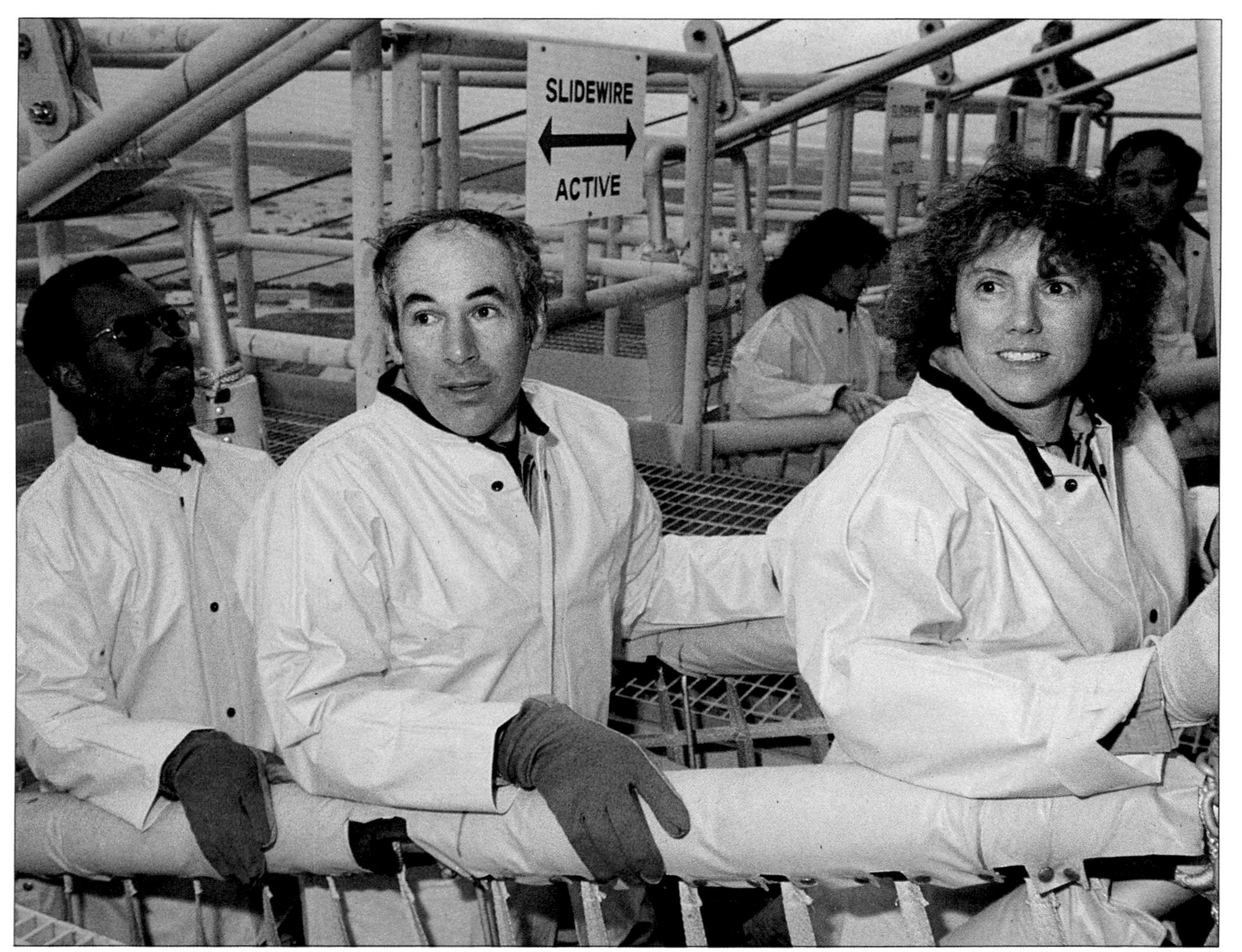

RESNIK, Judith Arlene (Mission Specialist *Challenger* 10)
Civilian, born April 5, 1949 at Akron, Ohio, and died January 25, 1986 following the mid-air explosion of *Challenger* above KSC, Florida. She gained a BS degree in Electrical Engineering from Carnegie Mellon University (1970) and a PhD in Electrical Engineering from the University of Maryland (1977). She was employed by RCA Missile and Surface Radar at Moorestown, New Jersey (1970-71) but transferred to RCA Services Co. at Springfield, Virginia, working as a design engineer on a variety of projects including circuit design and development of phased-array radar control systems, naval control systems, engineering support for the NASA sounding rocket programme, and administration for telemetric systems for naval and NASA tasks (1971-74). She served as a biomedical engineer and staff fellow in the Laboratory for Neurophysiology, National Institute of Health, Bethesda, Maryland (1974-77), and as senior systems engineer, Engineering Staff, Production Development, Xerox Corporation, El Segundo, California (1977-78). Selected in Group 8 for NASA training in January 1978, she completed the 12-month course in August 1979 and then worked on RMS development as member of the Core Group, performed SAIL tests for STS-2 (1980), flew as MS-1 on Shuttle 12 (41-D), the maiden flight of *Discovery* in August and September 1984, and was named MS-1 for Shuttle 51-L on January 29, 1985. Launched on January 28, 1986 as Shuttle 25 (51-L), the 10th flight of *Challenger* ended in disaster after 73 seconds.

RIDE, Sally Kristen (Mission Specialist *Challenger* 2 and Mission Specialist *Challenger* 6)
Civilian, born May 26, 1951 at Los Angeles, California. She gained a BA in English (1973), a BS degree in Physics (1973), an MS degree in Physics (1975) and her PhD in Physics (1978) all from Stanford University. Between 1973 and 1978 she held teaching, assistant and research assignments whilst a graduate student in the Physics Department of Stanford University, experience including one summer with the low-temperatures group working with experimental general relativity and three years in X-ray astrophysics whilst working on her thesis. Selected to NASA in January 1978 (Group 8), she completed training in August 1979. Thereafter she performed underwater zero-g simulations with the mock-up RMS, was a member of the RMS Core Group, and worked with SPAS/RMS deployment/retrieval procedures throughout 1980 and 1981. She was then CapCom for Shuttles 2 and 3 before being selected as MS-2 for Shuttle 7 on April 20, 1982. Flown as Shuttle 7 (31-C) on June 18-24, 1983, this was the second flight of *Challenger*. She also has the distinction of being the first American female in space. Following this mission she continued her astronaut training, serving as CapCom on several Shuttle flights, before flying for a second time in 1984. She was named in November 1983 for Shuttle 13 (41-G), the sixth flight of *Challenger*, and flew as MS-1 on October 5-13, 1984. She was later assigned to NASA HQ. At the time of the *Challenger* loss, Ride was in training as an MS with a new crew for a mission in July 1986 on Shuttle 61-M. She served as a member of the Presidential Commission to investigate *Challenger*'s accident (February-June 1986). Active astronaut.

SCOBEE, Francis Richard (Pilot *Challenger* 5 and Commander *Challenger* 10)
Major, USAF (Ret), born May 19, 1939 at Cle Elum, Washington, and died January 28, 1986 following explosion of *Challenger* above KSC, Florida. He gained a BS degree in Aerospace Engineering from the University of Arizona (1965). He joined the USAF in 1957, trained as an engine mechanic, attended night school at the University of Arizona, went to officer training school and completed flight training in 1966. He then completed a variety of USAF assignments, including a tour in Vietnam. After graduating from the USAF Aerospace Research Pilots' School in 1972 he participated in the flight test programmes of a variety of aircraft between 1972 and 1978 whilst assigned to Edwards AFB, California, including flying the X-24 lifting-body vehicle, one of the forerunners of the Shuttle. He flew that vehicle twice in 1975 and also qualified as a Boeing 747 pilot. Selected to NASA in January 1978, he completed his training in August 1979 and was designated a future Shuttle pilot. He retired the USAF in January 1980, and continued as a civilian astronaut, conducting cockpit integration tests on *Columbia* in 1980 as well as power-up simulations, and flying the SCA carrying *Columbia* back to KSC following Shuttle 1. He was selected for Shuttle 13, later designated Shuttle 11 (41-C), the fifth flight of *Challenger*, on February 22, 1983, flying as pilot on April 6-13, 1984. He also visited Europe during *Enterprise*'s fly around Western Europe in the summer of 1983, acting as one of the SCA pilots. He continued his training and on January 29, 1985 was named commander of Shuttle 51-L. Flown as Shuttle 25 (51-L), the 10th flight of *Challenger*, the mission was launched on January 28, 1986 and resulted in a mid-air explosion just 73 seconds after launch.

SCULLY-POWER, Paul Desmond (Payload Specialist *Challenger* 6)
Civilian, born May 28, 1944 in Sydney, Australia (becoming a US citizen on September 17, 1982). He gained a BS post-graduate diploma of education from the University of Sydney (1966), established and served as head of the first oceanographic group in the Royal Australian Navy (1967-72) and, whilst an exchange scientist with the USN, was invited to assist the Earth Observations team on Skylab. He has worked on space oceanography for each US manned spaceflight since that time. In 1974-75 he returned to Australia to plan and implement the EDDY project, the first combined US, Australian and New Zealand oceanographic and acoustic measurement of ocean eddies. He served as principle foreign investigator for the Heat Capacity Mapping Mission Satellite and has spent time at sea, completing 24 scientific cruises, 13 of them as chief scientist. He is a qualified naval diver and author of over 60 scientific articles on oceanography, marine biology, underwater acoustics and ocean engineering; since emigrating to the USA in October 1977 he has served as senior scientist and technical specialist at the US Naval Underwater Systems Center, New London, Connecticut. He was invited to fly as PS on a Shuttle flight in 1984, taking up this invitation as PS-2 for Shuttle 13 (41-G) on October 5-13, 1984. Returned USN, USC.

SMITH, Michael John (Pilot *Challenger* 10)
Commander, USN, born April 30, 1945 at Morehead City, North Carolina, and died January 28, 1986 in the *Challenger* tragedy, 73 seconds after launch above KSC, Florida. He gained a BS degree in Naval Sciences from the USN Academy (1967) and an MS degree in Aeronautical Engineering from the USN Postgraduate School (1968). He completed naval jet pilot training after graduation from postgraduate school, earning his wings in May 1969, and served two years with Training Squadron 21 of Advanced Jet Training Command and as an instructor with AJTC (May 1969 to March 1971). He flew A-6 Intruders for two years (1971-73) with Attack Squadron 52 aboard USS *Kitty Hawk*, completing a Vietnam tour. He was then a student at the USN Test Pilot School, graduating in 1974 before spending two years at the Strike Aircraft Test Directorate, Patuxent River, Maryland. He completed an 18-month tour as an instructor at the USN Test Pilot School, and in 1977 was assigned to Attack Squadron 75 as maintenance and operations officer, completing two Mediterranean cruises aboard the USS *Saratoga*. Selected for the NASA astronaut programme in May 1980 (Group 9), he completed pilot training in May 1981 and completed assignments as commander in the Shuttle Avionics Integration Laboratories, Department Chief at the Johnson Spaceflight Center Aircraft Operations Directorate and Technical Assistant to the Director of Flight Operations Directorate. He was also assigned to the Astronaut Office Developments and Test Group, worked on the crew for Shuttle Earth Observation Mission (51-H for a short time), and was named pilot for Shuttle 51-L on January 29, 1985. He

Above: (l to r) Scobee, Nelson, Van Hoften, Hart and Crippen, the 'ace' repair team of *Challenger* 5 (41C).

was killed following the explosion of *Challenger* 73 seconds after the launch of the orbiter.

STEWART, Robert Lee (Mission Specialist *Challenger* 4)
Colonel, US Army, born August 13, 1942 at Washington, DC. He gained a BS degree in Mathematics from the University of Southern Mississippi (1964) and an MS degree in Aerospace Engineering from the University of Texas (1972). He enlisted in the US Army during 1964. He served as Air Defence Artillery Director of the 32 NORAD Region Headquarters in Alabama, received rotary-wing training and was designated army aviator in July 1966, was Fire Team Leader Armed Helicopter Platoon, 'A' Company, 101st Aviation Battalion and served combat duties in Vietnam (1966-67), was an instructor pilot at the US Army Primary Helicopter School (1967-69), was a student at the US Army Air Defence School (1969-72), served in South Korea with the 309th Aviation Battalion as operations officer and executive officer, attended and completed the USN Test Pilot School Rotary-Wing Test Pilot Course (1973-74), and served as an experimental test pilot (1974-78) with US Army Aviation Engineering Flight Activity at Edwards AFB, California, completing a variety of assignments on rotary- and fixed-wing aircraft. Selected by NASA in January 1978 (Group 8), he completed MS training in August 1979 and was assigned to Shuttle development. He was the first US Army officer selected for astronaut training, and his technical duties in Astronaut Office included test and evaluation of the re-entry flight-control system for Shuttle 1, ascent abort procedures development and payload co-ordination, Support Crew for Shuttle 4 and Ascent/Orbit CapCom for Shuttle 5. He was named MS-1 (EV-2) for Shuttle 11 on February 4, 1983, and flew as MS-1 on the redesignated Shuttle 10 (41-B) on February 3-11, 1984, the fourth flight of *Challenger*. During the mission he became the 4th person to complete two EVAs from *Challenger*, these totalling 12 hours 12 minutes, and also flew the MMU unit. He also flew on the maiden mission of *Atlantis* in October 1985 as Shuttle 21 (51-J). Reassigned 1986, US Army Space Command.

SULLIVAN, Kathryn Dwyer (Mission Specialist *Challenger* 6)
Civilian, born October 3, 1951 at Paterson, New Jersey. She gained a BS degree in Earth Sciences from the University of California, Santa Cruz (1973) and a PhD in Geology from Dalhousie University, Halifax, Nova Scotia (1978). She spent most of her time after graduation from high school in 1969 in academic research and studies until selection by NASA in 1978. These activities included a tour as exchange student at the University of Bergen, Norway (1971-72) and completion of a series of doctoral studies (1973-78) including oceanographic expeditions with the US Geological Survey. She served as a first- and second-year laboratory and tutor instructor (1973-75) and worked for the Canadian Geological Survey as a researcher during the summer of 1975. Selected to NASA in January 1978 (Group 8), she completed astronaut training in August 1979 and was assigned as an MS. She qualified as a Systems Engineering Operator in NASA's RB-57F high-altitude research aircraft (1978) and continued research in spaceborne remote sensing, including participation in remote sensing projects in Alaska (1980). She served as Chase 1 photo/observe crew member for Shuttle 2 (November 1981), was assigned software development for Shuttles 1 and 2, was orbiter and payload test/checkout and launch support crew member at KSC for Shuttles 3, 4, 5 and 6, was EVA and spacesuit support crew for Shuttles 7 and 8, and became a co-investigator on the Shuttle Imaging Radar-B experiment flown on Shuttle 13 (41-G), a mission for which she was selected as MS-2 (EV-2) in November 1983. The mission was flown on October 5-13, 1984. She also completed a 3 hour 27 minute EVA, the first US woman to perform an EVA, and the 8th *Challenger* astronaut to do so. Following her first mission she continued her training and also served on the National Commission to investigate the future of US space exploration in the next 50 years which completed its work in May 1986. Active.

THAGARD, Norman Earl (Mission Specialist *Challenger* 2 and Mission Specialist *Challenger* 7)
Civilian, born July 3, 1943 at Marianne, Florida. He gained a BS degree in Engineering Science from Florida State University (1965), an MS degree in Engineering Science from Florida State University (1966) and an MD degree from the University of Texas Southwestern Medical School (1977). He held various teaching posts while studying for advanced degrees (1961-66) and entered active duty with USMC Reserve (1966). He took flight training and served with VMFA-333 and VMFA-115, the latter in Vietnam. He was Aviation Weapons Division Officer of VMFA-251 at Marine Corps Air Station Beaufort, South Carolina (1970-71). He was a medical student at the University of Texas (1971-77) and an intern in the Department of Internal Medicine, Medical University of South Carolina (1977-78). Selected with NASA Group 8 in January 1978, he completed training as an MS in August 1979 and was assigned to Shuttle development: he thus worked on Shuttle Avionics Integration Laboratories assignments for Shuttle 2. He was named MS-3 for Shuttle 7 on December 21, 1982 and flew this Shuttle 7 (31-C) mission, the second flight of *Challenger*, on June 18-24, 1983. He then worked on Shuttle 8 and 9 support assignments, and was selected for Spacelab 3 on February 22, 1983, flying *Challenger*'s seventh mission between April 29 and May 6, 1985. Active.

THORNTON, William Edgar (Mission Specialist *Challenger* 3 and Mission Specialist *Challenger* 7)
Civilian, born April 14, 1929 at Faison, North Carolina. He gained a BS degree in Physics from the University of North Carolina (1952) and an MD from the University of North Carolina (1963). He served in USAF (1952-55) as Officer in Charge Instrumentation Laboratory, Flight Test Proving Ground, later becoming consultant to Air Proving Ground Command. He was Chief Engineer, Electronics Division, Del Mar Engineering Laboratory, Los Angeles (1955-59) and attended the University of North Carolina Medical School before interning at Wilford Hall USAF Hospital, Lackland AFB, Texas (1959-64). He returned to active duty in the USAF, being assigned USAF Aerospace Medicine Division at Brooks AFB, Texas and completing two years of research in space medicine (1965-67). Selected for NASA in August 1967 (Group 6), he completed training in 1969 and was assigned to Skylab development. He was crew member for SMEAT, the Skylab ground simulation for medical experiments conducted at the Johnson Spaceflight Center in 1972, Support Crew/CapCom for all three Skylab missions and principal investigator on several Skylab experiments. He was then assigned to Shuttle support duties, participating in simulations of Spacelab life science missions during 1974 and 1977 before being reallocated to the Shuttle Operations Mission Development Group, responsible for the development of crew procedures and techniques of deploying Shuttle payloads. The primary task here was the development of equipment for the study of human adaptation to spaceflight, including equipment used by astronaut crews for inflight exercise. He continued medical associations within and outside NASA in areas of aerospace medicine, and investigated Space Adaptation Syndrome effects on crew members for Shuttles 4, 5, and 6. He was named MS-3 for Shuttle 8 (31-D), the third flight of *Challenger*, on December 21, 1982, flying the mission between August 30 and September 5, 1983. He was also selected as a mission specialist for Spacelab 3, eventually flown as Shuttle 17 (51-B), on February 22, 1983. He flew the mission as MS-3 (Gold Team) between April 30 and May 6, 1985. Active.

TRULY, Richard Harrison (Commander *Challenger* 3)
Rear Admiral, USN, born November 12, 1937 at Fayette, Mississippi. He gained a BS degree in Aeronautical Engineering from Georgia Institute of Technology (1959) and entered the USN upon graduation from Georgia Tech. He received flight training and was assigned to Fighter Squadron 33 (1960-63) flying F-8 Crusaders, and completed over 300 carrier landings. He attended the USAF Aerospace Research Pilots' School course at Edwards AFB, California, and was assigned as instructor there following graduation (1963-65). He was one of eight Group 1 MOL astronauts selected on November 12, 1965, and served as a MOL astronaut until the programme was cancelled in 1969. He transferred to NASA (Group 7) in August 1969 and worked on Skylab development. He was Support Crew/CapCom for all three Skylab missions and also Support Crew/CapCom for the Apollo-Soyuz Test Project (1969-75). Assigned to the Shuttle Approach and Landing Test programme, he flew *Enterprise* during the ALT flight programme with Astronaut Engle during 1977. He was back-up pilot for Shuttle 1 and flew as pilot of Shuttle 2, the second flight of the programme and second mission of *Columbia*. He was named commander for Shuttle 8 (31-D) on April 24, 1982 and flew his third *Challenger* mission between August 30 and September 5, 1983. He resigned from NASA September 30, 1983 and became the first commander (1983-86) of the US Naval Space Command upon its commissioning on October 1, 1983: the command is responsible for management and operational control of all USN satellites in current use, and provides direct space system support to the fleet worldwide. The command also co-ordinates the USN's efforts in space research. On February 20, 1986 he was named Associate Administrator for Space Flight, NASA Headquarters, and assumed position of head of NASA's Space Shuttle programme and director of the agency's Design and Data Analysis Task Force which reviewed the *Challenger* accident of January 28, 1986.

VAN DEN BERG, Lodewijk (Payload Specialist *Challenger* 7)
Civilian, born March 24, 1932 at Sluiskil, the Netherlands (US citizen). He gained an MS degree in Chemical Engineering from the Technical University Delft, the Netherlands (1961), an MS degree in Applied Science (1972) and a PhD in Applied Science (1975) both from the University of Delaware, USA. A chemical engineer and senior scientist, he had experienced over 20 years research and management experience in areas of crystal growth and investigations before his spaceflight. An international expert on vapour growth technique, he was co-investigator on the Spacelab 3 Vapor Crystal Growth System (VCGS) experiment. He has worked for the EG&G Corporation, Goleta, California since 1975. Selected for Spacelab 3 on June 8, 1983 as one of four PS candidates, he was named PS-2 (Materials – Science Expert, Silver Team) for Shuttle 17 (51-B)/Spacelab 3 on June 8, 1984. He flew the mission between April 29 and May 6, 1985. Returned to EG&G Corp.

VAN HOFTEN, James Dougal Adrianus (Mission Specialist *Challenger* 5)
Civilian, born June 11, 1944 at Fresno, California. He gained a BS degree in Civil Engineering from the University of California, Berkeley (1966), an MS degree in Hydraulic Engineering from Colorado State University (1968) and a PhD in Fluid Mechanics from Colorado State University (1976). He entered the USN in 1968 and completed flight training in November 1970 before being assigned NAS Miramar then Fighter Squadron 121 flying F-4 Phantoms. He flew combat missions in Vietnam from USS *Ranger*. Retiring from USN duties, he transferred to the USN Reserve in 1974 and resumed his academic studies. He was Assistant Professor of Civil Engineering at the University of Texas (September 1976 to July 1978), teaching fluid mechanics and conducting research on biomedical fluid flows in respect of flow in artificial internal organs and valves. Selected by NASA in January 1978 (Group 8), he completed training in August 1979 and was assigned to Shuttle development. As such he supported Shuttle re-entry and on-orbit guidance, navigation and flight-control testing at the Flight Simulation Laboratory, Rockwell Downey Plant, California (1979-80). He then became Head of the Astro Support Team at KSC, Florida, responsible for turnaround of the orbiter for Shuttle 2, as well as testing and flight preparations. Selected for Shuttle 10 (41-C) on February 22, 1983, he flew the mission as MS-3 (EV-2) on April 6-13, 1984. He was the 6th person to EVA from *Challenger*, completing two EVAs and logging 9 hours 13 minutes (2 hours 57 minutes and 6 hours 16 minutes), and also flew the MMU during the second EVA. Following his first flight he flew again as MS on Shuttle 20 (51-I) in August and September 1985. Resigned 1986.

WANG, Taylor G. (Payload Specialist *Challenger* 7)
Civilian, born June 16, 1940 at Shanghai, China (US citizen). He gained a BS degree in Physics (1967), an MS degree in Physics (1968) and a PhD in Physics (1971), all from the University of California, Los Angeles. He joined NASA's Jet Propulsion Laboratory in 1972, and at the time of his spaceflight was a senior scientist responsible for the inception and development of containerless processing technology, and for research into the dynamics of liquid drops and bubbles. As the principal investigator for the Spacelab 3 Drop Dynamics Module Experiment (DDME) he conducted precursor experiments in ground laboratories, neutral buoyancy systems, drop towers and NASA's KC-135 parabolic flight programme as well as on SPAR sounding rockets. Selected as a Spacelab 3 PS on June 8, 1983, he was named PS-1 (Fluids Science Expert, Gold Team) for Shuttle 17 (51-B)/Spacelab 3, the seventh flight of *Challenger*, on June 8, 1984. Returned to JPL.

WEITZ, Paul Joseph (Commander *Challenger* 1)
Captain, USN (Ret), born July 25, 1932 at Erie, Pennsylvania. He gained a BS degree in Aeronautical Engineering from Pennsylvania State University (1954) and an MS degree in Aeronautical Engineering from the USN Postgraduate School (1964). He served one year aboard USS *John A. Bole* (1954-55) following graduation from PennState University, and then completed flight training in September 1956. He was then A-4 tactics instructor with Attack Squadron 44, the project officer for various air-to-ground delivery tactics projects with Experimental Squadron 5. He attended USN Postgraduate School for two years, and completed a tour of combat duty in Vietnam whilst attached to Helicopter Attack Squadron 4. Selected to NASA in April 1966 (Group 5), he was assigned to the Apollo Command Module Branch of the Astronaut Office. He performed support work for Apollo 12 (original back-up CMP for Apollo 17 and prime CMP for the cancelled Apollo 20 lunar mission before budget cuts in 1969-70). He was assigned to the Skylab programme and flew as pilot of Skylab 2, the first manned flight of 28 days duration in 1973. He then moved to Shuttle development assignments (1974-82), including EVA simulation tasks and service as Deputy Chief of the Astronaut Office. Named commander of Shuttle 6 (31-B) on March 2, 1982, he flew the maiden flight of *Challenger*. Dep. Director NASA JSC. No longer active.

Below: (l to r) Thornton, Thagard, Lind, Overmyer, Gregory, Wang and Van Den Berg, *Challenger* 7's seven-man Spacelab crew for mission 51-B. They are seen preparing for breakfast before launch on April 29, 1985.

The Payloads

During its 10 missions *Challenger* lifted a wide variety of satellites, experiments and other payloads. This section lists briefly all the major elements of the 10 payload manifests. The payload weight for each mission was:

Mission	Approximate Cargo Launch Weight
Shuttle 6 (31-B)	46,615lb (21,145kg)
Shuttle 7 (31-C)	32,821lb (14,888kg)
Shuttle 8 (31-D)	26,163lb (10,507kg)
Shuttle 10 (41-B)	23,767lb (10,781kg)
Shuttle 11 (41-C)	32,267lb (14,636kg)
Shuttle 13 (41-G)	18,091lb (8,206kg)
Shuttle 17 (51-B)	31,893lb (14,467kg)
Shuttle 19 (51-F)	33,145lb (15,035kg)
Shuttle 22 (61-A)	31,131lb (14,121kg)
Shuttle 25 (51-L)	48,361lb (21,937kg)
OV-099 *Challenger's* Approximate Cargo Total:	324,254lb (145,723kg)

In addition to the payloads and experiments carried by *Challenger*, several support equipment items were also launched on some missions:
EVA suits, equipment and PLSS's, all Missions
Remote Manipulator System: Missions 2, 3, 4, 5, 6, 8, 9 and 10
Two MMUs and Flight Support Stations: Missions 4 and 5
Inertial Upper Stage (IUS) and Airborne Support Frame: Missions 1 and 10
Payload Assist Module (PAM) and Sun Shield/Support Frame: Missions 2 (2), 3 (1) and 4 (2) for a total of 5 PAMs
Spacelab Long Module and Tunnel: Missions 7 and 9
Spacelab Pallet: Mission 8 (3 plus Igloo and IPS)
Mission Peculiar Equipment Support Structure (MPESS): Missions 6, 7, 9 and 10
Fixed Service Structure for the Mission 5 Solar Max repair mission

Deployable Payloads

Tracking and Data-Relay Satellites
Missions: 1 (31-B) TDRS-A and 10 (51-L) TDRS-B
The Tracking and Data-Relay Satellites are a series of advanced communications platforms designed to enhance the on-orbit coverage of Shuttle missions in a more efficient way than from existing ground stations. A planned series of two active satellites (with an on-orbit backup available) was planned in the 1970s as part of the SSTS programme. *Challenger* deployed the first on its maiden flight, but faulty IUS systems and difficulties with this TDRS-A in space constantly delayed the second TDRS, which was launched on Shuttle 25 (51-L), *Challenger's* 10th mission. The loss of the vehicle also resulted in the destruction of TDRS-B. The deployment of the remaining two TDRS vehicles remains high on the payload schedule when flights resume. Deployed from Shuttle by IUS, the TDRS vehicles are the largest privately-owned telecommunications satellites so far built, and each weighs 4,700lb (2,132kg). Fully deployed, the satellite measures 57ft 2in (17.42m) across its solar panels, and its two main single-access antennae, which are fabricated of molybdenum plated with 14-carat gold, each measure 16ft (4.88m) in diameter and span 42ft 7in (12.98m) from tip to tip when deployed. In all, seven antennae are mounted on each satellite, which consists of two modules: the equipment module holding the subsystems that operate the satellite, and the telecommunications payload module housing the electronic equipment that links user spacecraft to ground terminals. The TDRS operates in the S-, Ku- and C-band frequencies, and has the capacity to support up to 23 user spacecraft at the same time in two types of service: a multiple-access service relaying data from up to 19 spacecraft at once, and a single-access service providing high data rate communications in two relays from each vehicle.

HS-376 Commercial Satellites
Missions: 2 (31-C) and 4 (41-B)
One of the most familiar sights of a Shuttle mission was the routine deployment of cylindrical communications satellites sent spinning out from an orbiter's payload bay into the depths of space. *Challenger* deployed several of these fare-paying satellites during its career, the most versatile being the Hughes 376 comsat. During *Challenger* missions this type was deployed under the Anik C, Palapa B and Westar names on the second and fourth missions. In stowed position the HS-376 measures about 108in (2.74m) in height (using only 14% of the payload bay) but on station folds out to 260in (6.60m) including a 72in (1.83m) antenna. Members of this large and multi-capable family can carry voice, video or facsimile transmissions in the C or Ku bands, or both.
Anik: Deployed on Challenger 2 and named Anik C-2. It is owned by Telesat of Canada, which operates a series of Anik satellites. This vehicle operates in the 14- and 12-GHz HF range with 16 transponders. Using spot beam antennae, much smaller ground stations are able to be used with this satellite. It operates between 104.5° and 117.5°, 22,300 miles (35,887km) above the Earth with antennae focussed on Canada, of which most parts fall in the satellite's range.
Palapa: Deployed on Challenger 2 and designated Palapa B, and on Challenger 4 designated Palapa B2 (see below). The Palapa B is operated by Indonesia and, serving the Association of South-East Asia Nations, operates in the C band (6/4 GHz) with a total of 24 transponders compared with only 12 on the A series. The satellite links the many islands of Indonesia by voice, video, telephone, telegraph and high-speed data transmission.

Westar: The Westar VI was deployed from *Challenger* on its fourth mission and, like Palapa B2, was promptly lost when malfunctions in the PAM motors fired each of the satellites into the wrong orbit. After many months of international wrangling, the two stranded satellites were finally retrieved during *Discovery's* second mission (51-A) in November 1984. Westar VI has 24 transponders and six backups, and is operated by the Western Union Company of the USA, providing telecommunications and other HS-376 services for the USA.

Insat 1B
Mission: 3 (31-D)
The Indian National Satellite (Insat) 1B was deployed from the third *Challenger* mission by PAM, which placed the satellite in a geosynchronous orbit over 74° East longitude. Built by Ford Aerospace Western Development Laboratories, the satellite operates in the C-band communications range and S-band TV range. In addition the satellite services India with weather surveillance and forecasting data from a data-collection platform, and with additional weather surveillance data from a Very High Resolution Radiometer. The satellite has a 7-year lifespan. The main box structure of the vehicle measures 7.15ft × 3.75ft × 5.09ft (2.18m × 1.42m × 1.55m) and includes a 100lb (45kg) thruster for attitude control.

Integrated Rendezvous Target
Mission: 4 (41-B)
The IRT was a 6.4ft (1.95m) diameter balloon deployed from a rack bolted to the forward end of the *Challenger's* port longeron, inside a deployable canister which split open one minute after ejection to reveal an automatically-inflated one-mil thick aluminized mylar balloon pressurized to 0.3lb/sq in (0.02 bar). Flat white in colour except for an IR gore (one of 24), the complete assembly weighed 200lb (91kg). The balloon departed from the orbiter at 1.5ft (0.46m) per second and a spin rate of 3rpm. Designed by NASA as a pathfinder for the Solar Max rendezvous attempt, it was launched so that the Challenger 4 crew could practise a variety of rendezvous approaches to the satellite.

Earth Radiation Budget Satellite (ERBS)
Mission: 6 (41-G)
One of three satellites of the Earth Radiation Budget Experiment research programme, this 5,087lb (2,307kg) satellite was built by Bell Aerospace Systems under contract from NASA, and carries three instruments: the ERBE Scanner, the ERBE Non-Scanner, and the Stratospheric Aerosol and Gas Experiment II. Deployed by the RMS, the ERBS used its Orbit Adjust Propulsion System for a gradual increase in orbit altitude to 379 miles (610km) at 57°. ERBE is 15ft (4.57m) wide, 12.5ft (3.81m) high and 5.2ft (1.58m) long. Its instruments provide measurements on the Earth's radiation budget on several spatial and temporal scales. The ERBE Non-Scanner has five sensors, four Earth-pointing and the fifth solar-pointing, the Earth-pointing sensors with cavity radiometer detectors viewing the planet from limb to limb. The ERBE Scanner has three sensors with radiometric thermistor bolometers for short-wave, long-wave and total radiation measurements. The SAGE-II experiment is designed to monitor the vertical global distribution of aerosols and gases in the stratosphere by measuring the reduction in intensity of the Sun's energy through the atmosphere during 15 sunrises and sunsets on each mission day.

Northern Utah Satellite (NUSAT) & Global Low Orbiting Message Relay (GLOMR) Satellite
Missions: 7 (51-B) and 9 (61-A)
Challenger was the first Shuttle to deploy satellites from the small GAS canisters, mounted on the port side of the payload bay near the forward hatch area during the seventh and ninth missions. Deployment was initiated automatically by a crew command from the aft flight deck opening the lid of the canister and the spring released satellite exited the canister at 3.5ft (1.07m) per second. The satellites provide clear proof of the Shuttle's facility for giving small groups or firms the chance to orbit inexpensive satellites by taking advantage of the orbiter's unique deployment opportunities.
NUSAT: Built by Morton Thiokol Inc. for a university team headed by Weber State College, Ogden, Utah in co-ordination with the FAA, this air traffic control radar system calibrator measured antenna patterns for ground-based radar in the USA and other member countries of the Civil Aviation Organization. The 115lb (52kg) 26-sided satellite had a design life of six months, and was deployed from *Challenger* on its seventh mission.
GLOMR: Also intended to be deployed on *Challenger's* seventh mission, this satellite did not in reality get deployed until the ninth mission due to a malfunction in the deployment sequence. Designed and built by Defense Systems Inc, it weighed 150lb (68kg) and had 62 sides. The data relay and communications satellite had a one-year design life, and was intended to read signals and command oceanographic sensors, locate oceanographic and other ground sensors and relay data from them to customers.

Retrievable Payloads

Shuttle Pallet Satellite (SPAS)
Missions: 2 (31-C) and 4 (41-B)
The SPAS is a reusable platform built by the Messerschmitt-Bölkow-Blohm (MBB) aerospace firm of West Germany. Capable of operation in the payload bay and of free-flying away from the orbiter for a limited period, this system allows groups of experiments and equipment to operate in free space outside the orbiter's sphere of influence, and can then be retrieved by the RMS for reuse on later flights after the onboard experiments have been changed.
SPAS-01: Flown on Challenger 2 and deployed by RMS, the SPAS-01 used its onboard TV camera to provide the first photos of the full orbiter against the backdrop of Earth and space. With experiments, the configuration measures 15.7ft (4.79m) across by 11ft (3.35m) high and 4.9ft (1.49m) wide, and weighs 5,022lb (2,280kg). With 40 hours of free flight time, it has its own power supply, data-processing and attitude-stabilizing systems.
SPAS-01A: The SPAS flew again on Shuttle 10, the fourth *Challenger* flight, but was not planned for free flight on this mission. Carrying the same experiment payload as on its previous mission, the SPAS should have been used in conjunction with the Shuttle 10 EVA task simulations for the Solar Max mission. However, full operation was not possible because of RMS equipment malfunction, but usable data were nonetheless recorded from the pallet.

Long Duration Exposure Facility (LDEF)
Mission: 5 (41-C)
Designed to accommodate a range of experiments in Earth orbit for up to one year, the NASA LDEF platform was specially designed for the Shuttle system and deployed on the fifth *Challenger* mission in 1984 for recovery in early 1985. However, changes in the manifest saw the attempt eventually arrive in a 1986 mission, well after the LDEF's designed life had passed, then the loss of *Challenger* put the plans for LDEF retrieval to rest for a further two or three years. When (or perhaps if) it is retrieved, several of the experiments will have been ruined by the extended on-orbit stay time dictated by Shuttle scheduling. Experience of long-term effects on the structure will, however, be of use in planning of later LDEF platforms. Constructed as a 12-sided open-grid structure of aluminium rings and longerons, the 57-experiment LDEF is 30ft (9.14m) long and 14ft (4.27m) in diameter, and weighs 8,000lb (3,629kg). Eighty-six experiment trays, each measuring 50in (1.27m) by 34in (0.86m) by 3, 6 or 12in (7.62, 15.24 or 30.48cm) deep, are located on the structure as 72 around the circumference, six on the Earth-pointing end and eight on the space-pointing end of the gravity-gradient-stabilized facility.

Ejectable Plasma Diagnostics Package (PDP)
Mission: 8 (51-F)
Previously flown but not released on Shuttle 3 in 1982, the PDP was again flown on the Challenger 8-Spacelab 2 mission of 1985. The free-flying PDP was deployed and retrieved by the RMS, and was designed to supplement the investigations of plasma environment experiments, measuring the process in the ionosphere in which the Shuttle travelled. The ionosphere is constantly affected by electrified gas or plasma that streams from the Sun, and the instrument-filled PDP investigated this phenomena.

Spartan-Halley
Mission: 10 (51-L)
In a low-budget attempt to examine the 1986 appearance of Comet Halley from space, NASA and the University of Colorado recycled several instruments and designs to record ultraviolet light from the comet's chemistry when it was closest to the Sun, with a view to assessing how fast water was broken down by sunlight, searching for carbon and sulphur atoms and related compounds, and understanding how the tail evolved. Using two spectrometers modified from the 1971 Mariner 9 backup spacecraft the science package also contained two film cameras (35-mm Nikon F3 with 105-mm and 155-mm lenses) loaded with 65-frame rolls. The whole package, including a microprocessor, measured 35 by 37in (0.89 by 0.94m) and weighed 175lb (79kg). It was mounted on an aluminium optical bench attached to the Spartan carrier, which measured 52 × 43 × 51in (1.32 × 1.09 × 1.30m) and weighed 2,250lb (1,021kg).

Major Payload-Bay Science Payloads

Office of Space and Terrestrial Applications (OSTA)-2
Mission: 2 (31-C)
The OSTA-2 payload, managed by the Marshall Spaceflight Center, was the first of a series of investigations into on-orbit materials-processing aboard the Shuttle. Comprised of four instrument packages containing six experiments, the investigations were a co-operative venture with the Federal Republic of Germany. The payload was located in the payload bay on a Mission Peculiar Equipment Support Structure, which provided mechanical support and elevated the package above the level of the cargo bay, allowing the unit to dissipate heat into space. The OSTA designation was changed on subsequent flights to MSL. The Materials Experiment Assembly developed by Marshall was designed to carry a range of materials experiments (providing data recording, thermal control, power distribution, and structural support) and required minimum attention by the crew. This package was designed to evaluate the system for later mission, the provision of data being a secondary task. Among the OSTA-2 experiments were the following.
1 Vapor Growth of Alloy Type Semi-Conductor Crystals: this experiment was designed to grow alloy semi-conductor (electronic materials) crystals and provide useful data for the understanding of fluid dynamics of vapour transport in space.
2 Liquid Phase Miscibility Gap Materials: this experiment was designed to produce space-formed alloys difficult to obtain on Earth (for later analysis of their physical, chemical and electrical properties) produced by mixing different liquid metals in space and letting them cool for analysis.
3 Containerless Processing of Glass Forming Melts: this experiment was designed to obtain data on high-temperature containerless processing of various compositions of glass-forming substances to eliminate impurities and flaws by acoustic methods.
4 Materialwissenschaftliche Autonome Experimente unter Schwerelosigkeit (MAUS) was the West German part of the materials research experiments, and contained two experiments in three GAS containers.
(i) Stability of Metallic Dispersions: contained in two GAS canisters this experiment developed a technique for taking X-ray photos of the melting and solidification of metals, each container having identical configurations but different heating/cooling cycles.
(ii) Solidification Front: using a general-purpose rocket furnace this experiment was designed to help determine particle movement during melting and solidification of metal alloys.

Below: The Canadian Anik C-2 comsat nudges into space after deployment from *Challenger's* payload bay on June 18, 1983.

Payload Flight Test Article (PFTA)
Mission: 3 (31-D)
An aluminium, lead-ballasted test structure weighing 8,500lb (3,856kg) and resembling a dumb-bell in shape, this NASA experiment was flown on Shuttle 8 after the removal of TDRS-B from that payload manifest. Simulating a large-mass payload for flight testing the RMS, it continued experiments conducted on Shuttles 2, 3, 4 and 7 in preparation for operational use of the RMS during the Solar Max rescue mission of 1984. The test article was 19ft 9in (6.02m) long and 15ft 6in (4.72m) wide.

Office of Space and Terrestrial Applications (OSTA)-3
Mission: 6 (41-G)
OSTA-3, carried on the 13th Shuttle flight (Challenger 6), consisted of four instruments which recorded by photographic and radar images areas of the Earth's surface as a means of measuring the global distribution of tropospheric carbon monoxide, and attempting autonomous classification of scenes. The images obtained were later used in making maps to interpret geological features in support of resource studies. The OSTA-3 system had the following items:
1 Shuttle Imaging Radar (SIR-B): an uprated version of the SIR-A system which flew on the second Shuttle mission in 1981, this experiment encompassed 44 different investigations in archeology, geology, cartography, oceanography and vegetation studies. Radar data were computer-reconstructed from the data memory to produce detailed imagery on photo-like black and white pictures. SIR-B featured a 35×7ft (10.7×2.1m) eight-array antenna and had the capability of acquiring data over virtually any region at any time regardless of weather or sunlight conditions.
2 Large Format Camera: reassigned from an earlier cancelled mission in June 1984, this experiment was a 900lb (408kg) space camera designed to produce 2,400 negatives from 70lb (31.75kg) of film in black and white or in colour. Evolved from instruments developed for the Apollo, Skylab and Viking Mars landers in the 1970s, this camera provided high resolution and a wide field of view for precise stereo photography. Once calibrated, it was used for worldwide exploration of oil and mineral resources, mapping, and monitoring of the Earth's environment. Film format was 9×18in (22.86×45.72cm), with a lens focal length of 12in (30.48cm) and aperture of f/6.0, providing images of 65ft (19.8m) features from an altitude of 185 miles (298km).
3 Measurement of Air Pollution from Satellites (MAPS): designed to provide information on what happens to industrial wastes after they enter the atmosphere by measuring the carbon monoxide in the troposphere on a global scale.
4 Feature Identification and Location Experiment (FILE): designed to develop more efficient remote-sensing equipment, the FILE instrument was operated during sunlight intervals by either ground or crew command. It consisted of two charged-coupled detectors, two TV cameras (one with an optical filter the other with near infrared filter), two Hasselblad 70-mm cameras, two tape recorders and a buffer memory.

Orbital Refueling System (ORS)
Mission: 6 (41-G)
This experiment was designed to evaluate the capabilities of Shuttle-based crew to refuel on-orbiting satellites once their own self-contained fuel supply had been used, thus making possible a resumption or extension of the useful operational life of Earth-orbiting satellites. The ORS was designed by the JSC Engineering Directorate. Two Shuttle 13 astronauts performed EVA during the mission to simulate a hook up of fuel lines from a simulated satellite panel to the fuel supply link of the fuel tank on an MPESS in the payload bay.

Spacelab Mission

Spacelab: Europe's contribution to the programme. Designed by the European Space Agency, who also provided several elements for Spacelab missions.

Spacelab Long Module
Missions: 7 (51-B/Spacelab 3) and 9 (61-A/Spacelab D-1)
Challenger flew two Spacelab missions with the Long Module/MPESS truss configuration. One was the dedicated micro-gravity mission (Spacelab 3) and the second a dedicated West German mission (Spacelab D-1).
1 Spacelab 3: this mission carried out 15 investigations in five areas of discipline, namely materials science, life science, fluid mechanics, atmospheric physics, and astronomy. In addition three experiments were carried in the orbiter mid-deck, and two experiments on the support structure outside the pressurized compartments in the payload bay, and two small satellites were carried in GAS canisters.
2 Spacelab D-1: the first of a series of West German Spacelab missions was a mission which investigated basic and applied microgravity research in fields of materials sciences, life sciences and technology, communications, and navigation. The mission included 17 fluid physics, 31 solidification, 17 biological, 5 medical, and 6 space-time interaction experiments. A small satellite was also deployed from a GAS canister, and a special pallet housed the Materials Experiment Assembly and Navex equipment.

Spacelab Pallet Configuration
Mission: 8 (51-F/Spacelab 2)
In addition to the Long Module Spacelab flights, *Challenger* also completed one flight carrying the pallet-only configuration of Spacelab modules. Controlled from the aft flight deck rather than from the inside of a pressurized payload-bay module, the Spacelab 2 investigations centred on solar and astronomical research, and represented the first flight of the pallet-only concept with the Igloo control module and Instrument Pointing System (IPS). Experiments were mounted on three U-shaped Spacelab pallets, with a further experiment mounted on a special support structure.

Get-Away Special Canisters

The Shuttle offers the opportunity for anyone to fly small experiments of scientific research and development nature. Officially called Small Contained Payloads, the GAS packages are flown on a space-available basis and are available to industry, educational organizations and domestic or foreign governments as well as private citizens for legitimate scientific purposes. Canisters measure 24in (60.96cm) in diameter and 36in (91.44cm) in height, and are usually grouped alongside one payload bay longeron, but can also be located at various other points in the payload bay. They must be completely self-contained, with minimum involvement by the crew or orbiter systems. *Challenger* carried 27 GAS experiments on five missions, and the complete list is as follows:
1 Mission 1 (Shuttle 6, 31-B) three GAS payloads
(i) Artificial Snow Crystal Experiment (Japanese)
(ii) Seed Experiment
(iii) Senic Fast Experiment (containing six USAF Academy engineering experiments)
2 Mission 2 (Shuttle 7, 31-C) seven GAS payloads
(i) A collection of five West German high school student experiments
(ii) Three experiments from Purdue University in space, biological sciences and fluid dynamics.
(iii) Two CalTech experiments (radish seed in zero-g, and oil/water mixing in zero-g)
(iv) Observations of a live ant colony
(v) Nine experiments on soldering and desoldering in space
(vi) One NASA Goddard Space Flight Center (GSFC) experiment to measure Shuttle bay environment on ultraviolet-sensitive film
(vii) One USAF experiment to examine film strips exposed to Shuttle environment, using first opening GAS canister
3 Mission 3 (Shuttle 8, 31-D) four GAS payloads
(i) Cosmic Ray Upset Experiment (G-0346)
(ii) Ultraviolet-Sensitive Photographic Emulsion Experiment (G-0347)
(iii) Japanese Snow Crystal Experiment (G-0475, a repeat of the Shuttle 6 GAS)
(iv) Contamination Monitor Package (G-0348, the first mounted outside a canister lid)
4 Mission 4 (Shuttle 10, 41-B) five GAS payloads
(i) Utah State University and University of Aberdeen, Scotland (G-004, containing two experiments from Utah students and one three-pack experiment from Scottish students)
(ii) AIAA-Utah Section (G-008, containing three experiment packs with two separate experiments and the third a reflight of the first GAS experiment as well as a new investigation)
(iii) Atomic Oxygen Flux Monitor from GSFC (G-349)
(iv) Arc Lamp Research (G-0051)
(v) Cosmic Ray Upset Experiment (G-0347 reflight of the Shuttle 8 GAS)
5 Mission 6 (Shuttle 13, 41-G) eight GAS payloads
(i) Space Processing and Transmitting Computer Voice on Amateur Radio Bands (G-0007)
(ii) Halogen Lamp Experiment (G-0013, HALEX)
(iii) Physics of Solids and Liquids in Zero-g (G-0032)
(iv) Vacuum Deposition (G-0038, Art in Space)
(v) Zero-g Fuel System Test (G-0074)
(vi) Trapped Ions in Space Experiment (G-0306, TRIS)
(vii) Cosmic Ray Upset Experiment (G-0469, CRUX III)
(viii) Physics and Materials Processing (G-0518)

Student Experiments

The Shuttle programme offers active participation to students in a way similar to the GAS programme: small experiments can be included in mission payloads, even when they at times need the attention of the flight crew depending on their other activities. The system was designed to generate student interest in the programme, and *Challenger* flew six Shuttle Student Involvement Program (SSIP) experiments on four missions:
1 Mission 3 (Shuttle 8, 31-D) one experiment
(i) Biofeedback Medicated Behavioral Training In Physiologic Self Regulator:
Application in Near Zero-g Environment (using rats in the Animal Enclosure Module)
2 Mission 4 (Shuttle 10, 41-B) one experiment
(i) Effects of Weightlessness on the Development of Arthritis (using six rats in the AEM)
3 Mission 5 (Shuttle 11, 41-C) one experiment
(i) Determine characteristics of Hive Construction of Honey Bees in Zero-g
4 Mission 10 (Shuttle 25, 51-L) three experiments
(i) Utilizing a Semi-Permeable Membrane to Direct Crystal Growth
(ii) Effects of Weightlessness on Grain Formation and Strength In Metals
(iii) Chicken Embryo Development In Space
(These three experiments were lost in the explosion of *Challenger* during the launch phase.)

Mid-deck Experiments

In addition to the range of payloads and experiments covered above, the mid-deck area of *Challenger* (as well as areas of the flight deck) provided locations for locker-located or astronaut-participant experiments.
1 Continuous-Flow Electrophoresis System (Shuttles 6, 7 and 8; 31-B, 31-C and 31-D)
Developed by McDonnell Douglas, this equipment was designed to verify the possibility of separating biological materials to purity levels four times higher than those possible on Earth. Designed to validate the concept of space-produced drugs, the system was flown on the mid-deck of *Challenger* during the first three flights of the orbiter as part of the NASA-McDonnell test programme to evaluate the operation of the system in the orbiter before flying a McDonnell Douglas engineer on a Shuttle flight to operate the system in a test production programme in 1984. The unit weighed 550lb (249kg) and was 6ft (1.83m) high.
2 Mono-disperse Latex Reactor (Shuttles 6 and 10, 31-B and 41-B)
A materials-processing experiment to study kinetics involved with the production of uniformly formed (mono-disperse) latex beads in low gravity. The experiment consisted of four 12in (30.48cm) tall reactors each containing a chemical forming latex recipe.
3 Night-time/Daytime Optical Survey of Thunderstorm Lightning (Shuttle 6, 31-B)
Using a 16-mm data-acquisition camera, a two-channel cassette tape recorder and a photo-optical detector mounted on the camera, the crew conducted a lightning survey from the crew compartment windows.
4 Animal Enclosure Module (Shuttles 8 and 17, 31-D and 51-B)
Used to house six rats as part of a preliminary evaluation of the self-contained system, the AEM was later flown on Shuttle 17 (51-B), the Spacelab 3/Challenger 7 mission. The AEM was designed to provide safe housing for research animals and provide a healthy environment for the occupants and minimum interruption to the astronaut crew.
5 Acoustic Containerless Experiment System (Shuttle 10, 41-B)
This was a materials-processing furnace experiment enclosed in two airtight canisters in the mid-deck. Activated 23 hours into the mission, it ran for a programmed 2 hours.
6 Isoelectric Focusing Experiment (Shuttle 10, 41-B)
Activated with ACES, this was another self-contained experiment stowed in a mid-deck locker and was designed to evaluate the effect of electro-osmosis on an array of eight columns of electrolyte solutions as DC power was applied and pH levels increased.
7 Canadian Experiments (Shuttle 13, 41-G)
Canada's first astronaut, Marc Garneau, conducted 10 experiments for NDC of Canada during the Shuttle 13 mission under space technology, space science and life science categories.
(i) NRC Space Vision System (tests with the RMS TV system)
(ii) Advanced Composite Materials Exposure Samples (attached to exterior of RMS; Garneau had no personal contact with this experiment)
(iii) Measurements Using a Sunphotometer (measurements of Solar radiation)
(iv) Atmospheric Emission and Shuttle Glow Measurements (using very high-resolution optical filters and an image intensifier, photos were obtained to identify reactions which cause these emissions)
(v) Space Adaptation Syndrome Experiment Studies (a set of experiments to isolate and measure several key adaptation processes which occur during the first few days in space: located in the mid-deck these examined vestibulo-ocular reflex, sensory functions in limbs, proprioceptive illusions, awareness of external objects, space motion sickness and taste in space)
8 Radiation Monitoring Equipment (Shuttles 13 and 25, 41-G and 51-L)
Handheld (Gamma and Electron Dosimeter) and pocket (Neutron and Proton Dosimeter) radiation meters were used to provide measurements of gamma radiation on individual crew members in the orbiter cabin. Used several times on the Shuttle 13 flight, the monitors were lost on the 25th mission in the explosion of *Challenger* during launch.
9 Thermoluminescent Dosimeter (Shuttle 13, 41-G)
A small portable dosimetry system developed in Hungary, the TLD was used to record cosmic radiation doses during a mission for comparison with other data-collection devices.
10 Protein Crystal Growth Experiment (Shuttle 19, 51-F)
Two crystal growth units were stowed in a mid-deck locker to examine the effects of low gravity to produce near perfect crystals, which grow many times larger than on Earth.
11 Shuttle Amateur Radio Experiment (Shuttle 19, 51-F)
MS England and Bartoe, both 'ham' radio operators, conducted several contacts with 'ham' radio enthusiasts on Earth during the Spacelab 2 mission, in a demonstration of the enthusiasm and participation of Shuttle followers world wide.
12 Plant Carry-On Container (Shuttle 19, 51-F)
Designed to study gravitropism (the development of a diet and delivery system which can provide purified diets in a noncontaminating process) this experiment by a group of selected students was stowed in a mid-deck locker of *Challenger*, and the students planning space science as a career evaluated pre- and post-flight data to determine how the physiology of the vestibular system (visual and orientation) and motion cope with zero g.
13 Teacher in Space Project (Shuttle 25, 51-L)
In a programme initiated by President Reagan, the first private citizen to fly in space aboard the Shuttle was to have been US teacher Christa McAuliffe, tragically killed in her attempt to reach orbit in January 1986. Had the mission reached orbit safely McAuliffe was to have conducted a programme of inflight lessons which were to be beamed to Earth or shown after the flight to educational institutes around the USA in order to promote the programme and generate interest in the younger community for the space programme.
14 Comet Halley Active Monitoring Program (Shuttle 25, 51-F)
Using a hand-held 35-mm camera and a windowscreen, a Shuttle 25 crewmember was to take photographic images and spectra images of Comet Halley during the week-long mission as part of the International Halley Watch programme. The objectives of CHAMP were the investigation of the dynamical/morphological behaviour as well as the chemical structure of the comet.
15 Phase Partitioning Experiment (Shuttle 25, 51-F)
Another payload package lost on Shuttle 25 was this small inexpensive experiment which established a two-phase system of separating biomedical materials such as cells and proteins. By adding polymers to a water solution it was expected that higher resolution separated cells would be obtained than those previously obtained on Earth.
16 Fluid Dynamics In Space (Shuttle 25, 51-F)
Challenger, Mission 10 astronaut Greg Jarvis was to have performed experiments on fluid dynamics in space in an attempt to understand how fluids act in zero g, with a view to refining the design of current fluid transfer systems in spacecraft (particularly Hughes satellites) to provide more efficient and less costly spacecraft. He was to perform experiments with fluid motions in enclosed tanks and fluid motion interactions with spacecraft motions.
17 Space Adaptation Syndrome Studies (Shuttle 6, 7, 8, 13, 17, 22, 31B, 31C, 31D, 41G, 51B, 61A)
Conducted on nearly all flights, experiments into human reactions to zero-g. Motion sickness was also investigated on these flights, especially by MS Thagard and Thornton.

Other Experiments

1 IMAX Camera (Shuttles 10, 11 and 13; 41-B, 41-C and 41-G)
Carried inside the mid-deck, the IMAX camera project was a joint NASA, National Air and Space Museum, IMAX Systems Group, and Lockheed agreement to produce a colour motion picture of shuttle flight operations from launch to landing on an IMAX film screen, which replays on a screen nine times larger than a conventional screen. Called 'THE DREAM IS ALIVE', the film reproduces a very vivid and spectacular account of a Shuttle flight from excerpts of several missions. The watcher does not see the IMAX film so much as 'fly' it!
2 CINEMA 360 (Shuttles 10 and 11, 41-B and 41-C)
Using film taken both inside and outside the orbiter, a second Shuttle film was taken especially for planetarium viewing.
3 Orbiter Experiments Program (Shuttle 7, 31-C)
As part of an ongoing NASA research and data-gathering programme to provide adequate flight data and research reserves for future SSTS operations and systems, *Challenger* continued the OEP programme begun by *Columbia*.
(i) Aerodynamic Coefficient Identification Package to provide aerodynamic data during launch, re-entry and landing (data on Shuttle aerodynamic performance and aerothermal/structural dynamic patterns).
(ii) High-Resolution Accelerometer Package to record changes in vehicle acceleration caused by aerodynamic forces in the high-altitude portions of the atmosphere during launch and re-entry.
4 Development Flight Instrumentation pallet (Shuttle 8, 31-D)
Though no DFI was carried during the Challenger 3 mission, the pallet used to support such instrumentation on *Columbia*'s first flights was flown by *Challenger* to carry the postal cover canisters and two small experiments.
5 Evaluation of Oxygen Inter-reaction with Materials (DSO 0301)
6 High-Capacity Heat Pipe Demonstration (DSO 0101)

Commemorative Payloads

1 Shuttle 8 (31-D): 260,000 US Postal Service philatelic covers were carried with a new stamp and the Shuttle 8 emblem.
2 Shuttle 25 (51-L): Two sets of three Liberty coins (a $5 gold coin, a $1 silver coin and a 50c coin) were aboard *Challenger* during its ill-fated 10th launch.

Flight Data

CHALLENGER'S ASTRONAUTS (IN ORDER OF EXPERIENCE)

Position	Astronaut	Total Flights	Mission Sequence	Separate Mission Totals Day:Hr:Mn:Sec	Orbits	Accumulated Mission Totals Day:Hr:Mn:Sec	Orbits
1	Crippen	3	Sh07/Ch02	06:02:23:59	98		
			Sh11/Ch05	06:23:40:07	107		
			Sh13/Ch06	08:05:23:33	133	21:07:27:39	338
2	Ride	2	Sh07/Ch02	06:02:23:59	98		
			Sh13/Ch06	08:05:23:33	133	14:07:47:32	231
3	Thagard	2	Sh07/Ch02	06:02:23:59	98		
			Sh17/Ch07	07:00:08:46	109	13:02:32:45	207
4	Bluford	2	Sh08/Ch03	06:01:08:43	97		
			Sh22/Ch09	07:00:44:51	112	13:01:53:34	209
5	Thornton	2	Sh08/Ch03	06:01:08:43	97		
			Sh17/Ch07	07:00:08:50	109	13:01:17:33	206
6	Musgrave	2	Sh06/Ch01	05:00:23:42	81		
			Sh19/Ch08	07:22:45:26	126	12:23:07:08	207
7	McBride	1	Sh13/Ch06	08:05:23:33	133	08:05:23:33	133
	Sullivan						
	Leestma						
	Garneau						
	Scully-Power						
12	McNair	2	Sh10/Ch04	07:23:15:55	127		
			Sh25/Ch10	00:00:01:13	0	07:23:17:08	127
13	Brand	1	Sh10/Ch04	07:23:15:55	127	07:23:15:55	127
	Gibson						
	Stewart						
	McCandless						
17	Fullerton	1	Sh19/Ch08	07:22:45:26	126	07:22:45:26	126
	Bridges						
	Henize						
	England						
	Acton						
	Bartoe						
23	Hartsfield	1	Sh22/Ch09	07:00:44:51	112	07:00:44:51	112
	Nagel						
	Dunbar						
	Buchli						
	Messershmid						
	Furrer						
	Ockels						
30	Overmyer	1	Sh17/Ch07	07:00:08:46	109	07:00:08:46	109
	Gregory						
	Lind						
	Wang						
	Van Den Berg						
35	Scobee	2	Sh11/Ch05	06:23:40:07	107		
			Sh25/Ch10	00:00:01:13	0	06:23:41:20	107
36	Hart	1	Sh11/Ch05	06:23:40:07	107	06:23:40:07	107
	Nelson						
	Van Hoften						
39	Hauck	1	Sh07/Ch02	06:02:23:59	98	06:02:23:59	98
	Fabian						
41	Truly	1	Sh08/Ch03	06:01:08:43	97	06:01:08:43	97
	Brandenstein						
	Gardner						
44	Weitz	1	Sh06/Ch01	05:00:23:42	81	05:00:23:42	81
	Bobko						
	Peterson						
47	Smith	1	Sh25/Ch10	00:00:01:13	0	00:00:01:13	0
	Resnik						
	Onizuka						
	McAuliffe						
	Jarvis						

CHALLENGER'S ASTRONAUTS (IN ORDER OF FIRST FLIGHT)

Position	Astronaut	Position	Astronaut	Position	Astronaut
1	Weitz, P.J.	18	McCandless, B.	35	Bridges, Jr, R.D.
2	Bobko, K.J.	19	McNair, R.E.	36	Henize, K.G.
3	Musgrave, F.S.	20	Scobee, F.R.	37	England, A.W.
4	Peterson, D.H.	21	Hart, T.J.	38	Acton, L.W.
5	Crippen, R.L.	22	Nelson, G.D.	39	Bartoe, J.D.
6	Hauck, F.H.	23	Van Hoften, J.D.A.	40	Hartsfield, Jr, H.W.
7	Fabian, J.M.	24	McBride, J.A.	41	Nagel, S.R.
8	Ride, S.K.	25	Sullivan, K.D.	42	Dunbar, B.J.
9	Thagard, N.E.	26	Leestma, D.C.	43	Buchli, J.F.
10	Truly, R.H.	27	Garneau, M.	44	Messerschmid, E.
11	Brandenstein, D.C.	28	Scully-Power, P.D.	45	Furrer, R.
12	Gardner, D.A.	29	Overmyer, R.F.	46	Ockels, W.J.
13	Bluford, Jr, G.S.	30	Gregory, F.D.	47	Smith, M.J.
14	Thornton, W.E.	31	Lind, D.L.	48	Resnik, J.A.
15	Brand, V.D.	32	Wang, T.G.	49	Onizuka, E.S.
16	Gibson, R.L.	33	Van Den Berg, L.	50	McAuliffe, S.C.
17	Stewart, R.L.	34	Fullerton, C.G.	51	Jarvis, G.B.

CHALLENGER'S ASTRONAUTS (IN ORDER OF SECOND FLIGHT)

Position	Astronaut	Position	Astronaut	Position	Astronaut
1	Crippen, R.L.	4	Thornton, W.E.	7	Scobee, F.R.
2	Ride, S.K.	5	Musgrave, F.S.	8	McNair, R.E.
3	Thagard, N.E.	6	Bluford, Jr, G.S.		

CHALLENGER'S ASTRONAUTS (IN ORDER OF THIRD FLIGHT)

Position	Astronaut
1	Crippen, R.L.

CHALLENGER EVAs (IN ORDER OF FIRST EVA PERIOD)

Mission Sequence	Astronaut	Designation of Astronaut	EVA No.	Date of EVA	Duration Hr:Min	MMU Use	Comments
Sh06/Ch01	Musgrave	MS-1/EV-1	1	07/04/83	04:17	No	First Shuttle EVA
	Peterson	MS-2/EV-2	1	07/04/83	04:17	No	
Sh10/Ch04	McCandless	MS-3/EV-1	1	07/02/84	05:55	Yes	1st use of MMU
	Stewart	MS-2/EV-2	1	07/02/84	05:55	Yes	units
	McCandless	MS-3/EV-1	2	09/02/84	06:17	Yes	2nd use of MMU
	Stewart	MS-2/EV-2	2	09/02/84	06:17	Yes	units
Sh11/Ch05	Nelson	MS-3/EV-1	1	08/04/84	02:57	Yes	Attempted capture
	Van Hoften	MS-2/EV-2	1	08/04/84	02:57	No	of Solar Max
	Nelson	MS-3/EV-1	2	11/04/84	06:16	No	Repair of Solar
	Van Hoften	MS-2/EV-2	2	11/04/84	06:16	Yes	Max
Sh13/Ch06	Leestma	MS-3/EV-1	1	11/10/84	03:27	No	Demonstration of
	Sullivan	MS-2/EV-2	1	11/10/84	03:27	No	orbital refuelling and 1st US female EVA

Total: 3 missions, 8 Astronauts, and 6 EVA periods: 63:16

Note: Shuttle EVAs are measured from the time Extravehicular Mobility Unit (EMU) power is switched from orbiter power to internal power, and completed once a switch back to orbiter power has been achieved inside the airlock. This of course occurs before and after hatch opening and/or astronaut egress and ingress, these times not being recorded.

CHALLENGER'S ASTRONAUTS (TOTAL PERSON HOURS BY MISSION)

Flight Sequence	Day:Hr:Mn:Sec for Mission	Crew Size	Person Accumulated Time Day:Hr:Mn:Sec	Mission Orbits	Person Accumulated Orbits
Sh06/Ch01	05:00:23:42	4	20:01:34:48	81	324
Sh07/Ch02	06:02:23:59	5	30:11:59:55	98	490
Sh08/Ch03	06:01:08:43	5	30:05:43:35	97	485
Sh10/Ch04	07:23:15:55	5	31:21:03:40	127	635
Sh11/Ch05	06:23:40:07	5	34:22:20:35	107	535
Sh13/Ch06	08:05:23:33	7	57:13:44:51	133	931
Sh17/Ch07	07:00:08:46	7	49:01:01:22	109	763
Sh19/Ch08	07:22:45:26	7	55:16:18:02	126	882
Sh22/Ch09	07:00:44:51	8	56:05:58:48	112	896
Sh25/Ch10	00:00:01:13	7	00:00:08:31	0	0
10 Missions	62:07:56:15	60 crew	366:03:54:07	990	5941

CHALLENGER'S ASTRONAUTS: EVA EXPERIENCE (IN ORDER OF EXPERIENCE)

Position	Astronaut	EVA Total	Flight Total	Hrs:Min	Order of 1st Challenger EVA	Use of MMU
1	McCandless	2	1	12:12	3	Yes
	Stewart	2	1	12:12	4	Yes
3	Nelson	2	1	11:42	5	Yes
	Van Hoften	2	1	11:42	6	Yes
5	Musgrave	1	1	4:17	1	No
	Peterson	1	1	4:17	2	No
7	Leestma	1	1	3:27	7	No
	Sullivan	1	1	3:27	8	No

Total 8 Astronauts, 12 EVAs and 8 flights: 63:16

CHALLENGER MMU OPERATIONS (IN ORDER OF FIRST MMU FLIGHT)

MMU Flight	Date of MMU Flight	Mission Sequence	EVA No.	Astronaut	MMU Unit	MMU Unit Flight No.	Duration Hr:Min
01	07/02/84	Sh10/Ch04	1	McCandless	3	3/01	01:22
02	07/02/84	Sh10/Ch04	1	Stewart	3	3/02	01:09
03	09/02/84	Sh10/Ch04	2	McCandless	2	2/01	00:47
04	09/02/84	Sh10/Ch04	2	Stewart	2	2/02	00:44
05	09/02/84	Sh10/Ch04	2	McCandless	3	3/03	01:08
Subtotal for Mission Sh10/Ch04							05:10
06	08/04/84	Sh11/Ch05	1	Nelson	2	2/03	00:42
07	11/04/84	Sh11/Ch05	2	Van Hoften	3	3/04	00:28
Subtotal for Mission Sh11/Ch05							01:10

Overall Flight time for MMUs on *Challenger* missions: 06:20

CHALLENGER ASTRONAUT EVA AND RMS TRAINED ASSIGNMENTS

Mission Sequence	EV-1 Astronaut	EV-2 Astronaut	RMS Operator	EVA Performed
Sh06/Ch01	Musgrave (MS-1)	Peterson (MS-2)	–	Yes
Sh07/Ch02	Fabian (MS-1)	Thagard (MS-3)	Ride (MS-2)/Fabian	No
Sh08/Ch03	Truly (Commander)	Gardner (MS-1)	Truly/Gardner	No
Sh10/Ch04	McCandless (MS-3)	Stewart (MS-1)	McNair (MS-3)	Yes
Sh11/Ch05	Nelson (MS-2)	Van Hoften (MS-3)	Hart (MS-1)	Yes
Sh13/Ch06	Leestma (MS-3)	Sullivan (MS-2)	Ride (MS-1)	Yes
Sh17/Ch07	Gregory (Pilot)	Thagard (MS-3)	–	No
Sh19/Ch08	Musgrave (MS-1)	England (MS-3)	Henize (MS-2)/England	No
Sh22/Ch09	Nagel (Pilot)	Buchli (MS-2)	Hartsfield/Dunbar (MS-1)	No
Sh25/Ch10	Onizuka (MS-2)	McNair (MS-3)	Resnik (MS-1)/McNair	No

Note: Majority of EVA assignments were fulfilled by Mission Specialist astronauts, except EV-1 positions on Sh08/Ch03 and Sh17/Ch07 missions, where the mission commander and pilot filled these assignments respectively, and the Sh22/Ch09 EV-1 position again filled by the mission pilot. More than one astronaut on each crew was usually a trained RMS operator. Astronauts listed under this heading are in order of primary RMS operator role. RMS was not carried on the first or seventh *Challenger* missions.

CHALLENGER RMS FLIGHT SUMMARIES

Flight	Designation	Arm	Payload(s)	Remarks
Challenger 2	(31-C)	DDT&E/201	SPAS-01	Payload deployment and retrieval performance
Challenger 3	(31-D)	DDT&E/201	PFTA	Medium loaded arm tests
Challenger 4	(41-B)	DDT&E/201	MFR	Manoeuvring astronaut on MFR
Challenger 5	(41-C)	FOP 2/302	LDEF; SMM; MFR	Deployment & release of LDEF; retrieval and deployment of SMM work platform for EVA astronauts
Challenger 6	(41-G)	FOP 2/302	ERBS	Deployment & release of ERBS; arm used to latch SIR-A antenna
Challenger 8	(51-F)	FOP 2/302	PDP	Deploy, release and retrieve PDP payload
Challenger 9	(61-A)	FOP 2/302	–	Used to monitor water dumps
Challenger 10	(51-L)	FOP 2/302	Spartan-Halley	Was to have been used to deploy, release and retrieve Spartan payload

Delivery dates
201: Developmental test and engineering model delivered April 20, 1981
302: Second operational model delivered December 14, 1983
(Information: courtesy Gail Macnaughton, PR Coordinator, RMS Division, Spar Aerospace Ltd)

CHALLENGER ENGINE BURN TIMES (Launch Profile Times Only Not Including Launch Aborts, FRFs or Test Firings)

Launch date	Mission designation	Position No. 1	Duration (seconds)	Position No. 2	Duration (seconds)	Position No. 3	Duration (seconds)
04.04.83	Sh06 (31-B)/Chal 01	2017	505.8	2015	505.9	2012	506.0
06.18.83	Sh07 (31-C)/Chal 02	2017	506.5	2015	506.6	2012	506.7
08.30.83	Sh08 (31-D)/Chal 03	2017	528.0	2015	528.1	2012	528.2
02.03.84	Sh10 (41-B)/Chal 04	2109	527.8	2015	527.9	2012	528.0
04.06.84	Sh11 (41-C)/Chal 05	2109	517.1	2020	517.2	2012	517.4
10.05.84	Sh13 (41-G)/Chal 06	2023	536.7	2020	536.8	2021	536.9
04.29.85	Sh17 (51-B)/Chal 07	2023	521.347	2020	521.465	2021	521.567
07.29.85	Sh19 (51-F)/Chal 08	2023	349.6	2020	587.73	2021	578.849
10.30.85	Sh22 (61-A)/Chal 09	2023	521.325	2020	521.465	2021	521.586
01.28.86	Sh25 (51-L)/Chal 10	2023	79.4	2020	79.56	2021	79.62
Total			4593.53		4832.72		4833.822

(Information: courtesy Joyce Lincoln, Rocketdyne)

CHALLENGER EXTERNAL TANKS

OV-099 Mission	STS Mission Designation	ET Serial Number	Production Start	(DD-250) Completed	Arrived at Launch Site	Launch Date
One	STS 06 (31-B)	ET-8 (LWT-01)	11.17.80	09.08.82	09.15.82	04.04.82
Two	STS 07 (31-C)	ET-6 (HWT-06)	05.25.79	07.26.82	08.02.82	06.18.83
Three	STS 08 (31-D)	ET-9 (LWT-02)	04.23.81	01.12.83	01.17.83	08.30.83
Four	STS 10 (41-B)	ET-10 (LWT-03)	07.30.81	03.01.83	03.07.83	02.03.84
Five	STS 11 (41-C)	ET-12 (LWT-05)	02.08.82	07.22.83	08.01.83	04.06.84
Six	STS 13 (41-G)	ET-15 (LWT-08)	09.01.82	12.15.83	01.11.84	10.05.84
Seven	STS 17 (51-B)	ET-17 (LWT-10)	11.10.82	03.16.84	04.10.84	04.29.85
Eight	STS 19 (51-F)	ET-19 (LWT-12)	02.08.83	05.24.84	09.07.84	07.29.85
Nine	STS 22 (61-A)	ET-24 (LWT-17)	07.11.83	11.16.84	05.08.85	10.30.85
Ten	STS 25 (51-L)	ET-26 (LWT-19)	10.10.83	03.15.85	08.26.85	01.28.86

(Information: courtesy Murray Forsman, Martin Marietta)
Note: *Challenger* 2 (Shuttle 7) flew the last of the Heavy-Weight Tanks (HWT) and the other nine *Challenger* missions all flew Light-Weight Tanks (LWT).
(DD-250): Final Test and Checkouts Program before shipment to KSC by ocean barge.

CHALLENGER ENGINE POSITIONS & SERIAL NUMBERS

Mission	No. 1	No. 2	No. 3	Date
Flight Readiness Firing (02)	2011	2015	2012	December 18, 1982
FRF (03)	2011	2015	2012	January 25, 1983
Ch 01 /Shuttle 6 (31-B)	2017	2015	2012	April 4, 1983
Ch 02 /Shuttle 7 (31-C)	2017	2015	2012	June 18, 1983
Ch 03 /Shuttle 8 (31-D)	2017	2015	2012	August 30, 1983
Ch 04 /Shuttle 10 (41-B)	2109	2015	2012	February 3, 1984
Ch 05 /Shuttle 11 (41-C)	2109	2020	2012	April 6, 1984
Ch 06 /Shuttle 13 (41-G)	2023	2020	2021	October 5, 1984
Ch 07 /Shuttle 17 (51-B)	2023	2020	2021	April 29, 1985
Ch 08 /Shuttle 19 (51-F) Abort	2023	2020	2021	July 12, 1985
Launch	2023	2020	2021	July 29, 1985
Ch 09 /Shuttle 22 (61-A)	2023	2020	2021	October 30, 1985
Ch 10 /Shuttle 25 (51-L)	2023	2020	2021	January 28, 1986

Engine positions

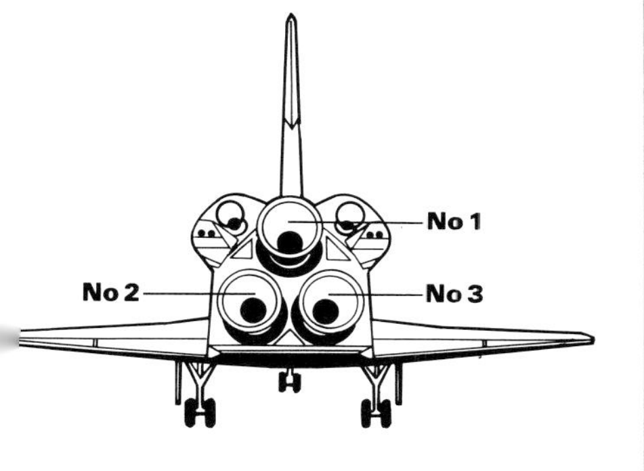

CHALLENGER SRB MOTOR COMPONENTS

SRB	Mission	FWD	CYL	CYL	CYL	CYL	CYL	CYL	ATT	STF	STF	AFT
06-A	Ch01/31-B	013	046	061	L03	L04	L05	L06	L01	L01	L02	005
		New	1-A	1-A	New	New	New	New	New	New	New	G-3
06-B		014	075	076	L07	L08	L09	L10	L02	L03	L04	L14
		New	1-B	1-B	New	New	New	New	New	New	New	New
07-A	Ch02/31-C	016	041	058	L17	L18	L19	L20	L04	L07	L08	016
		New	1-B	1-A	New	New	New	New	New	New	New	New
07-B		017	060	062	L21	L22	L23	L25	L05	L09	L10	017
		New	1-A	1-A	New	New	New	New	New	New	New	New
08-A	Ch03/31-D	019	066	067	L30	L31	L32	L33	L07	L13	L14	L19
		New	1-B	1-A	New	New	New	New	New	New	New	New
08-B		020	068	069	L34	L35	L36	L37	L08	L15	L16	020
		New	1-B	1-B	New	New	New	New	New	New	New	New
10-A	Ch04/41-B	009	023	031	L11	L51	L15	L42	012	011	012	009
		1-B	5-B	3-B	D-5	New	D-5	New	1-B	3-A	3-A	1-A
10-B		006	037	057	L38	L39	L40	L41	007	014	015	008
		1-A	3-A	3-B	New	New	New	New	G-3	3-B	3-B	2-A
11-A	Ch05/41-C	002	043	016	L43	L16	L44	L45	003	020	022	004
		3-A	3-A	D-5	New	D-5	New	New	5-A	1-B	1-B	3-A
11-B		012	045	013	L46	L47	L48	L49	008	026	027	011
		5-B	3-A	2-B	New	New	New	New	2-B	2-A	2-B	2-B
13-A	Ch06/41-G	024	056	024	L59	L60	L61	L62	L11	L19	L20	015
		New	3-B	5-B	New	New	New	New	New	New	New	D-5
13-B		022	022	035	L55	L64	L65	L66	L12	L21	L22	007
		New	5-A	5-B	New	New	New	New	New	New	New	5-B
17-A	Ch07/51-B	016	041	068	L17	L18	L19	L20	L04	L14	L26	005
		7-A	7-A	8-B	7-A	7-A	7-A	7-A	7-A	8-A	New	6-A
17-B		011	036	066	L21	L22	L37	L31	L02	L15	L16	017
		9-B	QM4	8-A	7-B	7-B	8-B	8-A	6-B	8-B	8-B	7-B
19-A	Ch08/51-F	010	055	054	L85	L90	L83	L84	011	016	011	010
		9-A	9-A	9-A	New	New	New	New	9-B	9-B	10A	9-A
19-B		029	072	077	L91	L92	L82	L80	007	024	013	029
		New	9-B	9-B	New	New	New	New	10B	9-A	9-B	New
22-A	Ch09/61-A	024	056	065	L97	L98	L88	L94	L20	L35	L36	033
		13A	13A	9-A	New	New	New	New	New	New	New	New
22-B		022	022	078	L100	L101	L95	L96	L23	L19	L37	007
		13B	13B	9-B	New	New	New	New	New	13A	New	13B
25-A	Ch10/51-L	035	045	083	L41	L16	L75	L76	L11	L25	L07	027
		New	11B	15B	10B	11A	15A	15A	13A	15A	15B	15B
25-B		026	082	085	L28	L106	L59	L60	L06	L02	L01	L26
		15A	15A	15A	15B	New	13A	13A	15A	15B	15A	15A

Notes: Shuttle missions listed as Shuttle 1 = 01, Shuttle 2 = 02 etc; SRB sets match accordingly. Set A = Left Hand Booster Set; Set B = Right Hand Booster Set.
FWD = Forward Assembly; CYL = Cylindrical Segment; ATT = Attachment; STF = Stiffener; AFT = Aft Segment Assembly; G = Ground Test; D = Development Motor; QM = Qualification Motor. L before number indicates Light construction; no number indicates Standard construction.
Shuttle *Challenger* Missions 1, 2 and 3, 6, 7, 9, 10 used lightweight SRBs; Missions 4, 5, 8 Middleweight SRBs.
Only previous use is listed; several components were used two, three or four times, though NOT in same position each time, segments are interchangeable.
(Information: courtesy Rocky Raab, Manager Public Relations, Morton Thiokol Inc. Wasatch Div.)

CHALLENGER TURNAROUND TIMESCALE

Arrive KSC	Days in OPF	Days in VAB	Days on Pad	Launch Date	Mission Days	Landing Date
July 5, 1982	141	7	126	April 4, 1983	5	April 9, 1982
April 16, 1983	34	5	28	June 18, 1983	6	June 24, 1982
June 29, 1983	26	7	28	August 30, 1983	6	September 5, 1983
September 9, 1983	67	6	22	February 3, 1984	8	February 11, 1984
February 11, 1984	32	4	19	April 6, 1984	7	April 13, 1984
April 18, 1984	69	5	23	October 5, 1984	8	October 13, 1984
October 13, 1984	129	5	15	Rolled back to VAB March 4, 1985 for remanifest of payloads from 51-E to 51-B; returned OPF March 7, 1985		
	33	5	15	April 29, 1985	7	May 6, 1985
May 11, 1984	43	5	14	(to abort July 12 on pad)		
			17	July 29, 1985	8	August 6, 1984
	61	4	15	October 30, 1985	7	November 6, 1985
	61	4	15	October 30, 1985	7	November 6, 1985
	35	6	37	January 28, 1985	(vehicle exploded 73 seconds after launch)	

Note: Times indicate only mission processing durations and not storage times in OPF/VAB at the Cape.
Construction at Palmdale lasted from February 1975 to June 1982, and rollout was on June 30 with transport to KSC in stages July 1-5, 1982.
Salvage of *Challenger* debris was carried out between January 28 and late July 1986.

CHALLENGER MISSION SUMMARY: 1983-1986

OV-099 Mission	Shuttle Flight	Launch Sequence	Launch Date	Crew Size	Duration (Hrs:Min:Sec)	Complete Orbits	Landing Orbit	Launch Complex	Landing Site
One	Six	31-B	04 Apr 83	4	120:23:42	80	81	KSC 39A	EAFB R.22
Two	Seven	31-C	18 Jun 83	5	146:23:59	97	98	KSC 39A	EAFB R.23
Three	Eight	31-D	30 Aug 83	5	145:08:43	96	97	KSC 39A	EAFB R.22
Four	Ten	41-B	03 Feb 84	5	191:15:55	127	127	KSC 39A	KSC SLF R.15
Five	Eleven	41-C	06 Apr 84	5	167:40:07	106	107	KSC 39A	EAFB R.17
Six	Thirteen	41-G	05 Oct 84	7	197:23:33	133	133	KSC 39A	KSC SLF R.33
Seven	Seventeen	51-B	29 Apr 85	7	168:08:46	108	109	KSC 39A	EAFB R.17
Eight	Nineteen	51-F	29 July 85	7	190:45:26	125	126	KSC 39A	EAFB R.23
Nine	Twenty-two	61-A	26 Nov 85	8	168:44:51	111	112	KSC 39A	EAFB R.17
Ten	Twenty-five	51-L	28 Jan 85	7	000:01:13	000	–	KSC 39B	–
Totals	Ten Missions			60	1,495:56:15	983			

Note: Total for Orbits indicates complete orbits only. Where *Challenger* landed at Edwards AFB runways (EAFB) each *Astronaut* log has been awarded an extra orbit for completeness, i.e. for Shuttle 6 they completed 80 orbits but landed during the 81st, so 81 orbits has been credited to those astronauts. For Kennedy Space Center Shuttle Landing Facility runway landings (KSC SLF) each mission landed where it started its first orbit so the crew is only credited with full orbits (i.e. Shuttle 13).

Glossary and abbreviations

Abort To end the mission suddenly, short of its planned duration. Usually as a result of an emergency situation or major malfunction.
AOA Abort-Once-Around. A launch abort mode used if one or two SSMEs fail after SRB separation but before a capability to reach a safe orbit is reached. All SSMEs and the twin OMS engines remaining, continue to burn until ET supplies are depleted and the tank jettisoned. The OMS engines are fired to attain the speed and altitude needed to reach one of the AOA landing sites such as White Sands in New Mexico. Following a further OMS burn to sustain the sub-orbital flight, entry is made as a normal mission.
ATO Abort-To-Orbit. A launch abort mode used if one or more SSMEs fail late in the launch phase. A safe orbit is attained, however, by firing the remaining engines for longer than usual and burning the OMS engines to compensate for the lost main engine thrust.
AFRSI Advanced Flexible Reusable Surface Insulation. A form of thermal protection material.
ASE Airborne Support Equipment. Payload support hardware.
AFB Air Force Base.
AFS Air Force Station.
AL Air Lock. Used in EVA for movement between the habitable, pressurized parts of the Shuttle and open space.
AHF Animal Holding Facility. Scientific container for holding research animals, usually rats and primates.
ALT Approach and Landing Tests. A series of airborne approach and landing tests flown in 1977 using the *Enterprise* orbiter launched from the back of the Shuttle Carrier Aircraft.
AMU Astronaut Maneuvering Unit. An early form of EVA back-pack developed for Gemini flights in 1966 but never fully used.
Atlantis OV-104, the fifth Orbital vehicle and the fourth operational flight vehicle. It made its maiden flight in October 1985.
APU Auxiliary Power Unit.
Blackout A period of re-entry during which radio communications between the flight crew and ground control are impossible due to an ionized sheath around the vehicle.
CAPCOM Capsule Communicator. The astronaut who usually talks to the crew on orbit, providing a vocal link between the flight crew and ground control.
CRT Cathode Ray Tube.
CITE Cargo Integration Test Equipment.
CDT Central Daylight Time GMT–5 hours.
CST Central Standard Time GMT–6 hours.
Challenger OV-099. Originally a Structural Test Article, this vehicle was brought to flight standard and became the third orbiter delivered and in 1983, the second to make an orbital mission.
Columbia The second orbital vehicle (OV-102) delivered, and the first to complete an orbital flight, in 1981.
CDR Commander. Most senior astronaut on the flight crew.
Contingency A backup or alternative method to achieve similar results.
CFES Continuous Flow Electrophoresis System. Developed by McDonnell Douglas, this experiment was designed to investigate the possibility of developing space-based production of drugs and medicines.
CT Crawler Transporter. A giant tracked vehicle used to transport the Shuttle stack to the launch pad at the Kennedy Space Center.
DYNA-SOAR Dynamic Soaring. Officially called X-20, this was a USAF programme to develop a manned orbital vehicle, and to investigate techniques for runway landings.
DoD Department of Defense.
DTOs Detailed Test Objectives. A series of mission investigations or goals.
Discovery The third orbital vehicle (OV-103), and the fourth of the fleet. Maiden flight, August 1984.
ERBE Earth Radiation Budget Satellite.
EDT Eastern Daylight Time GMT–4 hours.
EST Eastern Standard Time GMT–5 hours.
Enterprise OV-101 was the first production orbiter to be rolled out in 1976. For the next 10 years the vehicle provided an atmospheric, ground test and verification vehicle at Edwards AFB, KSC, MSFC and Vandenberg AFB.
ECLSS Environmental Control and Life Support System.
ESA European Space Agency.
ET External Tank.
EV 1/2 Extravehicular One or Two. EVA crew member identification call. EV1, the team leader, wears red identification stripes on his suit.
EVA Extra Vehicular Activity. Spacewalking.
EMU Extravehicular Mobility Unit. Spacesuit.
FRCI Fibrous Refractory Composite Insulation. A type of thermal protection.
FRSI Flexible Reusable Surface Insulation. A further type of thermal protection.
FD Flight Deck. In the orbiter, the uppermost level of the crew compartment, from where the control and operation of the Shuttle orbiter systems and its payload are managed.
FE Flight Engineer. The third member of the flight crew during the launch and re-entry phases of each mission. Usually a NASA Mission Specialist, this astronaut assists the two man flight crew with checkout procedures.
FRF Flight Readiness Firing. A SSME engine test, usually before the launch of a new orbiter.
GPC General Purpose Computer.
GAS Get-Away Special. Small simple experiments located in canisters in the payload bay.
GLOMR Global Low Orbiting Message Relay Satellite.
GET Ground Elapsed Time. Time of mission duration from moment of lift-off to touchdown of main landing gear *or* wheelstop. GET is usually measured from SRB ignition and timed as 00 hrs 00 min 00.0 sec.
HUT Hard Upper Torso. The chest element of the Shuttle spacesuit.
HAC Heading Alignment Circle. The final approach path during the re-entry glide slope.
HUD Heads-Up Display. The instrument readings displayed in light form onto the windshield of the orbiter.
HPU Hydraulic Power Unit.
HRSI High Temperature Reusable Surface Insulation. A fourth type of thermal protection.
IMU Inertial Measurement Unit.
IUS Inertial Upper Stage.
IPS Instrument Pointing System. A delicate directional system used in collaboration with specific scientific instruments.
IRT Integrated Rendezvous Target.
JSC Johnson Spaceflight Center. The home of the astronauts as well as the famous Mission Control. Located just outside Houston, Texas.
KSC Kennedy Space Center. The launch port for the first 25 shuttle launches.
LC39 Launch Complex 39, KSC, Florida. Using a former facility which supported Apollo flights and the Skylab space station in the 1960s and 70s, LC39 now provides the primary launch facilities for Shuttle missions.
LWT Light Weight Tank. A lighter form of External Tank.
LCVG Liquid Cooled Ventilation Garment.
LH Liquid Hydrogen.
LO Liquid Oxygen.
LDEF Long Delay Exposure Facility.
LM Long Module. The extended version of the Spacelab pressurized module.
LRSI Low Temperature Reusable Surface Insulation.
Mid-Deck The lower part of the pressurized crew compartment containing food, hygiene and sleeping stations; experiment and storage lockers; the airlock and hatch into the payload bay.
MLP Mobile Launch Platform.
MMU Manned Maneuvering Unit.
Max Q The point during launch at which the Shuttle experiences maximum aerodynamic pressure.
MSE Manned Spaceflight Engineer. A Department of Defense Payload Specialist.
MS Mission Specialist. A NASA Mission Specialist.
MECO Main Engine Cutoff. The termination of the SSME burns under normal flight conditions.
MCC-H Mission Control Center-Houston. Located at JSC this is the nerve centre of each Shuttle mission, from where the flight is controlled.
MIT Massachusetts Institute of Technology.
MPSS Mission Peculiar Support Structure.
MSFC Marshall Space Flight Center. Located at Huntsville, Alabama.
NASA National Aeronautics and Space Administration.
OV Orbital Vehicle. The orbiter part of the Shuttle system.
Orbiter The official name of the major element of the Shuttle system, the manned element of the stack and payload carrier.
OPF Orbiter Processing Facility.
OMS Orbital Maneuvering System.
OFT Orbital Flight Test. A programme of four flight test missions in 1981-82 designed to prove the basic Shuttle system and profile.
OIT Orbiter Integration Test.
OSTA Office of Space and Terrestial Applications.
OEP Orbiter Experiments Programme.
ORS Orbital Refueling System.
PLB Payload Bay.
PLBD Payload Bay Doors.
Pod The structure containing the OMS engines, RCS thrusters and associated fuel tanks, fuel lines and equipment.
PLSS Portable Life Support System. The EVA astronauts back pack, containing consumables.
PDP Plasma Diagnostics Package. Measures the plasma particles around the orbiter in orbit, recording levels of contamination.
PAM-D Payload Assist Module – Delta. The small spinning upper stage developed for the Delta unmanned expendable launch vehicle but adopted for Shuttle use.
PLT Pilot.
PS Payload Specialist. A non career astronaut.
PST Pacific Standard Time GMT–8 hrs.
PDT Pacific Daylight Time GMT–7 hrs.
POCC Payload Operations Control Center.
PFTA Payload Flight Test Article.
Prox Ops Close formation flying with another object in orbit.
PCR Payload Changeout Room.
Personal Hygiene Facility The orbiter's washroom, located on the side of the gallery on the mid-deck.
Re-Entry The terminal phase of the mission as the spacecraft 're-enters' the Earth's atmosphere.
RCS Reaction Control System.
RSS Rotating Service Structure.
RTLS Return To Launch Site. An abort mode which is used if an engine fails before or after the SRBs separate. The crew jettisons the SRBs if it has not already done so, burns excess SSME propellant and turns the vehicle 180 degrees, jettisoning the ET and performing a hazardous glide approach to an emergency landing near the launch site.
RSI Reusable Surface Insulation.
RCC Reinforced Carbon-Carbon.
RMS Remote Manipulator System.
RTV Room Temperature Vulcanizer. A TPS tile bonding agent.
STS Space Shuttle Transportation System.
SRB Solid Rocket Booster.
SRM Solid Rocket Motor.
Spacelab The European pressurized module or unpressurized pallets, designed to provide additional scientific work area for in-orbit research on the orbiter.
SSME Space Shuttle Main Engine.
Snoopy Cap A skull cap carrying communications gear, worn during EVA beneath the helmet of the spacesuit.
SFP Space Flight Participant. A person specially selected to fly one mission for their talents in arts, education and journalism.
'SEP' The call-up to confirm the separation of elements of the vehicle during ascent (such as the SRBs or ET).
STA Shuttle Training Aircraft.
SCA Shuttle Carrier Aircraft. A modified Boeing 747 Jumbo jet.
SIT Shuttle Integrated Test.
SAS Space Adaptation Syndrome. The official description of space sickness.
SPS Shuttle Pallet Satellite.
SLF Shuttle Landing Facility.
SAIL Shuttle Avionics Laboratory.
SMEAT Skylab Medical Experiments Altitude Test. A 56 day ground simulation in 1972 of a Skylab mission to collect baseline medical data for the missions flown in 1973.
SSIP Shuttle Student Involvement Program.
Screed The normal name for RTV, used to smooth surfaces prior to tile bonding.
TPS Thermal Protection System.
T-0 The moment of launch. T-minus numbers denote the time to lift off; the T-plus numbers count the mission's duration after lift-off.
TPAD Trunnion Pin Attachment Device.
TDRS Tracking Data and Relay Satellite.
TAL Trans Atlantic (Abort) Landing.
TAEM Terminal Area Energy Management.
VPF Verticle Processing Facility.
VAB Vehicle Assembly Building.
VAFB Vandenberg Air Force Base.
VFTI Verification Flight Test Instrument.
X-1 The first vehicle to break the sound barrier in 1947.
X-15 Hypersonic research aircraft programme of 1959-68.

US

KT-409-116

The Complete Book of

Cooking

The Complete Book of wok Cooking

APPLE

石湾米酒

Contents

Recipe list **6**
Introduction **10**
Equipment **12**
Ingredients **18**
Preparing ingredients **24**
Appetizers and entrées **30**
Chicken and duck **56**
Beef, lamb and pork **84**
Fish and seafood **112**
Vegetables and salads **142**
Rice and noodles **172**
Desserts **198**
Sauces, stocks and condiments **216**
Glossary **233**
Index **236**
Guide to weights and measures **239**

Recipe list

Appetizers and entrées

Beer-battered prawns with mango salsa 32
Carrot, coconut and ginger soup 33
Chicken, spinach and ginger dumplings 34
Chickpea patties 35
Chili-chicken dumplings 36
Cilantro and lime fish cakes 38
Crispy fried wontons with chicken filling 39
Fish balls 40
Fish wraps 41
Fried chicken wontons 42
Ginger-sesame pork rolls 43
Mini noodle baskets with crab and avocado 44
Miso with scallops and ginger 45
Mixed vegetable pakoras 46
Peanut and chili bundles 47
Portuguese-style shrimp 48
Pot stickers 49
Rice flour crisps 50
Savory rice bites 51
Shrimp and coconut fritters 52
Shrimp and lemongrass sticks 53
Sweet corn fritters 54
Vegetarian spring rolls 55

Chicken and duck

Braised duck with pineapple 58
Chicken and cashew stir-fry 60
Chicken chow mein 61
Chicken satay salad 62
Chicken stir-fry with bean sprouts 63
Chicken with ginger 64
Chicken with lemongrass and chili 65
Chili chicken and vegetables 66
Crispy wontons with duck 67
Duck with long beans 68
Green chicken curry 69
Grilled chicken drumsticks 70
Indonesian-style chicken fried rice 71
Larb salad with chicken 72
Orange rice with chicken 73
Peking duck pancakes 74
Red curry with roasted duck 75
Steamed chicken buns 76
Stir-fried chicken breast in roasted curry paste sauce 78
Stir-fried ginger chicken 79
Sweet chicken wings 80
Sweet-and-sour chicken and noodles 81
Teriyaki chicken 82
Thai curry with chicken 83

Beef, lamb and pork

Beef braised in rice wine 86
Beef chow mein 88
Beef kabobs 89
Beef stir-fry on crisp noodles 90
Beef stir-fry with Chinese greens 91
Beef with bamboo shoots 92
Beef with basil leaves 93
Chinese barbecue pork stir-fry 94
Chinese beef and vegetable stir-fry 95
Dry beef curry with sweet potato 96
Fried pork in endive 97
Ginger pork 98
Lamb with dried fruit 99
Long beans with pork and red curry paste 100
Meatballs in tomato sauce 101
Pork and lime patties 102
Pork and nectarine stir-fry 103
Pumpkin with pork 104
Red curry beef 105
Salt bulgogi 106
Shredded pork and bean sprouts 107
Sliced beef, mushrooms and vegetables in oyster sauce 108
Steamed pork ribs 109
Stir-fried beef with eggs 110
Stir-fried beef with red curry paste 111

Fish and seafood

Braised octopus and onions 114
Braised shrimp in ginger-coconut sauce 115
Cha ca fish with turmeric 116
Crab in black bean sauce 117
Crab with yellow curry powder 118
Crispy fried fish 119
Fish curry 120
Fish fillets with coconut rice parcels 121
Fish with green curry paste 122
Ginger fish in nori wrapper 123
Lobster salad 124
Mussels with garlic and lime butter 125
Pad Thai with shrimp 126
Sautéed squid with leeks 127
Scallops with arugula pesto and sweet potato puree 128
Seafood, basil and almond stir-fry with mixed greens 129
Semolina-crusted shrimp 130
Spiced shrimp and rice 131
Spicy snapper with parsnip chips 132
Squid bulgogi 133
Steamed fish in banana leaves 134
Stir-fried chili-lime shrimp 135
Stir-fried octopus with long beans and snow peas 136
Stir-fried seafood with noodles 137
Stir-fried squid with chili 138
Thai curry fish in banana leaf cups 139
Thai red curry shrimp 140
Whole fried fish with chili and basil 141

Vegetables and salads

Asian greens stir-fry with shiitake mushrooms 144
Asian greens with lemon and ginger oil 145
Asian greens with tempeh and oyster sauce 146
Beans foogarth 147
Black-eyed pea and sugar snaps stir-fry 148
Butternut squash and lentil salad 149
Chickpeas with spinach 150
Deep-fried tofu with vegetables 151
Fried tofu salad 152
Green beans in oil 153
Homemade cottage cheese with spinach 154
Japanese seaweed salad 155
Korean mung bean pancakes 156
Mango and yogurt curry 158
Mixed vegetable curry 159
Mushroom and sesame stir-fry 160
Pumpkin dumplings in malai sauce 161
Stir-fried Asian greens with tempeh 162
Stir-fried choy sum with ginger 163
Stir-fried fennel, celery, snow peas and bean sprouts 164
Stir-fried vegetables 165
Stir-fried vegetables with soy and ginger 166
Stuffed eggplants 167
Sweet-and-sour potatoes 168
Tofu and vegetable stir-fry 169
Vegetarian green curry 170
Vegetarian stir-fry 171

Rice and noodles

Bell peppers and mushrooms with noodles 174
Chili broccoli with noodles 175
Chili fried rice 176
Chinese fried rice 177
Fried cellophane noodles 178
Fried glass noodles with fish or eel 179
Fried noodles with pork 180
Fried rice with pineapple 181
Garlic and cumin lentils 182
Ginger-coconut rice 183
Herb and lemon noodle salad with ponzu dressing 184
Indian noodle stir-fry 185
Indian pilaf 186
Metropole fried rice 187
Mushroom and noodle stir-fry 188
Nasi goreng 189
Noodles with baked vegetables 190
Noodles with squash and green papaya 191
Pad Thai noodles 192
Salmon laksa 193
Soba noodles with bell peppers 194
Spicy cellophane noodle salad 195
Steamed rice in lotus parcels 196

Desserts

Almond cream pudding 200
Banana tempura 201
Chinese lemon, date and walnut cake 202
Cream and berry stack 203
Creamy coconut black rice 204
Figs in syrup 204
Ginger and nutmeg sweet potato pudding 206
Grand Marnier crème caramels 208
Hot mocha and brandied raisin soufflé 207
Lime and coconut pudding with lime-ginger syrup 210
Panfried pineapple 211
Polenta pudding with mango sauce 212
Rose water doughnuts 213
Spicy fruit salad 214
Sweet date wontons 215

Sauces and condiments

Adjat sauce 218
Chili and coriander dipping sauce 222
Chili jam 219
Chili oil 223
Coconut cream, milk, and water 224
Chicken stock 220
Dashi 222
Fish sauce with chilies 223
Fish stock 221
Garam masala 225
Garlic dipping sauce 226
Green curry paste 231
Hot chili sauce 226
Mango, papaya and green chili relish 227
Massaman curry paste 227
Mint raita 228
Nuoc cham nem sauce 228
Paneer 229
Penang curry paste 225
Red curry paste 231
Sambal oelek 230
Sweet chili relish 219
Tahini sauce 230
Teriyaki sauce 225
Thai chili dipping sauce 232
Tomato salsa with chili and cilantro 232
Vegetable stock 221

Introduction

The beauty of stir-fried food is not just that the dishes are quick to prepare and an extremely energy-efficient way to cook. Nor is it that the most tantalizing aromas are released when the ingredients mingle and sizzle during cooking, although this is quite wonderful. This method beats all others simply because it seals in the flavors and nutrients of the foods and preserves their original color and textures, making meals tasty, satisfying and healthy.

Stir-frying is the most popular way to cook food in Asia. The technique originated from China and over the centuries it was adopted throughout Asian kitchens. Vietnamese cuisine, for example, is a fusion of the best culinary elements of China's traditions with its use of chopsticks and woks, stir-fried dishes and plethora of noodles. Today, stir-frying has well and truly conquered the world, used frequently by Western chefs and home cooks alike.

With only four of the most ancient and rudimentary implements—cleaver, board, wok and spatula—plus a source of intense heat, stir-fries are easy to prepare. The success in cooking depends on having all the ingredients ready before cooking starts. The ingredients should be cut into pieces of about the same size, and the meat and poultry cut across the grain (partially frozen meat is easier to slice) to ensure they don't become tough during cooking. The food is then cooked in a wok or frying pan with very little oil over a high heat, constantly turning the ingredients.

The wok provides many other easy and effective ways to prepare foods. With a wok you can also steam, boil, braise and deep-fry. In this book we provide a number of recipes that use the wok in these versatile fashions. For example, desserts couldn't be simpler than using a wok with a bamboo steamer, and there is very little that needs cleaning up afterwards. So be adventurous with your wok and you'll find the rewards are more than the tasty food you prepare.

Recipes for stir-fries can often be adapted to suit whatever the refrigerator yields, a bonus when time and budget are short. A simple family meal can be created by making up two or three dishes using meat or seafood and vegetables. You can contrast the dishes by making one mild and one more highly seasoned. Steamed white rice usually accompanies stir-fried dishes, but you may choose to add interest to the rice by stirring in cooked green peas, baby shrimp (prawns) and chopped scallions (spring onions). You can also use noodles instead of rice, whatever you prefer.

When eating stir-fries, serve with Chinese-style tableware—bowls and chopsticks—as these add to the relaxed ambience this style of cooking affords. Tea is one of the best drinks to accompany stir-fries—try the lighter green teas, and plain or scented teas with jasmine blossoms are refreshing—as they cleanse the palate to enable you to enjoy the characteristics of each dish.

As a method of cooking it's obvious that stir-frying has several advantages: the ingredients can be prepared in advance to make cooking time no more than a few minutes, the dishes are economical to make, and the quick cooking ensures minimum loss of nutrients. Since stir-fried dishes cook quickly, they should be cooked just before serving so they are fresh and piping hot.

Enjoy!

Equipment

The wok

The wok is synonymous with stir-fries. The word wok simply means "cooking vessel" in Cantonese—an indication of how versatile and, indeed, indispensable this piece of equipment is for Asian cooks. Its shape, which has remained unchanged for centuries, was originally dictated by the Chinese stove. The stove had an opening in the top into which the round-bottomed wok securely fit.

A wok is a wonderful and practical addition to the contemporary kitchen. The shape accommodates small or large quantities of ingredients and allows control over how they are cooked. The large cooking surface evenly and efficiently conducts and holds heat, making a wok especially well suited for stir-frying. There are few ingredients that cannot be cooked in a wok, whether a recipe is Asian or Western in style.

Of the many woks available, all are basically bowl shaped with gently sloping sides. Some have looped handles on opposite sides; others have a long wooden handle on one side. Woks were traditionally made from cast iron and therefore were quite heavy. They are now available in many different materials and finishes. Carbon or rolled steel is one of the best materials. Nonstick woks are easy to clean but may not promote browning of foods as thoroughly as those made of rolled or carbon steel. Other options include stainless steel woks and electric woks, which may not reach temperatures as high as those of cast iron or carbon steel. Round-bottomed woks work best on gas stoves. A stand may be necessary to provide stability; the best choice is a stand with large perforations that promote good heat circulation. Flat-bottomed woks are suited for electric stove tops because they sit directly and securely on the heating element.

Woks are available in a range of sizes. A wok with a diameter of 14 inches (35 cm) is a versatile size appropriate for the recipes in this book and for other dishes that yield four to six servings. If you don't have a wok, use a large frying pan, a cast-iron skillet, or a russe.

Left: Carbon steel wok

Pictured opposite
Clockwise from top left: electric wok, stainless steel wok, cast iron wok, frying pan, nonstick woks

Breville

Preparing a new wok

Woks of carbon steel or rolled steel, the popular inexpensive vessels sold in Asian stores, are coated with a thin film of lacquer to prevent rusting. The film needs to be removed before a wok can be used. The best way to do this is to place the wok on the stove top, fill with cold water and add 2 tablespoons of baking soda (bicarbonate of soda). Bring to a boil and boil rapidly for 15 minutes. Drain and scrub off the coating with a nylon pad. Repeat the process if any coating remains. Then rinse and dry the wok. It is now ready to be seasoned.

Carbon steel, rolled steel and cast iron woks require seasoning before use, which creates a smooth surface that keeps food from sticking to it and prevents it from discoloring.

1 To season a wok: Wipe the wok lightly with oil and place it over high heat until smoking. Immediately plunge it into hot water, then return to heat to dry. Wipe again with oil and repeat these steps three times. At no time should you use soap.

2 To keep a wok clean: Rinse with hot water immediately after use and scour with a plastic or nonmetallic brush. Never use soap, or you will need to season the wok all over again. Do not wipe dry, but place over a low heat to dry. Wipe lightly with oil and store.

3 To heat a wok: Because of the wok's conical shape, a gas flame is preferable to electric as it disperses the heat upward along the sides of the wok. Gas also allows instant regulation of the heat.

4 To cook with a wok: Always preheat the wok before adding any ingredients, including oil. After adding oil, rotate the wok to spread the oil evenly up the sides, then heat before adding anything else.

Versatile cooking methods with a wok

Deep-frying: The wok is ideal for deep-frying as it uses less oil than a deep fryer and can accommodate ingredients without crowding. Make sure the wok is secure on its stand or heating element before adding the oil. Pour the oil into the wok and heat until it reaches 375°F (190°C) on a deep-frying thermometer or until a cube of bread sizzles and turns golden when dropped into the hot oil.

Steaming: This method cooks foods by moist heat supplied by steadily boiling water. A bamboo steamer set over but not touching simmering water in a wok is ideal for cooking buns, dumplings, fish, vegetables and puddings. Half fill the wok with water (the steamer should not touch the water) and bring to a boil. Arrange the food in the steamer, cover, place the steamer in the wok and steam for the required time, adding more water when necessary.

Boiling: A wok can serve as a saucepan, a frying pan and a stewing pot, suitable for simmering a delicate coconut sauce, boiling vegetables, simmering a soup or reducing a sauce.

Braising: Meat or seafood can be browned to seal in the juices. Once liquid is added, the wok can be covered for slow simmering.

Other useful kitchen equipment

Electric rice cookers are rapidly replacing conventional saucepan cooking. They cook rice perfectly and keep it warm throughout a meal. A saucepan with a tight-fitting lid also produces excellent results.

A good hardwood board is indispensable for proper cutting and other preparations. After use, cutting boards may be scraped clean with the back edge of the cleaver, rinsed with warm water, and hung to dry.

A good cleaver is the most versatile implement in the kitchen. It can cut, chop, slice, shred, mince (grind), pound, peel, scrape, flatten, and otherwise process every type of ingredient. A light cleaver is good for fine cuts such as shredding and mincing (grinding) and a heavy cleaver can be used for chopping through meat with bone. A properly used and cared-for cleaver will last a lifetime. Steel is best for heavy choppers, but iron is infinitely superior for lighter cleavers used in most cutting. Stainless steel cleavers tend to lose their edge quickly.

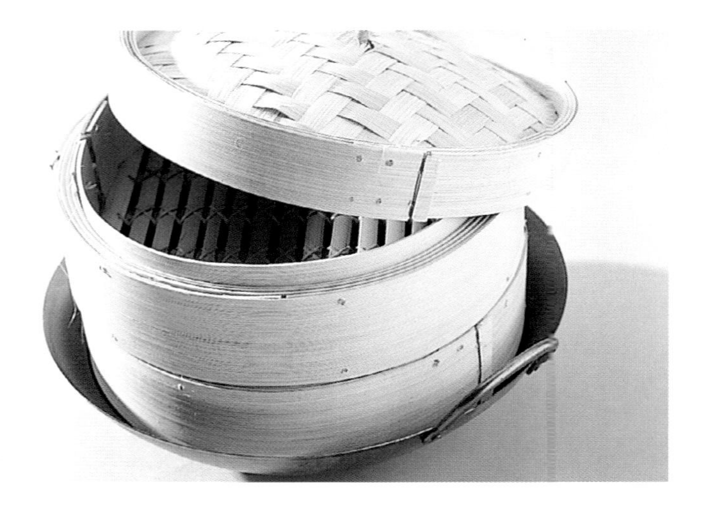

The two-level bamboo steamer is one of the cheapest and most attractive utensils for steaming. It is available in many sizes from Asian supermarkets and specialty cookware shops. The open-slat base allows steam to circulate easily and efficiently. The lid has an almost perfect design, allowing excess steam to escape through the tightly woven bamboo, with little condensed steam dripping back onto the food.

Wooden and metal wok spatulas or shovels are used for lifting and stirring foods in the wok. They are designed with a rounded end, facilitating scraping along the contours of the wok. If unavailable, use any wooden or metal spatula or pancake turner.

Mortar and pestles are essential for preparing traditional curry pastes. Their weight is ideal for pulverizing fibrous herbs and spices. Substitute with a food processor.

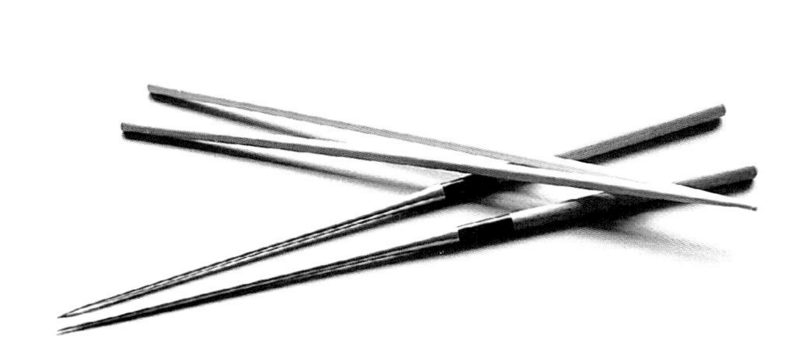

Cooking chopsticks are a jumbo version of the smaller type used for eating. They are long enough to reach into a wok without getting the hands burned or spattered. They are useful for plucking, arranging, stirring, turning, testing, and otherwise manipulating various types of food in the kitchen.

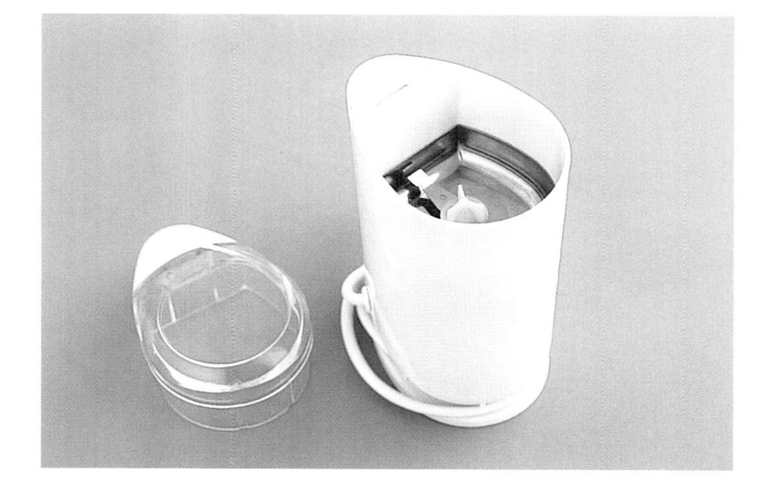

Electric spice grinders can be used in lieu of a mortar and pestle. Some grinders have both dry and wet mix attachments. You can use a coffee grinder (kept only for spices), but they do not have the two settings. For wet spice mixes, you will need to use a spice grinder to first grind dry spices and then a small food processor to finish the spice mix with the fresh or wet ingredients.

Ingredients

Today's cook can make superb use of an extensive array of ingredients. Each culture's culinary style seems to favor specific foods for its recipes. Basil, garlic, and chili are a popular combination for Thai cooking. The Vietnamese love garlic and coriander. The Chinese prefer a subtle blending of sweet and sour, hence the use of lemongrass, ginger, and star anise. The opportunities to create new flavors are endless—there's a whole world of ingredients to explore. Here are some of the ones we use in this book, but don't forget to look at the glossary for more choices.

Bay leaves
Dried leaves from a large, evergreen tree belonging to the laurel family, and native to the Mediterranean region. The leaves impart a lemon-nutmeg flavor. They are used in cooking, but are not edible.

Bean sprouts
These sprouting green mung beans are sold fresh or canned. Fresh sprouts tend to have a crisper texture and a more delicate flavor. Store in the refrigerator for up to 3 days.

Bok choy
Asian variety of cabbage with thick white stalks and mild-flavored dark green leaves. Sizes of bunches vary, from longer than celery stalks to baby bok choy about 6 inches (15 cm) long. Also known as Chinese cabbage. If unavailable, use Chinese broccoli or choy sum.

Cardamom

This member of the ginger family produces pods that contain seeds with a strong lemony flavor. It is available ground but for best flavor, grind your own just before using.

Cilantro (coriander)

These pungent, fragrant leaves from the coriander plant resemble parsley and are also called Chinese parsley and coriander. They have a sharp, tangy, fresh flavor and aroma. The leaves, stems, and roots are all essential seasonings in Asian cooking.

Chili oil

Spicy oil produced by steeping dried red chilies in oil. Use this hot oil only by the drop. Store in refrigerator after opening.

Chilies

Fresh chilies are available in a combination of sizes and are either red or green. The seeds and membranes are the "hot" parts, so if you prefer less heat in your food remove them before chopping or grinding. You could also reduce (or add) the amount of chilies used in a recipe. Chilies are also available dried.

Chili powder

Made from the long Thai chili, chili powder is not as piquant as cayenne pepper, nor is it the equivalent to Mexican chili powder, which is a combination of spices. When unavailable, use red chili flakes ground to a powder in a mortar or a food processor.

Choy sum

Popular and widely available Chinese green with yellow flowers and thin stalks. Every part of this mild-flavored vegetable can be used. Also known as flowering cabbage.

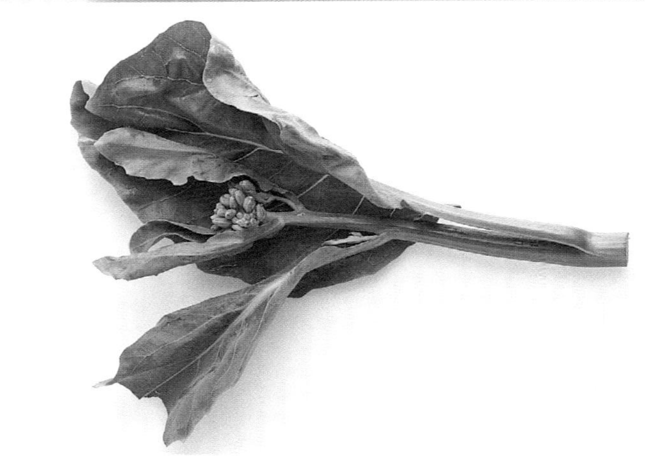

Daikon

This giant white radish, eaten in a variety of forms as an aid to digestion, is enormously popular in Japan and suits stir-fry dishes perfectly.

Galangal

A rhizome with a sharp flavor, sometimes called Thai ginger, it has reddish skin, orange or white flesh and a peppery gingerlike flavor. Fresh galangal should be peeled before use, then sliced or grated. It is also available dried.

Garlic

This edible bulb is indispensable in innumerable dishes. It goes well with meat, especially lamb, and many vegetables. If you find peeling a garlic clove a problem, simply drop them in boiling water for a few seconds, drain and then run cold water over them. You should be able to just slip off the skins afterwards.

Ginger

Thick rootlike rhizome of the ginger plant, a tall flowering tropical plant native to China. It has a sharp pungent flavor. Once the tan skin is peeled from fresh ginger, the ivory to greenish yellow flesh is grated or sliced. Used fresh in sweet and savory cooking and beverages.

Kaffir lime leaves

Fragrant, shiny, dark green leaves from the kaffir lime tree used fresh or dried, whole or shredded, for their enticing citrus flavor.

Leek

This member of the onion family looks like a large scallion (shallot/spring onion). Choose small to medium–size leeks with crisp white bottoms and fresh green tops. Store them unwashed in the refrigerator in the vegetable crisper or a plastic bag.

Lemongrass

Pale stalks of a tropical grass that contribute an intense lemon flavor to Southeast Asian dishes. After the green blades are removed, the stalks are bruised or sliced before use.

Noodles

Sold fresh in Asian markets, noodles, especially the thinner version, are more commonly bought from supermarkets in a dried form in packets. Although interchangeable, dried noodles should be soaked for 10 minutes in cold water, then drained before use. Fresh noodles can be used directly from the package. Noodles are made from bean thread, eggs, wheat, buckwheat or rice. Cellophane noodles (pictured) can be deep-fried for a crisp texture and then added to an already cooked stir-fry.

Saffron threads

If pepper is the king of spices, then saffron is the queen. Saffron threads are the dried stigmas from a variety of crocus flower, each of which produces only three stigmas. Harvesting saffron is labor-intensive, making it the most costly spice in the world. Saffron threads are generally soaked in a warm liquid to release their intense gold-yellow color and pungent, earthy aroma and flavor.

Shallots (French shallots)

Resembling clustered tiny onions, shallots are brown, gold or pink to purple in color. The white parts of scallions (shallots/spring onions) may be substituted.

Shiitake mushrooms

These are available fresh or dried. If dried, they should be soaked before use for 30 minutes in several changes of water. The stems are then removed and discarded.

Soy sauce

Made from fermented soybeans and used to enhance the flavor of many dishes, different soy have different tastes. Chinese soy sauce is saltier and stronger in taste than the Japanese style. Keep refrigerated once opened and use within 12 months.

Star anise

Dark brown, star-shaped spice with a flavor similar to aniseed but with more depth and sweetness. It is the dried fruit from a variety of evergreen magnolia tree. Commonly used in Chinese cooking, star anise also makes an appearance in Indian foods.

Tamarind

Tamarind paste and pulp are very sour. The paste, sold in block form, requires dilution in hot water and straining. More convenient is commercially available tamarind pulp, puree or water, sold in jars. Because there can be a difference in sourness between commercial and homemade puree, the quantities required are variable.

Preparing ingredients

Chopping an onion

1 Halve onion lengthwise through root and stem ends.
2 Peel onion by removing outer layers of skin.
3 Slice through each onion half 3 or 4 times, parallel to cut surface, to within ½ inch (12 mm) of root end.
4 Slice 4 or 5 times through onion, without cutting into root end.
5 Finally, cut through previous cuts.

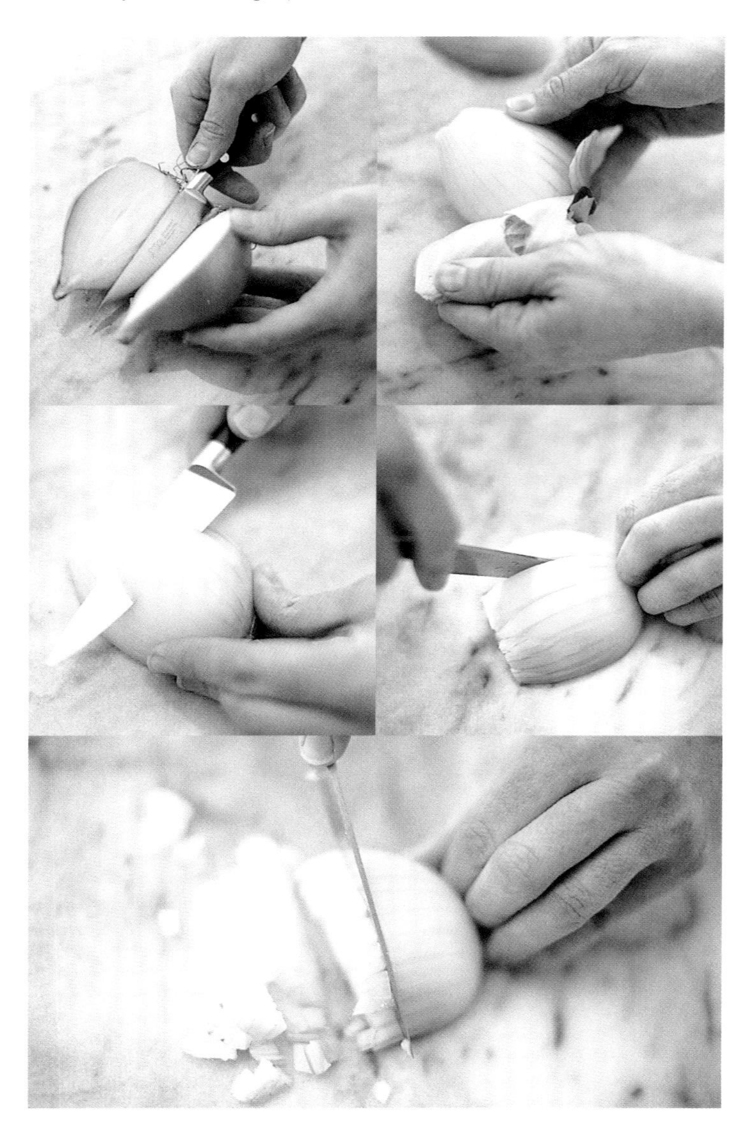

Chopping fresh herbs

Use sharp kitchen shears to snip fresh herbs.

Cutting fine shreds

Paper-thin shreds of herbs are achieved by rolling several leaves together into a tight cylinder, then slicing crosswise. Tender leaves such as basil and mint merely need to be pinched from their stems.

Chili flower

Medium chili

Medium length chilies are ideal for the simplest of chili flowers. Make sure that they are very crisp and fresh, either green or red.

1. Hold the chili flat on a board and use a thin sharp knife to cut lengthwise along the chili from stem to tip. Make about 5 parallel cuts just through the skin to the seeds, but not across them to the other side.
2. Plunge into ice water and the chili "petals" will curl back, while the seed cluster becomes the stamen. If parts of the flower remain closed, prod them gently with the knife and return the flower to the water. These will keep for up to 36 hours if refrigerated in cold water.

Long chili

Long chilies do not blossom as exquisitely as the shorter varieties. To make this garnish, which resembles the beautiful kiriboon flower of Southeast Asia, use a scalpel or preferably a thin V-shaped garnishing knife (available at cookware shops and from some cake-decorating suppliers).

1. Make small V-shaped incisions along the length of the chili, in parallel rows. They should be about 1/8 inch (3 mm) wide and no more than 1/4 inch (6 mm) long.
2. Plunge into ice water, as for medium chili, until the incisions curl back like a flower.

Note: For a more spectacular presentation, stick a thin carrot sliver into each of the chiseled holes.

Preparing thick asparagus

If asparagus spears are thick and woody, peeling away tough skin from stalk will result in more tender asparagus after cooking. Using a vegetable peeler or sharp knife, peel away a thin layer of skin beginning at lower part of stem, tapering off progressively as skin becomes more tender toward tip.

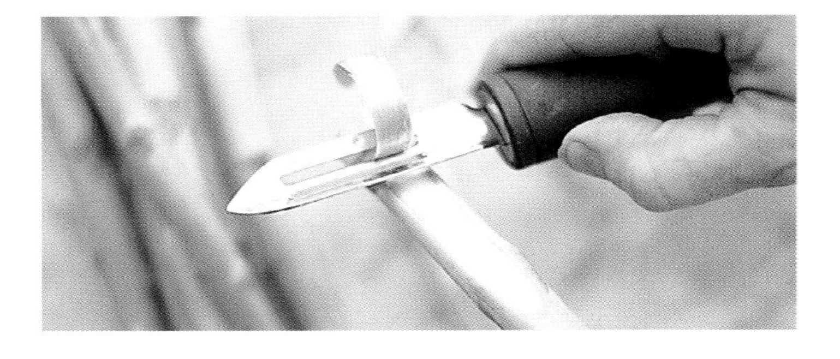

Removing corn from a fresh cob

1. Strip corn husks and silk down to stem end of corn.
2. Snap off husks and remove any remaining silk.
3. Grip stem firmly and use a sharp knife to slice away kernels. Slice close to woody cob.

Garnishes

Lemon and lime zest curls

Lemon and lime zest (rind) can be used to garnish and flavor your favorite recipes. Using a citrus zester, firmly scrape the zest from lemons, limes, oranges or grapefruits. If a zester is unavailable, remove zest with a vegetable peeler.

Remove any white pith from zest pieces. Using a very sharp knife, finely slice zest. Place zest in a bowl of ice water. Refrigerate until zest curls, about 15 minutes. (If you are using a zester, it is generally not necessary to place zest in ice water.)

Scallion brushes and curls

1. Using a sharp knife, remove the root section from each scallion (shallot/spring onion). Cut the paler green section into 2-inch (5-cm) sections. Discard the darker green section, or save for another use.
2. To make brushes: Make ¼-inch (6-mm) cuts in each scallion piece, forming a fringe. (Go to step 4.)
3. To make curls: Slice scallion pieces lengthwise into fine strips.
4. Place scallion brushes or strips in a bowl of ice water. Refrigerate until scallions curl, about 15 minutes. Drain and use as garnish.

Toasting seeds, nuts and spices

Because nuts, spices and seeds toast at different times, toast them separately. The general rule is to use your nose: once fragrant, remove from heat immediately. Do not overcook or they may become bitter or acrid.

1 Place nuts, spice or seeds in a dry wok or frying pan over medium heat, and toast, stirring constantly, until lightly golden and fragrant.
2 Alternatively, preheat oven to 400°F (200°C/Gas 6). Spread the nuts, spice or seeds on a rimmed baking pan and toast for 8–12 minutes, shaking the pan once to ensure even browning.
3 If spices need grinding, let cool then grind in a mortar.

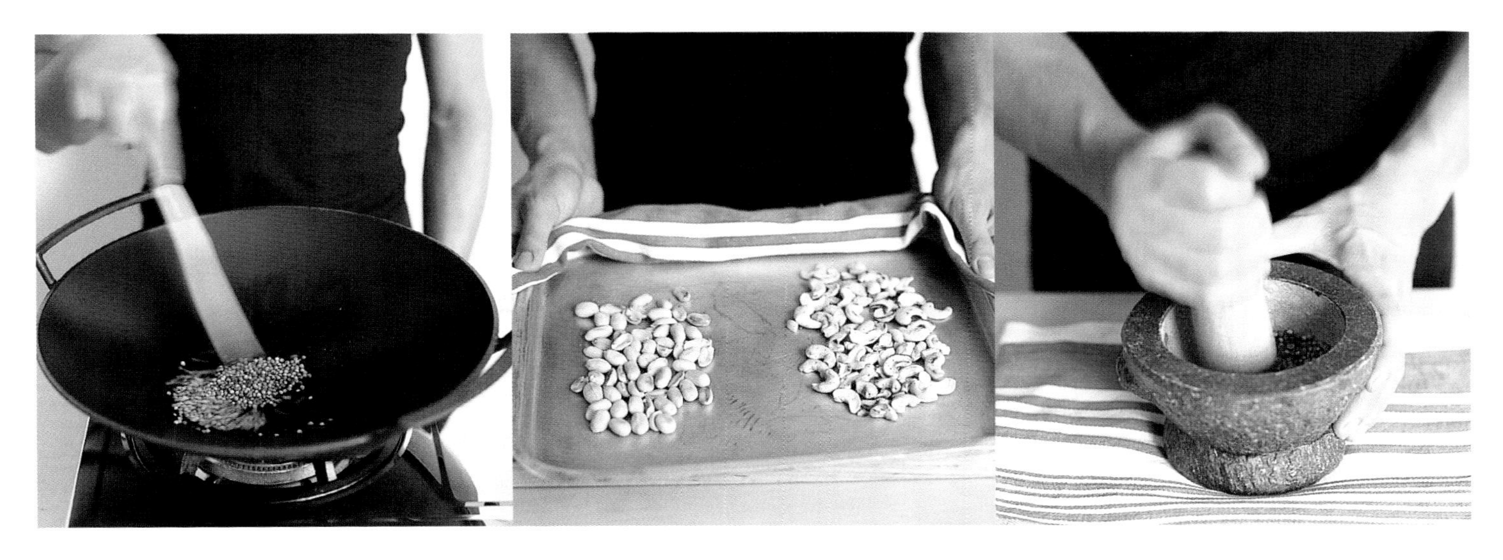

Removing seeds from a tomato

1 Slice tomato in half through stem.
2 Remove seeds, using a teaspoon.

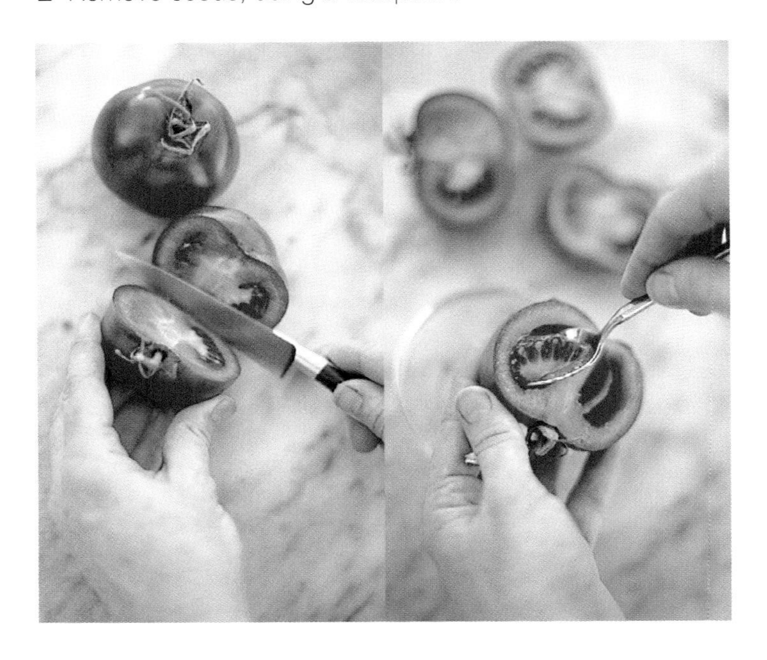

Deseeding a bell pepper (capsicum)

1 If recipe requires a whole bell pepper, slice top off with a sharp knife. If not, cut pepper in half through stem.
2 Using your fingers, remove and discard seeds and white pith from inside bell pepper.

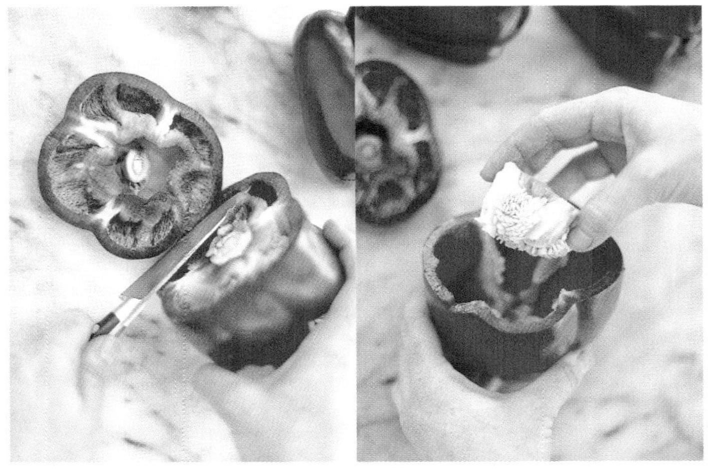

Preparing steamed rice

Though commonly referred to as "steamed rice", standard rice that accompanies most hot and spicy food is actually boiled. When cooked, rice swells to two and half times its volume. Estimate about 1–1½ cups cooked rice per person. If you are using an electric rice cooker follow the manufacturer's directions. If using a saucepan the steps are simple as 1, 2 and 3 below.

1 Rinse rice until the water runs clear, but do not overwork the rice or the grains may break. Drain the rice and put it in a deep, heavy saucepan with a tight-fitting lid.

2 Fill the pan with water to cover the rice by ¾ inch (2 cm). Traditionally, cooks measured by placing their index finger on the rice, adding just enough water to touch their first joint. Do not measure from the pan's bottom, but from the top of the rice. Over high heat, bring the water to a boil and cook until craters form on the rice's surface and the water has disappeared. Immediately cover tightly and reduce heat to a bare simmer. Cook for about 20 minutes, or until tender. Do not lift the lid during the cooking.

3 Use a wooden rice paddle or wooden spoon to fluff the rice up and loosen the grains. If cooking in a nonstick pan, using a bamboo or wooden implement avoids scratching the surface. Serve immediately with your stir-fried dishes.

Cooking noodles

Use the following cooking times as a guide only. Check the noodle package for the manufacturer's recommended cooking times and serving ideas. Always check the noodles during cooking by tasting a strand. Noodles for most dishes should be cooked through. There are basically two ways to cook noodles:

1 Place noodles in a heatproof bowl and cover with boiling water. Soak noodles until soft, then drain. This method is suitable only for fine noodles such as cellophane (bean thread) noodles, rice vermicelli and thin egg noodles.
2 Bring a large saucepan of water to a boil, add noodles and cook until tender, then drain. This method is suitable for all noodles.

Cellophane noodles: These need only be softened in boiling water for 10 minutes; they do not require boiling. Or for a crisp texture, deep-fry them in hot oil until golden and crisp, 1 minute or less.

Egg noodles: If fresh, cook in boiling water for about 3 minutes. If dried, cook in boiling water for about 5 minutes. Some precooked fresh egg noodles need only be soaked in hot water for 8–10 minutes; check package for directions.

Hokkien noodles: Cook in boiling water for 3–4 minutes or stir-fry in hot oil for 3–4 minutes. Some varieties are precooked; check package for directions.

Ramen noodles: Cook in boiling water for about 5 minutes.

Rice stick noodles: Soften dried noodles in hot water for 15 minutes or cook in boiling water for 2–3 minutes. Stir-fry fresh noodles for 2–3 minutes. Some thin rice stick noodles only require soaking in boiling water before adding to soups or stir-fries. Rice vermicelli can be deep-fried to create a crisp "bird's nest" for serving stir-fry dishes.

Soba noodles: If fresh, cook in boiling water for about 1½ minutes. If dried, cook in boiling water for 5–6 minutes.

Somen noodles: Cook in boiling water for about 3 minutes.

Udon noodles: If fresh, cook in boiling water for about 2½ minutes. If dried, cook in boiling water for 10–12 minutes.

Wheat flour noodles: If fresh, cook in boiling water for 3 minutes. If dried, cook in boiling water for 4–5 minutes.

From top: Ramen, somen, udon and soba noodles

appetizers and entrées

Beer-battered prawns with mango salsa

Serves 6–8 as appetizer, 4 as entrée

1 mango, peeled, pitted and chopped
½ cup (2 oz/60 g) chopped scallions (shallots/spring onions)
½ small red chili, seeded and chopped
3 tablespoons lime juice
2 teaspoons Asian sesame oil
½ cup (¾ oz/20 g) chopped fresh basil
ground pepper to taste
1½ cups (7½ oz/235 g) all-purpose (plain) flour
1 teaspoon baking powder (bicarbonate of soda)
1 teaspoon salt
½ teaspoon red chili flakes
1 teaspoon brown sugar
1¾ cups (14 fl oz/440 ml) beer
3 cups (24 fl oz/750 ml) vegetable oil for deep-frying
20 jumbo shrimp (king prawns), peeled and deveined, tails intact
lime wedges, for serving

To make salsa: In a bowl, combine mango, scallions, chili, lime juice, sesame oil, basil and ground pepper. Mix well and set aside.

Sift flour, baking powder and salt into bowl. Stir in red chili flakes and sugar. Pour in beer and mix with wooden spoon until batter is smooth.

In a wok, heat oil until it reaches 375°F (190°C) on deep-frying thermometer or until a small bread cube dropped in oil sizzles and turns golden. Dip prawns, one at a time, into batter, allow excess to drain off and carefully drop in hot oil. Deep-fry until golden, 30–60 seconds. Using slotted spoon, remove from wok and drain on paper towels. Continue until all prawns are cooked. Serve prawns hot with lime wedges and mango salsa.

Carrot, coconut and ginger soup

Serves 4

1 tablespoon vegetable oil
1 teaspoon Asian sesame oil
1 small red chili, seeded and chopped
4 cloves garlic, crushed
3 teaspoons peeled and grated fresh ginger
2 onions, chopped
2 lb (1 kg) carrots, peeled and sliced
1 teaspoon ground cumin
1 teaspoon ground turmeric
4 cups (32 fl oz/1 L) coconut milk
2 cups (16 fl oz/500 ml) vegetable stock (see page 221) or chicken stock (see page 220)
salt and ground pepper to taste
fresh tarragon leaves, for serving

In a wok over a medium heat, warm vegetable and sesame oils. Add chili, garlic and ginger and stir-fry until aromatic, about 1 minute. Add onions, carrots, cumin and turmeric and stir-fry until onions are softened, about 2 minutes.

Pour in coconut milk and stock. Bring to a boil, reduce heat to low and simmer, uncovered, until carrots are tender, 12–15 minutes. Remove from heat.

Working in batches, ladle soup into food processor or blender and process until smooth. Return to wok and heat through for 2 minutes. Taste and season with salt and pepper.

To serve, ladle into individual bowls and garnish with tarragon leaves.

Chicken, spinach and ginger dumplings

Makes 30

1 bunch spinach, stemmed, washed and chopped
8 oz (250 g) ground (minced) chicken
3 scallions (shallots/spring onions), finely chopped
1 teaspoon peeled and grated fresh ginger
2 cloves garlic, crushed
2 teaspoons soy sauce
1 teaspoon Asian sesame oil
½ teaspoon fish sauce
1 small red chili, seeded and finely chopped (optional)
3 teaspoons cornstarch (cornflour)
30 wonton wrappers
¼ cup (2 fl oz/60 ml) rice vinegar
2 tablespoons sugar
2 tablespoons water
1 teaspoon lemon juice
¾ teaspoon fish sauce
1 small red chili, finely chopped (seeds removed for milder taste)

Put spinach in a bamboo steamer or steamer basket. Partially fill a wok or pot with water (steamer should not touch water), and bring to a rapid simmer. Put steamer over water, cover, and steam until spinach is soft, 2–3 minutes. Remove from heat and let cool. Squeeze out excess water and chop finely.

In a medium bowl, combine spinach, chicken, scallions, ginger, garlic, soy sauce, sesame oil, fish sauce, chili and cornstarch. Mix well.

Place wonton wrappers on work surface and cover with a damp kitchen towel to prevent them from drying out. Working with 1 wrapper at a time, place 2 teaspoons filling in center and brush edges of wrapper with water. Gather edges together and twist to seal or fold wrapper in half, pressing edges together with fingers to seal. Cover with a damp kitchen towel and set aside. Repeat with remaining wrappers.

Line a large bamboo steamer or steamer basket with parchment (baking) paper. Partially fill a large wok or pot with water (steamer should not touch water) and bring to a rapid simmer. Arrange dumplings in steamer, making sure they do not touch. Place over water, cover, and steam for 10 minutes, adding more simmering water as necessary.

Meanwhile, combine rice vinegar, sugar, water, lemon juice, fish sauce and chili to make dipping sauce. Mix well.

Lift steamer off wok and carefully remove dumplings. Serve warm with dipping sauce.

Chickpea patties

Makes about 30 patties

1½ cups (10 oz/300 g) dried chickpeas (garbanzo beans)
4 cups (32 fl oz/1 L) cold water
1 medium yellow (brown) onion, coarsely chopped
2 cloves garlic
6 tablespoons chopped fresh flat-leaf (Italian) parsley
3 tablespoons chopped cilantro (fresh coriander)
pinch ground red chili
1 teaspoon ground coriander
½ teaspoon ground cumin
½ teaspoon baking soda (bicarbonate of soda)
1 teaspoon salt
freshly ground pepper to taste
vegetable oil for deep-frying
tahini sauce (see page 230), for serving

Put chickpeas in a bowl, add water and soak in a cool place for 12–15 hours or overnight.

Drain chickpeas and rinse well. (Do not cook chickpeas as patties would disintegrate when fried).

In a bowl, combine soaked chickpeas with onion, garlic, parsley, cilantro, ground chili, coriander, cumin, baking soda, salt and pepper. Toss ingredients lightly to mix.

In a food processor, process mixture in batches until finely ground. Alternatively, the mixture can be passed through a food grinder twice, using a fine screen.

Place the ground mixture in a bowl and knead well so that it just holds together. Cover and set aside for 30 minutes.

With moistened hands, shape generous tablespoonfuls of mixture into balls, then flatten into thick patties 1½ inches (4 cm) in diameter. Place on a baking sheet and set aside for 15 minutes.

In a wok over medium heat, pour oil to a depth of 1 inch (2.5 cm). When the oil reaches 375°F (190°C) on a deep-frying thermometer, add 6–8 patties at a time and cook, turning once, until deep golden brown, 3–4 minutes. Remove with a slotted spoon and drain on paper towels. Serve hot as an appetizer with tahini sauce.

Tip

Do not use a large onion as this will make the mixture too soft.

Chili-chicken dumplings

Makes 16

8 oz (250 g) ground (minced) chicken
4 scallions (shallots/spring onions), finely chopped
1/4 clove garlic, crushed
1/4 cup (1 1/2 oz/45 g) roasted peanuts, finely chopped
1/4 cup (1/3 oz/10 g) cilantro (fresh coriander) leaves, chopped
1 tablespoon sweet chili sauce
2 teaspoons soy sauce
1/2 teaspoon fish sauce
16 round wonton or pot sticker (gow gee) wrappers
1/4 cup (2 fl oz/60 ml) rice vinegar
1/4 cup (2 fl oz/60 ml) fresh lime juice
2 teaspoons fish sauce
1 tablespoon packed palm or brown sugar
1 tablespoon water
1 clove garlic, crushed
1 small fresh red chili, seeded and finely chopped (leave seeds in for more heat)

In a bowl, combine chicken, scallions, garlic, peanuts, cilantro, chili sauce, soy sauce and fish sauce. Place wrappers on a work surface and cover with a damp kitchen towel to prevent them from drying out. Take each wrapper and place in a gow gee press or place 1 wrapper on a work surface. Spoon 2 teaspoons filling in center of wrapper. Brush edges of wrapper with water, and close seal of press, or fold in half, pressing with fingers to seal and make a frilled edge. Cover with a damp kitchen towel and repeat with remaining wrappers and filling.

Place dumplings in a steamer or steamer basket lined with parchment (baking) paper, leaving some space for steam to circulate efficiently. Partially fill a wok or pot with water (steamer or basket should not touch water) and bring to a rapid simmer. Place steamer over boiling water and cover. Steam for 10 minutes.

For chili sauce: In a bowl, combine rice vinegar, lime juice, fish sauce, sugar, water, garlic and chili. Stir constantly until sugar dissolves. Serve dumplings warm with chili sauce.

Cilantro and lime fish cakes

Makes 36 cakes

1 lb (500 g) redfish fillets or skinless, boneless white-fleshed fish fillets
1 tablespoon red curry paste (see page 231)
1 tablespoon fish sauce
1 egg, beaten
2 teaspoons brown sugar
1 clove garlic, crushed
4 kaffir lime leaves, finely shredded, or 2 teaspoons grated lime zest (rind)
2 tablespoons chopped cilantro (fresh coriander)
2 scallions (shallots/spring onions), finely sliced
½ cup (2½ oz/75 g) finely sliced green beans
3 tablespoons vegetable oil, for frying
12 bamboo skewers
½ cup (4 fl oz/125 ml) light soy sauce, for dipping
lime wedges and extra skewers, for serving

In a food processor, combine fish fillets, curry paste, fish sauce, egg, sugar and garlic. Process until mixture forms a thick paste, about 20 seconds. Transfer to a bowl. Add lime leaves, cilantro, scallions and beans. Using wet hands, mix until well combined. Form mixture into 36 balls. Flatten each to form a patty shape.

In a wok, heat oil over medium heat. Working in batches, fry fish cakes until golden, about 1 minute on each side. Remove fish cakes from pan and drain on paper towels, then place 3 fish cakes on each skewer.

Serve with soy sauce for dipping and fresh lime wedges on skewers for garnish.

Crispy fried wontons with chicken filling

Serves 4

16 oz (500 g) ground (minced) chicken
2 teaspoons peeled and grated fresh ginger
4 scallions (shallots/spring onions), sliced
¼ cup (2 oz/60 g) finely chopped canned water chestnuts
1 teaspoon Asian sesame oil
2 tablespoons soy sauce
1 tablespoon dry sherry
24 wonton wrappers
vegetable oil, for deep-frying
1 tablespoon light soy sauce
1 teaspoon rice wine
1 teaspoon Asian sesame oil

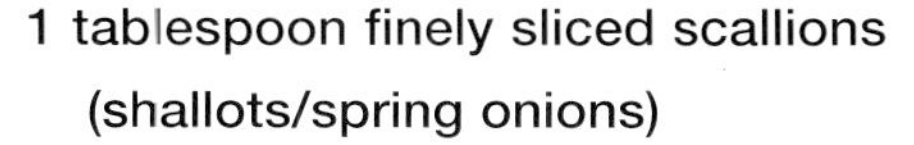

1 tablespoon finely sliced scallions (shallots/spring onions)
½ fresh small red chili, seeded and finely chopped
½ teaspoon chili sauce

In bowl, combine chicken, ginger, scallions, water chestnuts, sesame oil, soy sauce and sherry. Mix well. Place wonton wrappers on work surface and cover with damp kitchen towel to prevent them from drying out. Working with one wrapper at a time, lay it on work surface and place 1 teaspoon filling in middle. Brush edges with water. Gather wonton corners together and twist to seal. Set aside, covered with plastic wrap. Repeat with remaining wonton wrappers.

In a wok or frying pan, heat vegetable oil until it reaches 375°F (190°C) on a deep-frying thermometer or until a small bread cube dropped in oil sizzles and turns golden. Working in batches if necessary, fry filled wontons until golden and crisp, 1–2 minutes. Using slotted spoon, remove from oil and drain on paper towels.

To make dipping sauce: In a bowl, combine soy sauce, rice wine, sesame oil, scallions, chili and chili sauce. Mix well. Pour into serving dish and set aside.

Serve wontons hot with dipping sauce.

Fish balls

Serves 8–10

1½ lb (750 g) white-fleshed fish fillets
6 scallions (shallots/spring onions), chopped
3 tablespoons chopped fresh flat-leaf (Italian) parsley
1 teaspoon chopped fresh dill
1½ cups (3 oz/90 g) soft white bread crumbs,
  or more if needed
1 egg
1 teaspoon salt
freshly ground black pepper
all-purpose (plain) flour for coating
oil, for deep-frying
lemon wedges, for serving

Remove skin and any bones from fillets. Coarsely chop fillets, place in a bowl and stir in scallions, parsley and dill.

Pass the fish mixture through a food grinder using a fine screen, or process to a paste in a food processor in two batches. Return to bowl and add bread crumbs, egg, about 1 teaspoon salt and pepper to taste. Mix to a firm paste, adding more breadcrumbs if needed.

With moistened hands, shape the fish mixture into walnut-sized balls. If time allows, place on a baking sheet and refrigerate until firm, about 30 minutes.

Coat balls with flour. In a heavy wok over medium–high heat, pour oil to a depth of 1½ inches (4 cm). When oil reaches 375°F (190°C) on a deep-frying thermometer or when a small bread cube dropped in oil sizzles and turns golden, add eight balls at a time and cook, turning to brown evenly, for 6–8 minutes. Remove with a slotted spoon and drain on paper towels. Serve hot with lemon wedges.

Fish wraps

Makes 32

1 lb (500 g) firm white-fleshed fish fillets
2 teaspoons peeled and grated fresh ginger
2 tablespoons sweet chili sauce
6 scallions (shallots/spring onions), chopped
1 tablespoon fish sauce
1 egg, beaten
½ cup (1 oz/30 g) fresh white breadcrumbs
2 tablespoons chopped cilantro (fresh coriander)
32 betel leaves
32 toothpicks
½ cup (4 fl oz/125 ml) sweet chili sauce, for dipping

Place fish in a food processor and process until a thick paste is formed, about 30 seconds. Add ginger, chili sauce, scallions, fish sauce, egg, breadcrumbs and cilantro. Process until well combined, about 10 seconds. Using wet hands, divide mixture into 32 portions and shape into balls.

Line a medium-sized bamboo steamer with parchment (baking) paper. Half fill a medium-sized wok with water (steamer should not touch water) and bring water to a boil. Working in batches, arrange fish balls in steamer. Cover, place over boiling water and steam until cooked through, about 15 minutes, adding more water to wok when necessary. Lift steamer from wok and carefully remove fish balls. Wrap each ball in a betel leaf and skewer with a toothpick. Serve warm with chili sauce for dipping.

Tip

Use butter lettuce leaves or basil leaves if betel leaves are unavailable.

Fried chicken wontons

Serves 10–12 as appetizer, 6–8 as entrée

**1 tablespoon vegetable oil,
plus 4 cups (32 fl oz/1 L) oil for deep-frying**
1 onion, chopped
1 clove garlic, crushed
8 oz (250 g) ground (minced) chicken
2 tablespoon chunky peanut butter
1 tablespoon sweet chili sauce
1 tablespoon lemon juice
**¼ cup (⅓ oz/10 g) chopped cilantro
(fresh coriander)**
48 round wonton wrappers
chili oil, for serving

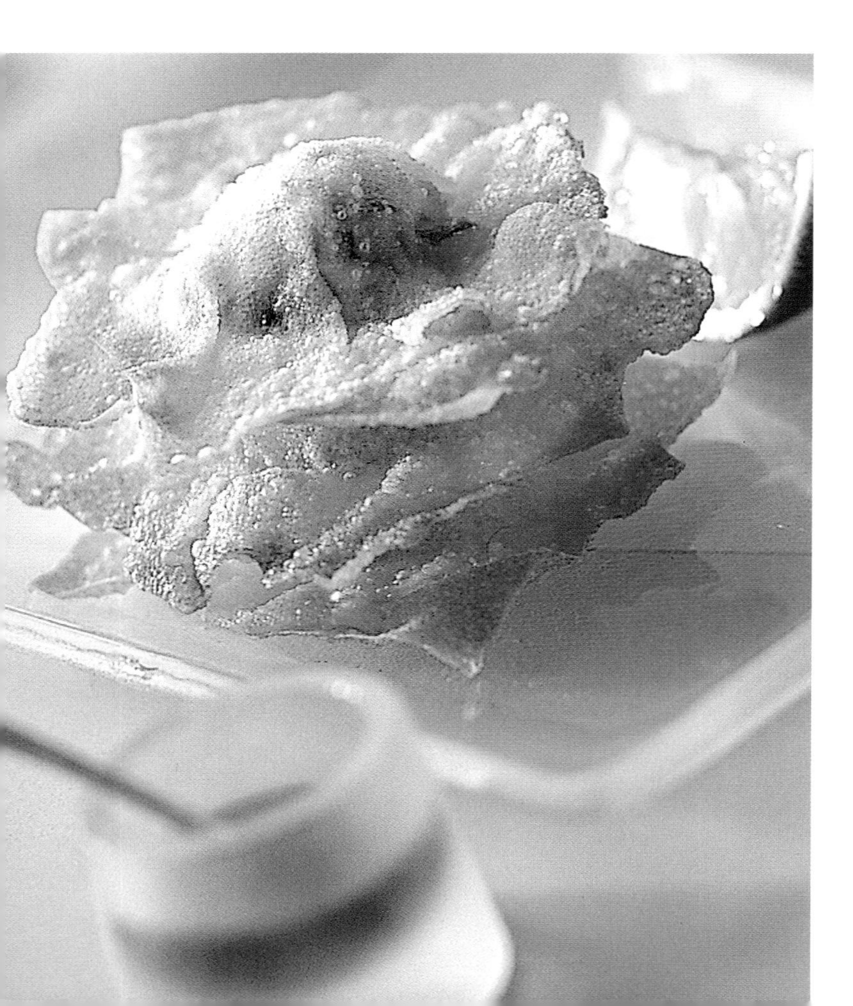

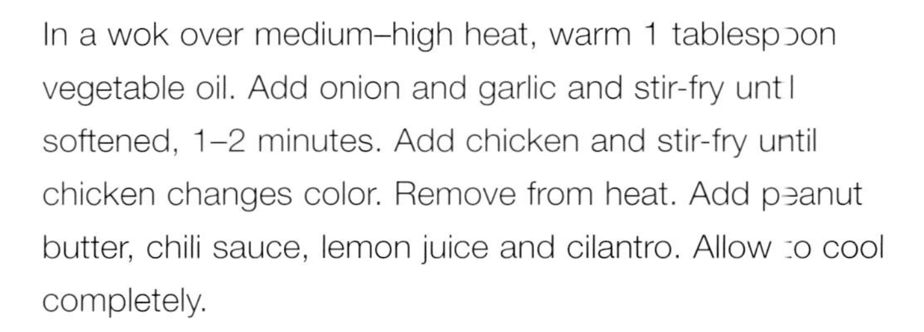

In a wok over medium–high heat, warm 1 tablespoon vegetable oil. Add onion and garlic and stir-fry until softened, 1–2 minutes. Add chicken and stir-fry until chicken changes color. Remove from heat. Add peanut butter, chili sauce, lemon juice and cilantro. Allow to cool completely.

Place wonton wrappers on work surface and cover with damp kitchen towel to prevent them from drying out. Working with one wrapper at a time, lay it on work surface and place 1 heaped teaspoon chicken filling in middle. Brush edges with water. Place another wonton wrapper on top and firmly press edges together. Set aside, covered with plastic wrap. Repeat with remaining wonton wrappers.

In a large wok, heat 4 cups (32 fl oz/1 L) vegetable oil until it reaches 375°F (190°C) on a deep-frying thermometer or until a small bread cube dropped in oil sizzles and turns golden. Working in batches, add wontons and fry until golden on both sides, 1–2 minutes. Using a slotted spoon, remove from wok and drain on paper towels. Serve wontons hot, accompanied with chili oil.

Tip

If round wonton wrappers are unavailable, purchase square wrappers and cut into rounds.

Ginger-sesame pork rolls

Makes 8 rolls

8 oz (250 g) ground (minced) pork
3 scallions (shallots/spring onions), finely chopped
2 tablespoons chopped canned bamboo shoots
1 teaspoon peeled and grated fresh ginger
¼ teaspoon five-spice powder
2 teaspoons soy sauce
1 teaspoon Asian sesame oil
8 bean curd sheets, 5 x 6 inches (13 x 15 cm)
¼ small red bell pepper (capsicum), seeded
and thinly sliced
4 scallions (shallots/spring onions), green tops
only, cut into 5-inch (13-cm) lengths
¼ cup (2 fl oz/60 ml) hoisin sauce
2 tablespoons shaoxing wine or dry sherry
2 teaspoons chopped fresh ginger
1 clove garlic, crushed
1 scallion (shallot/spring onion), finely chopped

In a bowl, combine pork, scallions, bamboo shoots, ginger, five-spice powder, soy sauce, and sesame oil. Mix well. Lightly brush bean curd sheets with cold water and lay flat on a work surface. Spread ⅛ of mixture along one end of each sheet. Lay strips of red bell pepper and scallions along meat and push gently until completely enclosed by meat. Fold two sides of sheet in and roll up, brushing remaining side lightly with water if needed. Press down firmly to seal.

Partially fill a large wok or pot with water (steamer should not touch water) and bring to a rapid simmer.

Line a bamboo steamer or steamer basket with parchment (baking) paper or leaves, leaving some space for steam to circulate efficiently. Arrange tofu rolls in a single layer in steamer. Place steamer over water, cover, and cook until pork mixture is firm and ready, about 10 minutes. Remove rolls from steamer.

For dipping sauce: In a bowl, combine hoisin sauce, wine, ginger, garlic and scallion. Mix well. Serve rolls whole or cut into diagonal pieces and stand with cut side up, with hoisin and ginger sauce for dipping.

Mini noodle baskets with crab and avocado

Makes 12

4 oz (125 g) fresh thin egg noodles
vegetable oil, for deep-frying
1 ripe avocado
juice of 1 lemon
4 oz (125 g) crabmeat, canned or fresh
4 oz (125 g) salmon roe

Soak noodles in boiling water for 10 minutes. Drain and pat dry with paper towels.

In a wok or frying pan, heat oil until it reaches 375°F (190°C) on a deep-frying thermometer or until a small bread cube dropped in oil sizzles and turns golden. Dip 2 strainers into oil to coat. Place 1 heaped tablespoon noodles in larger strainer. Press smaller strainer on top as firmly as possible. Plunge into oil and cook until golden and crisp, 1–2 minutes. Remove from oil. Lift basket from strainers and drain on paper towels. Repeat with remaining noodles. Set baskets aside and allow to cool. You should have 12 baskets.

Remove pit from avocado. Peel, cut into 12 thin slices and brush with lemon juice.

Place slice of avocado in each basket. Top with 1 teaspoon crabmeat and 1 teaspoon salmon roe. Serve immediately.

Tip

Noodle baskets not only look impressive but taste great. They can be made bite size or larger for serving individual portions. For this recipe, you can use a device specifically designed for making noodle nests and sold in Asian markets or specialty kitchen shops. Or you can use two heatproof strainers, one larger so that it holds the other. Be sure to dip the strainers in oil before putting the noodles in so they do not stick. The baskets can be made in advance of using and stored in an airtight container for up to five days.

Miso with scallops and ginger

Serves 4

8 oz (250 g) scallops, cut in half if large
¼ cup (1 oz/30 g) peeled and shredded fresh ginger
¼ cup (⅓ oz/10 g) chopped cilantro (fresh coriander)
1½ cups (12 fl oz/375 ml) water
1 lemongrass stalk, bruised and finely chopped
4 kaffir lime leaves, finely shredded, or 1 teaspoon grated lime zest (rind)
2 tablespoons red miso paste
1 teaspoon lime juice

In a wok, combine scallops, ginger, cilantro, water and lemongrass. Bring to a boil. Reduce heat, cover and simmer until scallops are opaque, 1–2 minutes.

Remove from heat and pour through strainer into bowl. Reserve liquid. Set scallops and spices aside and keep warm.

Measure liquid and add water to make 4 cups (32 fl oz/1 L). Return to wok and bring to a boil. Stir in miso and lime juice, reduce heat and simmer for 3 minutes.

To serve, divide scallops among individual plates. Ladle miso into small bowls.

Mixed vegetable pakoras

Makes about 28

2⅔ cups (14 oz/400 g) chickpea (garbanzo bean) flour
1 teaspoon whole ajwain seeds (see Tips below)
½ teaspoon chili powder
salt to taste
4 teaspoons vegetable oil
about 1¼ cups (10 fl oz/300 ml) water
vegetable oil for deep-frying
1 red bell pepper (capsicum), seeded and cut into ½-inch (12-mm) dice
1 medium desiree potato, peeled and cut into ½-inch (12-mm) dice
1 large red (Spanish) or yellow (brown) onion, cut into ½-inch (12-mm) dice
1 medium globe eggplant (aubergine), unpeeled, cut into ½-inch (12-mm) dice
mint raita (see page 228), for serving

In a bowl, combine flour, ajwain, chili powder and salt. In a small saucepan, heat oil until it begins to smoke, then quickly stir into flour mixture. Add enough water to form a thick smooth batter.

Fill a wok with vegetable oil to a depth of 3 inches (7.5 cm). Heat oil over medium–high heat to 375°F (190°C) on a deep-frying thermometer or until a small bread cube dropped in oil sizzles and turns golden. Meanwhile, add all diced vegetables to batter and mix well.

Working in batches of about seven pakoras, carefully drop 1 heaped tablespoon mixture for each pakora into hot oil. Cook, turning as necessary, until light golden brown, 1–2 minutes per side. Use a slotted spoon to remove pakoras to paper towels to drain. Repeat with remaining batter.

Just before serving pakoras, refry them in batches of seven, turning once, until crisp and golden brown, 1–2 minutes. Drain on paper towels. Serve immediately with mint raita.

Tips

- Ajwain seeds have the flavor of thyme with peppery overtones. Similar in appearance to celery seeds, they are used in Indian breads, fried snacks, and lentil and vegetable dishes.
- You can do the initial frying of pakoras up to 6 hours ahead. Instead of dicing vegetables, you can cut them into thin slices, dip them in batter, then deep-fry slices until golden brown.

Peanut and chili bundles

Serves 8–10 as appetizer, 6 as entrée

- 1 cup (5½ oz/165 g) unsalted roasted peanuts
- 1 small red chili, seeded and finely chopped
- 8 scallions (shallots/green onions), finely chopped
- ¼ cup (⅓ oz/10 g) chopped cilantro (fresh coriander)
- ½ cup (4 fl oz/125 ml) lemon juice
- ½ cup (1 oz/30 g) fresh white bread crumbs
- 1 teaspoon superfine (caster) sugar
- 24 wonton wrappers
- 4 cups (32 fl oz/1 L) vegetable oil, for deep-frying
- lime wedges and sweet chili sauce or soy sauce, for serving

In a food processor or blender, process peanuts until fine. Transfer to bowl. Add chili, scallions, cilantro, lemon juice, bread crumbs and sugar. Mix well.

Place wonton wrappers on work surface and cover with damp towel to prevent them from drying out. Working with one wrapper at a time, place 1 teaspoon peanut filling in middle. Brush edges with water, gather edges together and twist to seal. Set aside, covered with plastic wrap. Repeat with remaining wonton wrappers.

In a wok, heat oil until it reaches 375°F (190°C) on a deep-frying thermometer or until a small bread cube dropped in oil sizzles and turns golden. Working in batches, add wontons and fry until golden, 1–2 minutes. Using slotted spoon, remove from wok and drain on paper towels.

Serve bundles hot with lime wedges and with sweet chili sauce or soy sauce for dipping.

Portuguese-style shrimp

Serves 4–6

Reichado masala

4 dried red chilies, broken into small pieces
4 teaspoons black peppercorns
1 teaspoon cumin seeds
¼ cup (2 fl oz/60 ml) white vinegar
4 teaspoons crushed garlic
1½ teaspoons tamarind concentrate
½ teaspoon ground turmeric

2 lb (1 kg) medium shrimp (prawns), peeled and deveined
2 tablespoons vegetable oil
juice of 1 lemon

For reichado masala: In a spice grinder, grind chilies, peppercorns and cumin seeds (without roasting) to a powder. In a small bowl, combine vinegar, garlic and tamarind. Stir in ground spices and turmeric, and mix well. Set aside to stand for 10–20 minutes before using.

In a glass or ceramic bowl, combine reichado masala and shrimp and mix well to coat shrimp. Set aside to marinate for 5 minutes.

In a wok, heat oil over medium–low heat until hot. Cook shrimp in batches, turning once, until browned, about 1–2 minutes. Take care not to scorch marinade. Drizzle cooked shrimp with lemon juice and serve hot.

Tips

- Reichado masala can be kept in an airtight jar and stored in refrigerator for up to 6 months.
- As a variation, lightly brush shrimp with reichado masala. Cook shrimp in batches as above and set aside. In a small saucepan, heat 2 tablespoons vegetable oil over medium–high heat. Cook 20 curry leaves—or as many as desired—until fragrant, about 30 seconds. Drain on paper towels and toss with shrimp. If desired, add thinly sliced red (Spanish) onion for color.

Pot stickers

Serves 4

8 oz (250 g) ground (minced) lean pork
1 onion, finely chopped
1 cup (3 oz/90 g) finely shredded green cabbage
2 teaspoons peeled and grated fresh ginger
1 tablespoon Asian sesame oil
1 tablespoon soy sauce
1 teaspoon white pepper
24 round wheat wonton wrappers
4 tablespoons vegetable oil
2 cups (16 fl oz/500 ml) chicken stock (see page 220), or as needed
light soy sauce, for serving

In a bowl, combine pork, onion, cabbage, ginger, sesame oil, soy sauce and pepper. Mix well.

Place wonton wrappers on work surface and cover with damp kitchen towel to prevent them from drying out. Working with one wrapper at a time, lay it on work surface and place 1 teaspoon filling in middle. Brush edges with water, fold wonton in half and press edges together to seal. Using your fingertips, pinch frill around each folded wonton if desired. Set aside, covered with plastic wrap. Repeat with remaining wrappers.

In a heavy-bottomed pan over medium–high heat, heat 1 tablespoon vegetable oil. Swirl to cover entire bottom of pan. Working in batches, fry filled wontons until golden brown on both sides, about 1 minute. Coat pan as needed with remaining 3 tablespoons vegetable oil.

Return pot stickers to pan and add enough stock to come halfway up sides of pot stickers. Cover and simmer until stock is almost absorbed, about 10 minutes. Uncover and cook until stock is completely absorbed and bottoms of pot stickers are crisp. Repeat with remaining pot stickers. Serve pot stickers warm with soy sauce.

Tip

These panfried pork dumplings originally got their name because they tend to stick to the pot during cooking. Though messy, the dumplings have an authentic flavor and appearance.

Rice flour crisps

Serves 4

1½ cups (12 oz/375 g) rice flour
⅓ cup (2 oz/ 60 g) besan flour
1 tablespoon cumin seeds
1 teaspoon chili powder
1 teaspoon ground coriander
2 tablespoons ghee
about 1 cup (8 fl oz/250 ml) coconut milk
3 cups (24 fl oz/750 ml) vegetable oil, for deep-frying
2 teaspoons sea salt

Sift flours into a bowl. Add cumin seeds, chili powder and coriander. Rub ghee into dry ingredients, using your fingers. Make a well in the center and stir in enough coconut milk to make a soft batter. Spoon batter into a piping bag fitted with a ½-inch (12-mm) star tip.

In a large wok, heat oil until it reaches 375°F (190°C) on a deep-frying thermometer or until a small bread cube dropped in oil sizzles and turns golden. Working in batches, carefully pipe 2-inch (5-cm) lengths of batter into hot oil and fry until golden and crisp, about 1 minute. Using a slotted spoon, transfer to paper towels to drain. Sprinkle with salt and serve immediately.

Savory rice bites

Makes 16–20 squares

1½ tablespoons tamarind pulp
½ cup (4 fl oz/125 ml) boiling water
1 cup (7 oz/220 g) white glutinous rice
2 teaspoons grated fresh turmeric
1 teaspoon finely peeled and grated fresh ginger
¾ cup (6 fl oz/180 ml) thin coconut cream or coconut milk
2 scallions (shallots/spring onions), finely chopped
¼ cup (⅓ oz/10 g) cilantro (fresh coriander) leaves, finely chopped
3 kaffir lime leaves, spines removed, finely chopped
¼ teaspoon grated kaffir lime zest (rind)
1 red chili, seeded and finely chopped (optional)
6 oz (185 g) barbecued pork (available from Asian food stores) or barbecued chicken, sliced
Sweet chili, satay, or hoisin sauce, for serving

Place tamarind pulp in a small bowl and cover with boiling water. Mix well, breaking up pulp with a spoon to release flavor. Let stand for 5 minutes, then push through a fine-meshed strainer, discarding pulp and reserving liquid.

Wrap turmeric in a cheesecloth (muslin) square and tie with string. Put rice, turmeric and tamarind liquid in a medium bowl. Cover with cold water and let soak overnight. Drain, removing turmeric. Line a bamboo steamer or steamer basket with cheese-cloth (muslin) and spread rice evenly on top.

Partially fill a wok or pot with water (steamer should not touch water) and bring to a rapid simmer.

Place steamer over water, cover, and steam until rice is just tender, 30–35 minutes, adding more water to wok if required. Remove steamer from heat and put rice in a bowl.

Gently fold in ginger, coconut cream, scallions, cilantro, lime leaves, lime zest and chili. Spread rice evenly in an 8-inch (20-cm) square baking pan lined with parchment (baking) paper and refrigerate until set, about 2 hours. Cut into 16–20 squares to serve. Top with a small piece of barbecued pork or chicken and a dash of sweet chili, satay or hoisin sauce.

Shrimp and coconut fritters

Serves 6–8

10 oz (300 g) small raw shrimp (prawns), coarsely chopped
2 cups (16 fl oz/500 ml) water
1 cup (5 oz/150 g) self-raising flour
1/3 cup (1 oz/30 g) unsweetened dried (desiccated) shredded coconut
1/2 teaspoon baking powder
1 teaspoon salt
1 large egg
1/3 teaspoon black pepper
2 scallions (shallots/spring onions), finely chopped
1 small clove garlic, finely chopped
2 teaspoons fresh dill or cilantro (fresh coriander), chopped
2 tablespoons vegetable oil
sweet chili sauce, for serving

Peel the shrimp and place shells in a saucepan with water. Bring to a boil, simmer for 10 minutes, then strain liquid into a pitcher and let cool.

In a bowl, combine shrimp and remaining ingredients, except oil and chili sauce. Slowly add cooled, reserved liquid to make a creamy batter, adding extra cold water if necessary. Set aside for 25 minutes.

In a wok, heat oil over medium heat. Add large tablespoonfuls of batter and cook until golden brown underneath, then turn and cook other side. The fritters are done when they feel firm in the middle and no uncooked batter exudes when pressed. Remove from wok using a slotted spoon and drain on paper towels. Keep warm until remainder are cooked. Serve immediately with sweet chili sauce.

Shrimp and lemongrass sticks

Makes 12

1½ lb (750 g) jumbo shrimp (green king prawns), peeled and deveined
3 cloves garlic, chopped
2 teaspoons peeled and grated fresh ginger
6 scallions (shallots/spring onions), chopped
¼ cup (⅓ oz/10 g) chopped cilantro (fresh coriander)
1 teaspoon sambal oelek (see page 230)
3 teaspoons fish sauce
2 tablespoons cornstarch (cornflour)
6 lemongrass stalks, trimmed and cut into 12 pieces about 4 inches (10 cm) long
¼ cup (1 oz/30 g) cornstarch (cornflour), for dusting
3 cups (24 fl oz/750 ml) vegetable oil, for frying
soy sauce or chili oil (see page 223), for dipping

In a food processor, process shrimp until a thick paste forms, about 20 seconds. Add garlic, ginger, scallions, cilantro, sambal oelek, fish sauce and 2 tablespoons cornstarch and process until well combined, about 10 seconds. Using wet hands, divide mixture into 12 portions. Mold each portion around end of a lemongrass piece. Lightly dust with cornstarch, shaking off any excess.

In a large wok, heat oil until it reaches 375°F (190°C) on a deep-frying thermometer or until a small bread cube dropped in oil sizzles and turns golden. Working in batches, add lemongrass sticks and cook until golden, 3–4 minutes. Using a slotted spoon, remove from hot oil and drain on paper towels. Serve hot with soy sauce or chili oil for dipping.

Sweet corn fritters

Serves 4–5

1 lb (500 g) potatoes, peeled and cubed
1 egg, beaten
¼ cup (2 fl oz/60 ml) cream
¼ cup (1½ oz/45 g) all-purpose (plain) flour
kernels from 2 corn cobs, about 2 cups (12 oz/375 g)
¼ cup (¼ oz/7 g) cilantro (fresh coriander) leaves, finely chopped
1 egg white
sea salt and freshly ground black pepper to taste
3 tablespoons vegetable oil
⅓ cup (3 fl oz/90 ml) sweet chili sauce, for dipping

Preheat oven to 225°F (110°C/Gas ¼). Bring a saucepan of salted water to a boil. Add potatoes and cook until soft but not mushy, 6–8 minutes. Drain well, place in a bowl and mash with a fork or potato masher. Allow to cool slightly. Add egg and cream and mix well. Stir in flour, corn and cilantro.

In a bowl, using a balloon whisk or electric beater, beat egg white until soft peaks form. Gently fold egg white into corn mixture and season with salt and pepper.

In a heavy-bottomed wok, warm oil over medium heat. For each fritter, spoon 2 tablespoons corn mixture into hot pan. Cook fritters until golden, 2–3 minutes per side. Remove from pan and drain on paper towels. Keep warm in oven. Serve with sweet chili sauce for dipping.

Vegetarian spring rolls

Makes 18–20

4 Chinese dried mushrooms
2 oz (60 g) cellophane (bean thread) noodles or rice vermicelli
2 tablespoons vegetable oil
1 onion, finely chopped
2 cloves garlic, chopped
2 tablespoons peeled and grated fresh ginger
2 cups (6 oz/180 g) shredded green cabbage
2 carrots, peeled and grated
⅓ cup (½ oz/15 g) chopped cilantro (fresh coriander)
1 cup (4 oz/125 g) fresh bean sprouts, rinsed
2 teaspoons fish sauce
2 teaspoons cornstarch (cornflour) mixed in 2 tablespoons water
18–20 frozen spring roll wrappers, thawed
vegetable oil, for deep-frying
sweet chili sauce, for serving

Place mushrooms in a small bowl, add boiling water to cover and let stand for 10–15 minutes. Drain and squeeze out excess liquid. Thinly slice mushrooms, discarding tough stems.

Soak noodles in boiling water for 10 minutes. Drain and roughly chop into short lengths.

In a wok or frying pan over medium–high heat, warm 2 tablespoons oil. Add onion, garlic and ginger and cook until softened, about 2 minutes. Add cabbage and stir-fry until cabbage is softened, 1–2 minutes. Remove from heat and stir in carrots, cilantro, bean sprouts, noodles, mushrooms and fish sauce. Mix well and cool completely.

Separate spring roll wrappers, place on a work surface and cover with damp kitchen towel to prevent them from drying out. Working with one wrapper at a time, place on work surface. Using your fingertips, wet edges with cornstarch and water mixture. Place 1 heaped tablespoon filling in middle of wrapper. Roll up diagonally, tucking in edges. Seal edge with cornstarch and water mixture. Repeat with remaining wrappers.

In a wok or frying pan, heat oil until it reaches 375°F (190°C) on a deep-frying thermometer or until a small bread cube dropped in oil sizzles and turns golden. Working in batches, add rolls and fry until golden, 1–2 minutes. Using a slotted spoon, remove from pan and drain on paper towels. Serve hot, accompanied with chili sauce.

chicken and duck

Braised duck with pineapple

Serves 4

1 duck (about 3 lb/1.5 kg) or duck pieces (see Tips opposite)
½ cup (2 oz/60 g) finely chopped brown or pink shallots (French shallots)
6 cloves garlic, finely chopped
about ½ teaspoon ground pepper
2 tablespoons fish sauce
2–3 tablespoons vegetable oil
3 cups (24 fl oz/750 ml) chicken stock (see page 220)
2 tablespoons distilled rice alcohol or vodka
1 fresh pineapple, peeled, or one 28-oz (850-g) can pineapple rings, drained
1 tablespoon sugar
1 teaspoon salt or to taste
1 tablespoon arrowroot or cornstarch (cornflour) mixed with 1 tablespoon water
cilantro (fresh coriander) sprigs, for garnish
coarsely ground pepper to taste

If using whole duck, begin by placing duck on a cutting board. Pull each leg away from body and use a cleaver or large chef's knife to cut through the joint attaching it to the body. Likewise, pull each wing away from body and cut through its joint. Cut duck carcass in half lengthwise by cutting through bones connecting breast and back. Remove and discard any large bones as necessary. Now cut down along backbone, turn over duck, and cut lengthwise through breastbone. You should have 8 pieces. Cut each section crosswise through the bones into bite-sized pieces.

In a large bowl, toss duck pieces with shallots, garlic, pepper and fish sauce. Let stand at room temperature for 1 hour or refrigerate overnight. Using a slotted spoon, transfer duck to a plate, reserving marinade. Pat duck dry with paper towels.

In a large wok or frying pan, heat oil over medium heat. Add duck pieces, skin-side down, and cook until golden brown and all fat has been extracted, about 15–20 minutes. Drain off and discard fat. For a lighter, skin-free version, refer to the Tip opposite.

Transfer duck to a heavy pot. Add stock, liquor and reserved marinade. Bring to a very gentle boil, then immediately reduce heat to low, cover, and cook at a bare simmer until tender, about 20 minutes.

Meanwhile, cut fresh pineapple in half lengthwise, then into half-moons ½ inch (12 mm) thick. Use a small paring knife to remove core. Alternatively, cut canned pineapple rings in half crosswise. In a large, nonstick wok over medium heat, lightly brown pineapple pieces, sprinkling with sugar to create a light caramel glaze. Alternatively, use a large wok oiled with 1 tablespoon vegetable oil or butter, or vegetable oil cooking spray. Remove from heat and set aside.

When duck is almost done, add pineapple and taste for seasoning, adding salt to taste. Cook for a few minutes for flavors to meld. Using a slotted spoon, transfer duck and pineapple to a bowl; cover to keep warm. Strain cooking liquid. If liquid appears greasy, lightly float paper towels on the surface to absorb fat.

Add arrowroot mixture to sauce. Bring to a boil, stirring. Spoon some of this sauce over duck pieces. Serve additional sauce alongside. Garnish with cilantro sprigs and, sprinkle with coarsely ground pepper.

Tips

- For a lighter version, use skinless duck pieces. Fry duck pieces until lightly browned, for only 2–3 minutes. Likewise, boneless, skinless duck breast can be used; simmer until just tender, 10–15 minutes.
- For braised duck with orange, substitute an equal quantity of peeled orange segments for pineapple.

Chicken and cashew stir-fry

Serves 4

2 tablespoons vegetable oil
4 oz (100 g) cashew nut kernels
1 bunch scallions (shallots/spring onions), trimmed and sliced
4–5 sticks celery, thinly sliced
4 chicken breasts, skinned and cut in ½-inch (1.5-cm) cubes
6 oz (150 g) stir-fry yellow bean sauce
salt and pepper
steamed rice, for serving

In a wok or a heavy-based saucepan or skillet, add the oil and heat it until it smokes. Toss in the cashew nuts onions and celery and cook for 1–2 minutes, stirring frequently over a fairly fierce heat until the nuts are lightly browned. Add the chicken and cook quickly, stirring frequently for 2–3 minutes until sealed and just cooked. Add the yellow bean sauce, season lightly and cook for a further minutes or so until piping hot.

Serve at once with steamed rice.

Chicken chow mein

Serves 4

6 cups (48 fl oz/1.5 L) vegetable oil, for deep-frying, plus 2 tablespoons oil
6½ oz (200 g) fresh thin egg noodles
3 cloves garlic, crushed
1 tablespoon peeled and grated fresh ginger
1 onion, cut into eighths
1 lb (500 g) skinless chicken thigh fillets, cut into ¾-inch (2-cm) cubes
1 red bell pepper (capsicum), seeded and sliced
1 green bell pepper (capsicum), seeded and sliced
1 bunch choy sum or spinach, trimmed and cut into 2-inch (5-cm) lengths
3 tablespoons hoisin sauce
¼ cup (2 fl oz/60 ml) chicken stock (see page 220) mixed with 1 teaspoon cornstarch (cornflour)

In a wok, heat 6 cups (48 fl oz/1.5 L) oil until it reaches 375°F (190°C) on a deep-frying thermometer or until a small bread cube dropped in oil sizzles and turns golden. Working in small batches, add noodles and fry until golden and crisp, 1–2 minutes. Using slotted spoon, remove from oil and drain on paper towels.

In a wok over medium-high heat, warm 2 tablespoons vegetable oil. Add garlic, ginger and onion and stir-fry until onion softens slightly, about 3 minutes. Add chicken and stir-fry until browned, 3–4 minutes. Add bell peppers and choy sum or spinach and stir-fry until tender-crisp, about 2 minutes. Stir in hoisin sauce and stock and cornstarch mixture and cook until sauce boils and thickens slightly, about 2 minutes.

To serve, arrange crisp noodles in nest on serving plates. Top with chicken and vegetables.

Chicken satay salad

Serves 4

1 cup (8 fl oz/250 ml) coconut milk
½ cup (5 oz/155 g) crunchy peanut butter
1 tablespoon fish sauce
1 tablespoon soy sauce
1 tablespoon peeled and grated fresh ginger
1 tablespoon palm sugar or brown sugar
1 teaspoon red chili flakes
6½ oz (200 g) rice stick noodles
4 cloves garlic, crushed
3 tablespoons fish sauce
1 tablespoon soy sauce
1 tablespoon minced lemongrass or 2 teaspoons grated lemon zest (rind)
1 lb (500 g) skinless chicken breast fillets, sliced
2 tablespoons vegetable oil
3 carrots, peeled and julienned
1 cup (4 oz/125 g) fresh bean sprouts, rinsed
¼ cup (⅓ oz/10 g) chopped cilantro (fresh coriander)
1 bunch mizuna or 1 head butter lettuce, leaves separated and trimmed
lime wedges for serving

In a food processor, combine coconut milk, peanut butter, fish and soy sauces, ginger, sugar and red chili flakes. Process 10 seconds. Transfer to bowl and set aside.

Cook noodles, then drain and allow to cool. In a glass or ceramic bowl, combine garlic, fish and soy sauces and lemongrass or zest. Add chicken and turn to coat in marinade. Cover and allow to marinate in refrigerator 1 hour. Drain.

In a wok, heat oil over medium-high heat. Add chicken and cook, stirring, until golden and tender, 4–5 minutes. Add to satay sauce and toss.

In bowl, combine carrots, bean sprouts, noodles and cilantro.

To serve, arrange mizuna or lettuce leaves on individual plates. Top with vegetable-noodle mixture. Spoon on chicken and sauce. Serve warm or chilled with lime wedges.

Chicken stir-fry with bean sprouts

Serves 4

4 boneless chicken breasts, skinned
salt and pepper
3 tablespoons oil, preferably sesame or walnut
1 clove garlic, crushed
6 oz (185 g) carrots, peeled and cut into thin sticks
2 cups (8 oz/250 g) fresh bean sprouts
3–4 oz (90–125 g) snow peas (mange-tout), trimmed
7-oz (220-g) can pineapple pieces in natural juice
2 tablespoons light soy sauce
1 tablespoon sesame seeds
steamed rice, for serving

Cut chicken into strips and season lightly with salt and pepper.

In a wok or large heavy-based pan, heat 2 tablespoons oil and stir-fry chicken pieces briskly until browned and cooked through. Remove from wok and set aside.

Add remaining oil, garlic and carrots to wok and stir-fry for 3–4 minutes, stirring constantly. Add bean sprouts and snow peas and cook for 2–3 minutes, stirring.

Drain pineapple, reserving 2 tablespoons juice. Add pineapple to wok with cooked chicken, reserved pineapple juice and soy sauce, and season to taste. Heat through thoroughly. Sprinkle with sesame seeds.

Serve immediately with steamed rice.

Chicken with ginger

Serves 4–6

1 cup (2 oz/60 g) cloud or tree ear mushrooms (black or white fungus)
¼ cup (2 fl oz/60 ml) vegetable oil
6 cloves garlic, coarsely chopped
1 small onion, thinly sliced
12 oz (375 g) boneless, skinless chicken breasts, thinly sliced
1 cup (4 oz/125 g) loosely packed, julienned fresh ginger, preferably young ginger
1 tablespoon fish sauce
3 tablespoons oyster sauce
1 tablespoon soy sauce
1 tablespoon soybean paste
2 fresh long red chilies, cut into large pieces
½ cup (4 fl oz/125 ml) chicken stock (see page 220)
8 scallions (shallots/spring onions), white part only, chopped

If using dried mushrooms, soak in water for 10 minutes; drain. Use scissors to trim hard core, then cut mushrooms into pieces.

In a wok or large, heavy frying pan, heat oil over high heat and fry garlic just until it starts to brown. Immediately add onion and chicken, and stir-fry until meat is opaque on all sides, about 2 minutes.

Add ginger and mushrooms, then fish sauce, oyster sauce, soy sauce, and soybean paste. Stir-fry for 1 minute. Add chilies and stock or water, bring to a boil, and cook for 1 minute. Stir in scallions. Transfer to a serving dish and serve.

Tip

If cloud or tree ear mushrooms are unavailable, use an equal quantity of straw mushrooms or standard mushrooms.

Chicken with lemongrass and chili

Serves 6

1½ lb (750 g) chicken (thigh portions)
1 tablespoon fish sauce
salt and black pepper to taste
2 lemongrass stalks, trimmed
2 scallions (shallots/spring onions), trimmed
3 tablespoons vegetable oil
1 cup (8 fl oz/250 ml) water
2 fresh red chilies, seeded and sliced
1 teaspoon crumbled palm or brown sugar
steamed rice, for serving

Cut chicken portions in half, through bone. Using a sharp skewer, prick chicken. Place chicken in a dish and pour over fish sauce, sprinkle on salt and pepper and let stand for 15 minutes.

Very finely chop lemongrass and scallions. In a wok, heat oil and brown chicken evenly. Add lemongrass and scallions and water. Cover and cook until chicken is almost tender, about 15 minutes, turning several times. Add chilies and sugar and cook for a further 5–7 minutes. The liquid should evaporate, leaving chicken free of sauce. Serve immediately with steamed rice.

Chili chicken and vegetables

Serves 4

2 tablespoons peanut oil
1 small red chili, seeded and
  finely chopped
5 oz (150 g) skinless chicken breast or thigh
  fillet, cut into 1-inch (2.5-cm) cubes
6 asparagus spears, cut into 1¼-inch (3-cm) pieces
1 bunch bok choy, trimmed and large leaves halved
4 oz (125 g) sugar snap peas or snow peas
  (mange-touts), trimmed
4 oz (125 g) shiitake mushrooms, sliced
¼ cup (2 fl oz/60 ml) chicken stock (see page 220)
2 teaspoons soy sauce
1 tablespoon rice wine
1 teaspoon Asian sesame oil
crisp fried egg noodles for serving (optional)

In a wok over medium heat, warm peanut oil. Add chili and chicken and stir-fry until chicken is golden, 4–5 minutes. Raise heat to medium–high, add asparagus, bok choy sugar snap peas or snow peas and mushrooms and stir-fry until vegetables soften slightly, 3–4 minutes.

In a small bowl, combine stock, soy sauce, rice wine and sesame oil. Add to wok, reduce heat to medium and cook until heated through.

Serve hot, with crisp fried egg noodles if desired.

Crispy wontons with duck

Serves 4

10 scallions (shallots/spring onions), pale portion only, cut into 2-inch (5-cm) pieces
2 carrots, peeled and julienned
1 Chinese roasted duck
6 cups (48 fl oz/1.5 L) vegetable oil, for deep-frying
16 wonton wrappers
½ cup (4 fl oz/125 ml) hoisin sauce

Using sharp knife or scissors, make ¼-inch (6-mm) cuts into ends of each scallion piece to make fringe. Place scallions and carrots in bowl of ice water. Refrigerate until scallions curl, about 15 minutes.

Remove meat and skin from duck and coarsely chop; discard skin if desired. In a wok, heat oil until it reaches 375°F (190°C) on a deep-frying thermometer or until a small bread cube dropped in oil sizzles and turns golden. Working with one wonton at a time and using two sets of tongs, hold wonton in taco shape and lower into oil. Continue to hold wonton until golden and crisp, about 1 minute. Drain on paper towels. Repeat with remaining wontons.

To serve, fill wontons with scallions, carrots and duck. Drizzle with hoisin sauce and serve immediately.

Duck with long beans

Serves 4

1 Chinese roasted duck
2 teaspoons vegetable oil
4 scallions (shallots/spring onions), chopped
1 tablespoon peeled and shredded fresh ginger
8 long beans, cut into 2½-inch (6-cm) lengths
2 tablespoons shredded orange zest (rind)
2 tablespoons mirin
1½ tablespoons light soy sauce
steamed white rice, for serving

Cut duck into serving pieces, leaving flesh on bone. Set aside. In a wok over medium–high heat, warm vegetable oil. Add scallions and ginger and stir-fry until softened, about 2 minutes. Add beans, orange zest, duck, mirin and soy sauce and stir-fry until heated through, 3–4 minutes.

Serve hot, accompanied with steamed white rice.

Green chicken curry

Serves 4–6

2 tablespoon vegetable oil
1 onion, chopped
1 tablespoon green curry paste or to taste
1 lb (500 g) skinless chicken thigh fillets, cut into thin strips
5 oz (150 g) green beans, trimmed
1¾ cups (14 fl oz/440 ml) coconut milk
4 kaffir lime leaves
1 tablespoon fish sauce
1 teaspoon grated lime zest (rind)
1 tablespoon lime juice
1 tablespoon brown sugar
2 tablespoons chopped cilantro (fresh coriander)
steamed white rice, for serving

In a wok over medium heat, warm vegetable oil. Add onion and curry paste and stir-fry until onion softens, 1–2 minutes. Add chicken and stir-fry until lightly golden, 3–4 minutes. Add beans, coconut milk and lime leaves and bring to a boil. Reduce heat to low and simmer, uncovered, until beans are tender-crisp, 3–4 minutes. Add fish sauce, lime zest and juice, sugar and cilantro. Cook for 1 minute.

Serve hot, accompanied with steamed white rice.

Grilled chicken drumsticks

Serves 4

5 chicken drumsticks
1 tablespoon ginger juice (obtained by grating fresh ginger)
1 tablespoon vegetable or sunflower oil
2 tablespoons light soy sauce
1 tablespoon sugar
1 tablespoon malt liquid (mullyeot)
1 tablespoon rice wine
1 tablespoon chopped parsley, for garnish

Score drumsticks all over with tip of a knife to allow ginger flavor to penetrate. Place drumsticks in a medium bowl and drizzle with ginger juice. Marinate for 15 minutes, turning frequently to coat with juice.

In a wok over medium heat, heat 1 tablespoon of oil. Add drumsticks and fry until golden, about 5 minutes. Remove and keep warm. Keep sauce in pan.

Add soy sauce, sugar, malt liquid and rice wine to pan juices. Boil over high heat until liquid is reduced by half, about 5 minutes.

Using a brush, coat drumsticks with the sauce. Return to wok and cook over high heat until sauce caramelizes and chicken is cooked, 5–8 minutes. Test with a skewer; chicken is done when juices run clear.

Transfer drumsticks to a serving plate and wrap the bone ends in foil. Garnish with parsley and serve as finger food with steamed rice.

Tip

Malt liquid has a slightly sweet flavor. It is added to dishes for presentation as it adds a shine.

Indonesian-style chicken fried rice

Serves 4

2 cups (12 oz/375 g) long-grain rice
1 tablespoon vegetable oil
1 tablespoon Asian sesame oil
1 lb (500 g) chicken breast fillet, chopped
1 carrot, sliced into thin strips
1 medium-size green bell pepper (capsicum), seeded and thinly sliced
1 teaspoon Chinese five-spice powder
1 teaspoon ground coriander
½ teaspoon ground cumin
1 tablespoon finely grated fresh ginger
2 cloves garlic, minced
1 small chili, finely chopped
¼ cup (2 fl oz/60 ml) soy sauce
8 oz (250 g) bean sprouts
6 scallions (shallots/spring onions), sliced

Cook the rice according to package instructions. Drain, then return to pan, cover tightly with lid and set aside.

In a wok or large frying pan, heat the vegetable and sesame oil. Add chicken and stir-fry until lightly browned and tender, about 4 minutes. Add carrot and bell pepper and continue stir-frying for 2 minutes. Stir in spices.

Stir rice with fork and add to wok with remaining ingredients. Cook, stirring, 3 minutes to mix and heat through.

Larb salad with chicken

Serves 4–6

2 tablespoons sticky (glutinous) rice
2 thin slices fresh galangal
12 oz (375 g) boneless, skinless chicken breasts, ground (minced)
2 tablespoons thinly sliced shallots (French shallots), preferably pink
3 tablespoons fish sauce
2 tablespoons fresh lime juice
2–3 teaspoons chili powder, to taste
1 tablespoon coarsely chopped cilantro (fresh coriander) leaves and stems
1 scallion (shallot/spring onion), including green part, coarsely chopped
1 tablespoon coarsely chopped fresh mint

In a wok or small frying pan over low-medium heat, stir rice until golden brown, 3–5 minutes. Transfer to a mortar and pound to a coarse powder with a pestle. Transfer to a bowl and set aside. Pound galangal in the mortar until pulverized.

In a medium bowl, combine ground chicken, galangal, shallots, fish sauce, lime juice, and chili powder to taste; mix thoroughly. Heat a wok or large, heavy frying pan over medium heat and add chicken mixture all at once, stirring vigorously to keep it from sticking into lumps. Cook until opaque throughout, about 5 minutes.

Transfer to a bowl, and let cool slightly, then toss with ground rice and all remaining ingredients. If desired, garnish with additional mint leaves, and accompany with vegetable crudités, such as cabbage, carrot, cucumber, and long beans.

Tips

- Ask your butcher to grind the chicken, or do it yourself in a food processor.
- For Larb with Pork: Substitute an equal quantity ground pork for chicken, and cook as above.

Orange rice with chicken

Serves 5–6

2 oranges
2 cups (16 fl oz/500 ml) water
1 cup (8 oz/250 g) white sugar
4 tablespoons ghee or oil
½ cup (2 oz/60 g) slivered blanched almonds
2 lb (1 kg) boneless chicken breasts, quartered
1 tablespoon salt, plus extra salt to taste
freshly ground black pepper
1 medium-sized yellow (brown) onion, sliced
2 cups (14 oz/440 g) basmati rice
½ cup (1 oz/30 g) shelled, blanched pistachio nuts, chopped
½ teaspoon saffron threads, steeped in 2 tablespoons hot water for 10 minutes

Remove zest (rind) from oranges with vegetable peeler and cut into fine shreds about 1¼ inches (3 cm) long. In a small saucepan, bring water to a boil. Add zest and boil for 5 minutes. Drain and rinse.

Place 1 cup (8 fl oz/250 ml) water in same saucepan. Add sugar and orange zest, bring to a boil, reduce heat to medium–low and boil until syrup is thick, about 10 minutes. Set aside.

In a wok over medium–low heat, heat 1 tablespoon ghee or oil. Add almonds and fry gently until golden. Remove from pan and set aside. Heat remaining ghee or oil in the wok, add chicken and brown. Move chicken to a plate, leaving fat in wok, and season with salt and pepper. Add onion to the wok and fry gently over medium–low heat until soft and slightly browned, about 10 minutes. Add 1 cup (8 fl oz/250 ml) water and stir to deglaze wok. Add chicken, cover and simmer for 10 minutes.

In a large pot, bring 8 cups (64 fl oz/2 L) water to a boil. Add rice and 1 tablespoon salt. Return to boil and cook for 8 minutes. Drain rice in a sieve or colander and turn into a bowl. Strain syrup from orange over rice, reserving zest.

Preheat oven to 300°F (150°C/Gas 2). Butter a large baking dish (casserole) and spread half of the rice in it. Arrange chicken pieces and onion on top of rice. Add half the cooking liquid from chicken. Sprinkle with half the orange zest and almonds. Spread remaining rice on top, pour remaining chicken cooking liquid evenly over top, cover and bake for 40 minutes. Remove top layer of rice from dish and arrange around the edge of a warm serving platter. Remove chicken to a plate and place remaining rice in center of platter. Top with chicken pieces and garnish with remaining orange zest and almonds. Sprinkle with pistachio nuts. Pour saffron liquid over the rice around chicken.

Peking duck pancakes

Makes 15

Pancakes

3/4 cup (4 oz/125 g) all-purpose (plain) flour
1/3 cup (1 1/2 oz/45 g) cornstarch (cornflour)
2 eggs, beaten
3/4 cup (6 fl oz/180 ml) water
1/4 cup (2 fl oz/60 ml) milk
2 teaspoons superfine (caster) sugar
1 tablespoon vegetable oil

Filling

15 scallions (shallots/spring onions)
2 carrots, peeled and cut into thin sticks
1 Chinese roasted duck
1/4 cup (2 fl oz/60 ml) hoisin sauce
1 tablespoon rice wine

15 chives
1/3 cup (3 fl oz/90 ml) hoisin sauce, for dipping

To make pancakes: Sift flour and cornstarch into a bowl. In a separate bowl, whisk together eggs, water, milk and sugar. Make a well in center of dry ingredients, gradually add egg mixture and beat until smooth.

In a frying pan, heat oil over medium heat, pour in 2 tablespoons of pancake batter and swirl pan gently to form a round pancake. Cook until golden, about 2 minutes. Turn and cook other side for 10 seconds. Remove from pan and repeat with remaining batter and oil.

To make filling: Cut into each end of scallions with a sharp knife or scissors to form a fringe. Place scallions and carrots in a bowl of iced water and refrigerate for 15 minutes, or until scallions curl. Remove meat and skin from duck and roughly chop. Combine hoisin sauce and rice wine.

Lay pancakes on work surface and place 1 tablespoon of duck meat and skin in center of each one. Top with 1 teaspoon of hoisin and rice wine mixture. Add a scallion curl and 3–4 carrot sticks. Roll and secure with a chive, trimming off any excess chive. Serve with hoisin sauce for dipping.

Red curry with roasted duck

Serves 4–6

2 cups (16 fl oz/500 ml) coconut milk
2–3 tablespoons vegetable oil (optional)
3 tablespoons fresh or commercial red curry paste (see page 231)
3 kaffir limes leaves, stemmed
12 oz (375 g) roasted, boneless duck meat
1 cup (1 oz/30 g) loosely packed fresh sweet Thai basil leaves
½ cup (2 oz/40 g) fresh green peppercorns on the stem, or 2–4 tablespoons canned green peppercorns, drained
1 cup (4 oz/125 g) eggplant (aubergine) cut into ½-inch (12-mm) pieces or 4 round Thai eggplants
½ cup (2 oz/60 g) pea eggplants (optional)
1 cup (6 oz/185 g) fresh or canned pineapple chunks, drained
6 cherry tomatoes
10 grapes
1 fresh long red chili, coarsely chopped
2 tablespoons fish sauce
2 tablespoons soy sauce
1 tablespoon granulated (white) sugar
1 tablespoon palm sugar

Let coconut milk stand, allowing the thick coconut milk to rise to the top. Spoon thick coconut milk into a small bowl, reserving 2 tablespoons for garnish.

In a wok or large, heavy frying pan over medium–high heat, fry the thick coconut milk, stirring constantly, until it begins to separate, 3–5 minutes. If it does not separate, add the optional oil. Add red curry paste and fry, stirring constantly, until fragrant, 1–2 minutes. Tear 2 kaffir lime leaves and basil into pieces.

Add remaining thin coconut milk to the wok, increase heat, and bring to a gentle boil. Add duck and simmer until heated through, about 5 minutes. Add torn lime leaves, green peppercorns, both varieties of eggplants, pineapple and cherry tomatoes. Reduce heat and simmer for 3 minutes. Add water, if necessary. Add all remaining ingredients, reserving a few basil leaves and the remaining kaffir lime leaf for garnish.

Transfer to a serving bowl, garnish with reserved basil, and drizzle with reserved thick coconut milk. Roll the remaining kaffir lime leaf into a tight cylinder and cut into fine shreds; sprinkle over curry.

Tip

Roasted ducks are readily available in Chinese delicatessens and at numerous Asian markets.

Steamed chicken buns

Makes 16

Dough

2½ cups (10 oz/300 g) all-purpose (plain) flour
3 teaspoons baking powder
½ cup (3¾ oz/110 g) superfine (caster) sugar
½ cup (4 fl oz/125 ml) milk
⅓ cup (3 fl oz/90 ml) water
¼ cup (2 fl oz/60 ml) vegetable oil

Filling

6 Chinese dried mushrooms
1 tablespoon vegetable oil
3 teaspoons peeled and grated fresh ginger
8 oz (250 g) ground (minced) chicken
2 tablespoons chopped, drained canned bamboo shoots
4 scallions (shallots/spring onions), chopped
1 tablespoon oyster sauce
1 teaspoon soy sauce
1 teaspoon Asian sesame oil
¼ teaspoon salt
2 teaspoons cornstarch (cornflour) mixed with 2 tablespoons chicken stock (see page 220)

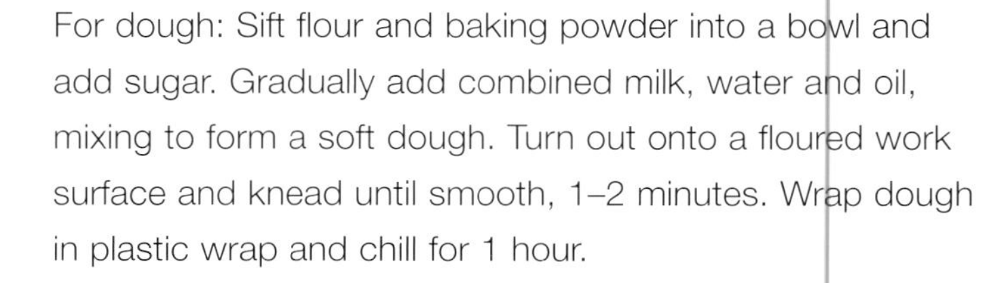

For dough: Sift flour and baking powder into a bowl and add sugar. Gradually add combined milk, water and oil, mixing to form a soft dough. Turn out onto a floured work surface and knead until smooth, 1–2 minutes. Wrap dough in plastic wrap and chill for 1 hour.

For filling: Place mushrooms in a small bowl, add boiling water to cover and allow to stand until softened, 10–15 minutes. Drain, squeeze excess liquid from mushrooms and finely chop, discarding thick stems. In a wok or frying pan, heat oil over medium heat, and fry ginger until aromatic, about 1 minute. Add ground chicken and cook until meat changes color, about 3 minutes. Stir in bamboo shoots, scallions, oyster sauce, soy sauce, sesame oil, salt and cornstarch mixture. Bring to a boil and stir until sauce thickens. Remove from heat, transfer filling to a plate and allow to cool completely.

Roll dough into a sausage shape 16 inches (40.5 cm) long. Cut into 16 1-inch (2.5-cm) pieces and roll each into a ball. Cover with a damp kitchen towel. Working with one piece of dough at a time, press into a cup shape. Place 1 tablespoon of filling in the center of dough. Gather edges together, twist and seal. Cover with a damp kitchen towel and repeat with remaining dough.

Cut out 16 squares of parchment (baking paper) and place buns, sealed side down, on paper. Half fill a medium wok with water (steamer should not touch water) and bring to a boil. Working in batches, arrange buns in steamer, cover and place steamer over boiling water. Steam for 20 minutes, adding more boiling water to wok when necessary. Lift steamer off wok and carefully remove buns.

Step-by-step basic buns

1. Divide dough into walnut-sized rounds.

2. Roll or press each piece out to a circle. Cover dough with a damp kitchen towel to prevent it from drying out.

3. Working with one dough round at a time, spoon filling into the center. Gather edges together and twist to seal dough. Cut out squares of parchment (baking paper) and place buns, sealed side down, onto paper.

Stir-fried chicken in roasted curry paste sauce

Serves 4–6

2 tablespoons vegetable oil
2 rounded tablespoons red curry paste (see page 231)
4 garlic cloves, chopped
2 shallots, sliced
1 lb (500 g) boned and skinned chicken breasts, cut into 1½-inch (3.5-cm) cubes
1 teaspoon sugar
3 tablespoons fish sauce
½–¾ cup (2 ½–4 fl oz/80–125 ml) thin coconut milk or water
20 basil leaves
steamed rice, for serving

In a wok, heat half the oil, swirling to coat the sides. Stir-fry the curry paste, garlic and shallots over medium heat for 2–3 minutes. Add the chicken and stir-fry briefly, basting to coat each piece.

In a bowl, combine the sugar, fish sauce and coconut milk, and add to the chicken. Bring to a boil, stirring constantly. Add the basil leaves, and toss.

Serve immediately with steamed rice.

Stir-fried ginger chicken

Serves 6

6 whole boneless chicken breasts
2 tablespoons fish sauce
2 tablespoons soy sauce
1 teaspoon sugar
2 tablespoons vegetable oil
1 red onion, sliced
6 garlic cloves, chopped
2-inch (5-cm) piece fresh ginger, peeled and thinly sliced
3 red or green serrano chilies, stemmed and cut lengthwise into fine strips
¼ teaspoon red chili flakes
¼ cup (½ oz/15 g) coarsely chopped mint or basil leaves
whole mint or basil leaves, for garnish
steamed rice, for serving

Cut the chicken breasts into 1½ x 1 x ½-inch (3.5 x 2.5 x 1-cm) pieces. Set aside.

In a bowl, combine the fish sauce, soy sauce and sugar. Set aside.

In a wok, warm oil over medium heat, add the onion and garlic and sauté until golden brown. Add the chicken pieces and stir-fry until white and opaque. Add the ginger, chilies, chili flakes and fish sauce mixture and cook until chicken is just cooked through, about 4 minutes. Transfer to a serving plate.

Garnish with mint or basil leaves and serve immediately with rice.

Sweet chicken wings

Serves 4

6 chicken wings, wing tips removed
pinch sesame salt
1 tablespoon ginger juice (obtained by grating fresh ginger)
1/4 cup (1 oz/30 g) cornstarch (cornflour)
1 1/2 cups (12 fl oz/375 ml) vegetable or sunflower oil, for frying
2 tablespoons light soy sauce
1 tablespoon malt liquid (mullyeot)
1 tablespoon sugar
1 teaspoon ginger juice (obtained by grating fresh ginger)
1 tablespoon rice wine
3 tablespoons water
5 whole cloves garlic
2 fresh red chilies, halved lengthwise, seeds removed
2 fresh green chilies, halved lengthwise, seeds removed
Asian sesame oil to taste

Wash chicken wings and pat dry with paper towels. Combine sesame salt and 1 tablespoon ginger juice in a bowl, then add chicken wings. Mix well to coat in juice. Remove wings and coat with cornstarch.

In a wok or deep frying pan, heat oil until very hot. Fry wings until golden, about 10 minutes. Remove from oil and drain on paper towels.

In a wok, combine soy sauce, malt liquid, sugar, 1 teaspoon ginger juice, rice wine and water and bring to a boil. Add garlic and red and green chilies and stir in well. Continue boiling sauce until reduced by half. Add chicken wings and mix to coat with sauce. Transfer chicken wings, garlic and chilies to a serving plate, sprinkle with sesame oil and serve with steamed rice.

Sweet-and-sour chicken and noodles

Serves 4

8 oz (250 g) rice stick noodles
vegetable oil for deep-frying, plus 2 tablespoons
8 oz (250 g) skinless chicken breast fillet, cut into 1-inch (2.5-cm) pieces
1 onion, sliced
2 tablespoons tomato paste (purée)
2 tablespoons palm sugar or brown sugar
1 tablespoon fish sauce
3 tablespoons lime juice
1 piece grapefruit zest (rind), 2 inches (5 cm) long, shredded
2 tablespoons water
2 tablespoons cilantro (fresh coriander) leaves
thin strips grapefruit zest (rind), for garnish
lime wedges, for serving

Place noodles in plastic bag and roughly break up into bite-sized pieces.

In a wok or frying pan, heat oil until it reaches 375°F (190°C) on a deep-frying thermometer or until a small bread cube dropped in oil sizzles and turns golden. Working in batches if necessary, add noodles and fry until golden and crisp, about 30 seconds. Using slotted spoon, remove from pan and drain on paper towels.

In another wok over medium–high heat, warm 2 tablespoons oil. Add chicken and cook, stirring occasionally, until golden, 4–5 minutes. Remove from pan. Add onion to same pan and cook until softened, about 2 minutes.

In a small bowl, combine tomato paste, sugar, fish sauce, lime juice, shredded zest and water. Add to pan, reduce heat to low and simmer, stirring occasionally, until sauce thickens, 3–4 minutes. Stir in chicken and noodles, raise heat to medium and cook until heated through, 1–2 minutes.

To serve, spoon chicken and noodles onto individual plates. Sprinkle with cilantro leaves and garnish with zest strips. Accompany with lime wedges.

Teriyaki chicken

Serves 4

4 boneless chicken breasts
½ cup (2½ oz/75 g) all-purpose (plain) flour
2 tablespoons vegetable oil
½ cup (4 fl oz/125 ml) Teriyaki sauce (see page 225)
2 cups (16 oz/500 g) hot cooked rice
1 teaspoon sesame seeds, toasted
2 scallions (shallots/spring onions), thinly sliced, for garnish
nori, cut into fine strips, for garnish

Remove skin and trim any fat from chicken breasts. Place each breast on a cutting board and pound gently with a meat mallet to flatten slightly. Place flour on a plate. Dredge chicken in flour.

In a wok, heat oil over high heat. Add chicken and brown well on both sides, about 4 minutes. Remove breasts from pan and place in a clean wok with teriyaki sauce. Bring sauce to a boil, then reduce heat to low and simmer, covered, turning chicken three times, until cooked through, about 5 minutes. Remove from pan and cut into slices ½ inch (12 mm) wide.

Divide chicken among 4 plates with rice and top with teriyaki sauce from pan. Garnish with toasted sesame seeds, scallions and nori strips.

Thai curry with chicken

Serves 4–6

1 tablespoon sticky (glutinous) rice
1/4 cup (2 fl oz/60 ml) vegetable oil
1/4 cup (2 fl oz/60 ml) red curry paste (see page 231)
12 oz (375 g) boneless chicken thighs or breasts, thinly sliced
1/2 cup (2 oz/60 g) chopped eggplant (aubergine) or 1 round eggplant or 1/4 long green eggplant
1/4 cup (1 oz/30 g) pea eggplants (optional)
2 long beans or 6–8 green beans, cut into 1-inch (2.5-cm) pieces
2 cups (16 fl oz/500 ml) chicken stock (see page 220) or water
2 tablespoons fish sauce
7 fresh eryngo (sawtooth coriander) leaves or 6 sprigs cilantro (fresh coriander), coarsely chopped or torn
4 fresh piper (beetle) leaves, or 2 cabbage leaves, coarsely chopped
1 cup fresh acacia leaves, coarsely chopped (optional)
1 fresh long red chili, seeded and cut into large pieces
1/4 teaspoon salt

In a wok or small frying pan over low heat, stir rice until golden brown, 3–5 minutes. Transfer to a mortar and pulverize with a pestle; set aside.

In a wok or large, heavy frying pan, heat oil over medium–high heat and fry curry paste, stirring constantly, until fragrant, 1–2 minutes. Add chicken and stir-fry until opaque on all sides, about 2 minutes. Add eggplants and beans; stir together well.

Add 1 cup (8 fl oz/250 ml) chicken stock or water; simmer for 2 minutes. Add remaining stock or water, fish sauce, remaining ingredients and ground rice. Bring to a boil, reduce heat, and simmer 2 minutes for chicken breasts, 5–7 minutes for thighs. Transfer to a serving bowl and serve.

Tips

- In Thailand, the availability of local ingredients allows for variations to this dish. For example, this recipe can be made with frog instead of chicken.
- In the north of Thailand, 1/4 teaspoon prickly ash (kamchatton) would be added with the chicken stock. Substitute with 1/4 teaspoon Szechuan peppercorns if desired.

beef, lamb and pork

Beef braised in rice wine

Serves 4

⅓ cup (3 fl oz/90 ml) dry rice wine or dry sherry
3 tablespoons fish sauce
1 teaspoon sugar
2 teaspoons ground pepper
2 lb (1 kg) boneless beef blade or chuck, trimmed and cut into 1-inch (2.5-cm) cubes (see Tips below)
3 tablespoons vegetable oil
½ cup (2 oz/60 g) brown or pink shallots (French shallots), crushed
cloves from ½ bulb garlic, crushed
2 sticks cinnamon, or ½ teaspoon ground cinnamon
½ teaspoon aniseed
about 1¼ cups (10 fl oz/310 ml) water
3 tomatoes, peeled and seeded
¼ cup (2 oz/60 g) butter
¼ cup (1 oz/30 g) all-purpose (plain) flour
cilantro (fresh coriander) sprigs, for garnish (optional)
crusty bread rolls or baguette, for serving

In a glass or earthenware bowl, combine rice wine, fish sauce, sugar and 1 teaspoon pepper. Stir to blend. Add beef and let stand at room temperature for 2 hours, or cover and refrigerate for up to 24 hours. Stir several times during this period. Using a slotted spoon, transfer beef from marinade and pat dry; reserve marinade.

In a large wok, heat oil over medium heat and sauté half of shallots and half of garlic until soft, about 3 minutes. Using a slotted spoon, transfer to a bowl. Add half of beef and cook, stirring frequently, until all sides are lightly seared, about 5 minutes. Using a slotted spoon, transfer to a bowl. Repeat with remaining meat.

In same wok, combine meat, cinnamon, aniseed and cooked shallots and add remaining garlic. Add 1 cup (8 fl oz/250 ml) water plus any marinade. Cover and simmer over medium-low heat just until beef is tender, about 2 hours. Shake occasionally to prevent scorching. If the braise cooks dry, add a little more water.

Meanwhile, peel and seed tomatoes: Use a small knife to cut away and remove each tomato core. Turn tomato over and lightly score underside with an X. Plunge into a large pot of rapidly boiling water and cook for exactly 10 seconds. Remove immediately from water and plunge into ice water to stop cooking. The skin should now pull easily from pulp; discard. Cut tomatoes in half and squeeze over a strainer to extract all seeds. Discard seeds and retain tomatoes and juice.

In a medium saucepan, combine tomatoes, strained tomato juice and remaining raw shallots, garlic and 1 teaspoon pepper. Add remaining ¼ cup (2 fl oz/60 ml) water and cook until tomatoes are just starting to break up, about 3 minutes. In a separate saucepan, melt butter over low heat and whisk in flour. Cook, stirring constantly, until it barely begins to brown, about 2–3 minutes. Whisk into tomato mixture and remove from heat.

When beef is barely tender, remove cinnamon sticks, if using, from braise. Stir in tomato mixture. Reduce heat to a simmer, cover, and cook until fork tender, 30–60 minutes. If desired, garnish with cilantro sprigs. Serve with bread rolls or baguette.

Tips

- Inexpensive beef cuts work best in this braised dish. Do not use premium cuts like loin (saddle), or lean meat like round (topside), as they can become tough and dry during long, slow cooking.
- This is a classic example of Vietnamese fusion food, created, presumably, after the French colonists' departure, when red wine flowed less freely and the local substitute of rice wine was used. This recipe's European prototype is arguably boeuf bourguignon or a Flemish-style carbonnade.

Beef chow mein

Serves 4–6

- 6½ oz (200 g) wheat flour, rice stick or thick egg noodles
- 2 tablespoons soy sauce
- 3 tablespoons hoisin sauce
- 2 cloves garlic, crushed
- 2 teaspoons peeled and grated fresh ginger
- 12 oz (375 g) round (topside) or sirloin (rump) steak, thinly sliced
- 2 tablespoons vegetable oil
- 8 fresh shiitake mushrooms, brushed clean and sliced
- 6 scallions (shallots/spring onions), sliced
- 6 oz (180 g) broccoli, cut into florets
- 2 tablespoons beef stock (see page 220)
- 1 tablespoon dry sherry
- 1 teaspoon Asian sesame oil

Cook noodles, then drain and set aside. In glass or ceramic bowl, combine soy and hoisin sauces, garlic and ginger. Add steak slices, turn to coat in marinade, cover and marinate for 30 minutes. Drain and reserve marinade.

In a wok or frying pan over medium–high heat, warm vegetable oil. Add steak and stir-fry until meat changes color, 3–4 minutes. Remove from wok or pan. Return wok or pan to medium–high heat, add mushrooms, scallions and broccoli, and stir-fry for 2 minutes. Add noodles, steak, reserved marinade, stock, sherry and sesame oil. Cook until heated through, 1–2 minutes.

Serve immediately, divided among individual plates.

Beef kabobs

Serves 4

7 oz (220 g) beef tenderloin or scotch fillet
1 oz/30 g scallions (shallots/spring onions)
1 green bell pepper (capsicum)
4 skewers, 5 inches (12 cm) long, soaked in water for 30 minutes
vegetable or sunflower oil, for frying
lettuce leaves, for serving

For marinade
2 tablespoons light soy sauce
2 teaspoons sugar
1 scallion (shallot/spring onion), finely chopped
1 teaspoon pan-toasted, ground sesame seeds to a powder
1 teaspoon sesame oil

Cut beef into strips about 3⁄4 inch (2 cm) wide by 1⁄4 inch (6 mm) thick by 2 1⁄2 inches (6 cm) long. Score surface with the tip of a sharp knife.

To make marinade: In a medium glass or ceramic bowl, combine soy sauce, sugar, chopped scallions, sesame seeds and sesame oil. Mix beef strips in marinade and marinate for 15–20 minutes.

Cut scallions into strips 2 inches (5 cm) long. Remove core and seeds from bell pepper and cut into slices 2 inches (5 cm) long.

Thread alternate pieces of beef, scallions and bell pepper alternately onto each skewer, leaving about 1 1⁄4 inches (3 cm) free for holding skewer.

In a wok over a high heat, heat 1 tablespoon oil. Fry kabobs for 2 minutes on each side. Arrange lettuce leaves on a serving plate, place kabobs in center and serve.

Beef stir-fry on crisp noodles

Serves 4

vegetable oil for deep-frying, plus 1 tablespoon
8 oz (250 g) fresh thin egg noodles
1 tablespoon soy sauce
3 cloves garlic, chopped
12 oz (375 g) sirloin (rump) steak, thinly sliced
2 onions, cut into eighths
6–7 oz (180–220 g) asparagus, trimmed and cut into 1-inch (2.5-cm) pieces
2 tablespoons oyster sauce
1 teaspoon cornstarch (cornflour) mixed with 2 tablespoons beef stock (see page 220)

In a wok or frying pan, heat oil until it reaches 375°F (190°C) on a deep-frying thermometer or until a small bread cube dropped in oil sizzles and turns golden. Working in batches, add noodles and fry until crisp, about 30 seconds. Using a slotted spoon, remove from pan and drain on paper towels.

In a glass or ceramic bowl, combine soy sauce and garlic. Add steak slices, turn to coat with marinade, cover and marinate for 30 minutes. Drain and reserve marinade.

In a wok or frying pan over medium–high heat, warm 1 tablespoon oil. Add steak and stir-fry until meat changes color, 3–4 minutes, remove from pan. Return pan to medium–high heat, add onion and stir-fry until softened, about 2 minutes. Return meat to pan, add asparagus and cook until asparagus is tender-crisp, about 2 minutes. Stir in oyster sauce and cornstarch and stock. Continuing to stir, cook until sauce thickens, 1–2 minutes.

To serve, arrange noodles on individual plates. Top with beef stir-fry and serve immediately.

Beef stir-fry with Chinese greens

Serves 4

10½ oz (315 g) sirloin (rump) or round (topside) steak
3 tablespoons vegetable oil
4 cloves garlic, crushed
1 tablespoon peeled and grated fresh ginger
2 small red chilies, seeded and chopped
1 bunch Chinese broccoli or 6 celery stalks, trimmed and cut into 1¼-inch (3-cm) lengths
7 oz (220 g) sugar snap peas or snow peas (mange-tout), trimmed
3½ oz (105 g) fresh bean sprouts, rinsed
1 tablespoon oyster sauce
1 teaspoon sambal oelek (see page 230)
steamed white rice, for serving

Enclose steak in freezer wrap and freeze until slightly firm, about 30 minutes. Remove from freezer and thinly slice. In a bowl, combine beef, 1 tablespoon vegetable oil, garlic and ginger. Cover and refrigerate for 30 minutes.

Drain beef from marinade, discarding marinade. In a wok over medium–high heat, warm remaining 2 tablespoons vegetable oil. Working in batches, add beef and stir-fry until brown, 1–2 minutes. Remove from wok and drain on paper towels. Add chilies, broccoli or celery, sugar snap peas or snow peas and bean sprouts and stir-fry until tender-crisp, 2–3 minutes. Add beef, oyster sauce and sambal oelek. Stir-fry until heated through, about 1 minute.

Serve hot, accompanied with steamed white rice.

Beef with bamboo shoots

Serves 4

2 tablespoons vegetable oil
2½ lbs (1.25 kg) sirloin or round steak, thinly sliced
2 small fresh red chilies, chopped
2 cloves garlic, minced
1 tablespoon very finely chopped fresh lemongrass
1 teaspoon grated fresh ginger
2 tablespoons Thai fish sauce
1 tablespoon soy sauce
1 can (12 oz/375 g) bamboo shoots, drained
2 tablespoons chopped fresh basil
2 scallions (spring onions/shallots), chopped
cooked rice or noodles, for serving

In a large wok, heat oil over high heat. Add meat in batches (to ensure even browning and so that the meat does not cook in its own juices) and stir-fry until browned all over. Add chilies, garlic, lemongrass and ginger and stir-fry until fragrant, about 2 minutes. Stir in sauces and bamboo shoots and stir-fry until bamboo shoots are just starting to soften, about 2 minutes. Stir in basil and scallions. Serve immediately on a bed of rice or noodles.

Beef with basil leaves

Serves 4–6

3 tablespoons vegetable oil
15 cloves garlic, crushed
10 fresh red or green chilies, coarsely chopped
1 lb (500 g) ground (minced) beef
1 tablespoon oyster sauce
2 tablespoons fish sauce
1 teaspoon sweet (thick) soy sauce
1 tablespoon granulated (white) sugar (or to taste)
2 fresh long red chilies, cut into large pieces
1 cup (8 fl oz/250 ml) chicken stock (see page 220) or water
1½ cups (1½ oz/45 g) loosely packed fresh basil leaves, preferably holy basil

In a wok or large, heavy frying pan, heat oil over high heat. Add garlic and chilies and stir-fry until garlic just begins to brown.

Add beef, stirring vigorously to break it up, about 2 minutes. Add oyster sauce, fish sauce, sweet soy sauce, and sugar to taste. Stir well to combine, then add chilies.

Add chicken stock or water and bring to a boil. Add basil, cook for 1 minute, then remove from heat.

Transfer to a serving plate and serve.

Tip

For a less piquant dish, keep the chilies whole, or seed them.

Chinese barbecue pork stir-fry

Serves 4

- 3 oz (90 g) cellophane (bean thread) noodles
- 1 tablespoon vegetable oil
- 6 scallions (shallots/spring onions), cut into 1-inch (2.5-cm) pieces
- 1 red bell pepper (capsicum), seeded and sliced
- 4 oz (125 g) Chinese barbecue pork, sliced
- 2 bok choy or Chinese broccoli, trimmed
- 1½ cups (6 oz/180 g) fresh beans sprouts, rinsed
- 2 tablespoons soy sauce

Soak noodles in boiling water for 10 minutes. Drain and set aside. In a wok or frying pan, heat oil over medium–high heat. Add scallions and bell pepper and cook until softened, about 2 minutes. Add pork and bok choy and stir-fry until pork is tender, about 2 minutes. Stir in noodles, bean sprouts and soy sauce. Cook until heated through, about 1 minute.

Serve hot, divided among individual plates.

Chinese beef and vegetable stir-fry

Serves 4

1 oz (30 g) dried shiitake mushrooms, soaked in boiling water for 20 minutes
2 tablespoons sunflower oil
4 oz (115 g) snow peas (mange-tout)
4 oz (115 g) whole baby corn cobs
4 oz (115 g) bean sprouts
1 large bunch scallions (shallots), chopped
1 red bell pepper (capsicum), seeded and sliced
1¼ lb (550 g) rib-eye steak, thinly sliced
2 tablespoons oyster sauce
2 tablespoons Chinese rice wine or dry sherry
3 tablespoons light soy sauce
3 tablespoons beef stock (see page 220)
1 tablespoon cornstarch (cornflour)
fried rice or noodles, for serving

Drain and dry mushrooms and cut in half if large.

In a large wok or frying pan, heat 1 tablespoon oil. Stir-fry mushrooms, snow peas, corn, bean sprouts, scallions and bell pepper for 2–3 minutes, then remove from pan.

Heat remaining oil. Stir-fry beef until brown, 2–3 minutes. Return vegetables to pan. In a bowl, combine oyster sauce, rice wine, soy sauce, stock and cornstarch. Pour into pan, mix well, and bring to a boil, stirring continuously.

Transfer to a warmed serving dish and serve immediately with fried rice or noodles.

Dry beef curry with sweet potato

Serves 4

1 onion, chopped
2 cloves garlic
1 teaspoon shrimp paste
1 teaspoon ground cumin
2 teaspoons ground coriander
1 tablespoon chopped lemongrass
½ teaspoon ground turmeric
1 teaspoon ground paprika
1 teaspoon grated lime zest (rind)
2 tablespoons vegetable oil
11 oz (330 g) sirloin (rump) or round (topside) steak, cut into 1¼-inch (3-cm) cubes
1 cup (8 fl oz/250 ml) water
7 oz (220 g) sweet potato, peeled and finely diced
1 long red chili, seeded and sliced
1 long green chili, seeded and sliced
steamed white rice, for serving

In a food processor, combine onion, garlic, shrimp paste, cumin, coriander, lemongrass, turmeric, paprika and lime zest. Process until smooth. Set aside.

In a wok over medium–high heat, warm vegetable oil. Working in batches, add beef and stir-fry until brown, 3–4 minutes. Remove from wok and drain on paper towels. Add spice blend to wok and cook until aromatic, about 1 minute.

Add beef and water and bring to a boil. Reduce heat to low, cover and simmer, stirring occasionally, for 30 minutes. Stir in sweet potato and simmer, uncovered, until sweet potato is tender, about 10 minutes. (Add a little more water if necessary.)

To serve, divide among individual plates and sprinkle with sliced chilies. Accompany with steamed white rice.

Fried pork in endive

Serves 4

1 tablespoon vegetable oil
2 cloves garlic, crushed
1 tablespoon peeled and grated fresh ginger
6 scallions (shallots/spring onions), chopped
½ teaspoon shrimp paste
1 tablespoon chopped lemongrass
2 teaspoons sambal oelek (see page 230)
7 oz (220 g) pork fillet, finely chopped
8 oz (250 g) cherry tomatoes, quartered
1 tablespoon coconut milk
3 tablespoons chopped cilantro (fresh coriander)
3 heads Belgian endive (chicory/witloof), cored and leaves separated

In a wok over medium heat, warm vegetable oil. Add garlic, ginger, scallions, shrimp paste, lemongrass and sambal oelek and stir-fry until aromatic, about 2 minutes. Add pork and cook until pork changes color, about 3 minutes.

Stir in tomatoes and coconut milk and stir-fry until tomatoes soften slightly, 1–2 minutes. Remove from heat and stir in cilantro.

To serve, spoon pork filling into endive leaves. Divide among individual plates and serve hot.

Ginger pork

Serves 4

½ cup (4 oz/124 g) sugar
½ cup (4 fl oz/125 ml) soy sauce
1 teaspoon mirin
2 tablespoons chicken stock (see page 220) or water
1 lb (500 g) pork fillet, trimmed of sinew, cut into slices ½ inch (12 mm) thick
½ cup (2½ oz/ 75 g) peeled and finely grated fresh ginger
2 tablespoons vegetable oil
2 scallions (shallots/spring onions), thinly sliced
1 teaspoon sesame seeds, for garnish

In a small saucepan over medium–high heat, combine sugar, soy sauce, mirin and stock or water and bring to a boil, stirring to dissolve sugar. Remove sauce from heat and set aside.

Dip both sides of each pork slice into grated ginger. Reserve any leftover ginger. In a wok, heat oil over medium–high heat. Add pork and fry, turning once until pork is no longer pink, 3–4 minutes. Add sauce to pan with any remaining grated ginger and bring to a boil. Reduce heat to low and simmer for 1 minute. Remove pork from pan and divide among 4 warmed plates. Spoon any remaining sauce from pan over slices. Garnish with sliced scallions and sprinkle with sesame seeds. Serve immediately.

Lamb with dried fruit

Serves 5–6

2 lb (1 kg) boneless lamb shoulder
¼ cup (2 oz/60 g) ghee or ¼ cup (2 fl oz/60 ml) vegetable oil
1 medium yellow (brown) onion, chopped
2 cups (16 fl oz/500 ml) water
salt
small piece cinnamon stick
1 dried lime or zest (rind) from ½ lemon
½ cup (3 oz/90 g) chopped pitted dates
¾ cup (4 oz/125 g) dried apricots
¾ cup (4 oz/125 g) dried prunes, pitted
¼ cup (1½ oz/45 g) golden raisins (sultanas)
2 tablespoons brown sugar
steamed rice, for serving

Cut lamb into ¾-inch (2-cm) cubes. In a heavy saucepan over high heat, heat half of the ghee or oil. Add lamb and cook, turning as needed, until browned on all sides, 8–10 minutes.

Push meat to one side, add onion and cook for 5 minutes. Reduce heat to low and add 1 cup (8 fl oz/250 ml) water, salt to taste, cinnamon stick and dried lime (pierced twice with a skewer) or lemon zest. Cover and simmer 45 minutes.

Place chopped dates in a small pan with remaining 1 cup (8 fl oz/250 ml) water. Set over low heat until dates soften. Press through a sieve into a bowl to purée.

Add date purée, apricots, prunes, raisins and brown sugar to pan. Stir to combine, cover tightly and simmer until lamb is tender, about 1 hour. Add more water during this time if the meat and fruit seem dry.

Remove cinnamon and dried lime or lemon zest and discard. Serve lamb with steamed rice.

Tip

When dates are being dried, they exude a thick syrup resembling molasses. Iraqi cooks add some of the syrup to this dish. Soaked and puréed, dried dates with brown sugar added, provide a similar flavor.

Long beans with pork and red curry paste

Serves 4

¼ cup (2 fl oz/60 ml) vegetable oil

1 cup (8 fl oz/250 ml) commercial or fresh red curry paste (see page 231)

20 oz (625 g) boneless pork butt or loin, thinly sliced

15 kaffir lime leaves, stemmed

1 lb (500 g) long beans or green beans, cut into 1-inch (2.5-cm) pieces

5 fresh long red chilies, seeded and cut into strips

1 tablespoon palm sugar

2 tablespoons granulated (white) sugar

¼ cup (2 fl oz/60 ml) fish sauce

1 cup (1 oz/30 g) loosely packed fresh sweet Thai basil leaves, coarsely torn

In a wok or large, heavy skillet, heat oil over medium–high heat. Add curry paste and cook, stirring constantly, until fragrant, 1–2 minutes. Add meat and stir until opaque on all sides, 2–3 minutes. Add 10 kaffir lime leaves, beans, and chilies. Cook, stirring frequently, for about 2 minutes, or until meat is barely tender.

Add palm sugar—if using a wok, add it along the edge of the wok so that it melts before stirring into the other ingredients; if using a standard saucepan, add directly to the pan. Add granulated sugar, then fish sauce and basil. Stir well, then remove from heat and transfer to a platter.

Roll remaining kaffir lime leaves into a tight cylinder and cut into fine shreds. Sprinkle over the dish and serve.

Meatballs in tomato sauce

Serves 5–6

1½ lb (750 g) finely ground (minced) beef or lamb
1 clove garlic, crushed
1 small yellow (brown) onion, finely grated
2 thick slices stale white Italian bread, crusts removed
1 egg
1 teaspoon ground cumin
2 tablespoons finely chopped fresh flat-leaf (Italian) parsley
salt
freshly ground black pepper
all-purpose (plain) flour, for coating
¼ cup (2 oz/60 g) butter or ¼ cup (2 fl oz/60 ml) olive oil
1½ cups (9 oz/280 g) chopped, peeled tomatoes
½ cup (2½ oz/75 g) finely chopped green bell pepper (capsicum)
½ teaspoon sugar
½ cup (4 fl oz/125 ml) water
steamed rice, for serving

In a bowl, combine beef or lamb with garlic and onion. Soak bread in cold water, squeeze dry and crumble into bowl. Add egg, cumin, parsley and salt and pepper to taste. Mix thoroughly to a smooth paste. With moistened hands, form 1 tablespoon portions of meat mixture into oval, sausagelike shapes. Coat lightly with flour.

In a deep wok or frying pan over high heat, heat butter or oil and fry meatballs until lightly browned on all sides. Remove to a plate. Add tomatoes and bell pepper to wok or frying pan and cook over medium heat for 5 minutes. Add sugar and season with salt and pepper to taste, then stir in water. Bring sauce to a boil and return meatballs to wok or pan. Reduce heat to low. Cover and simmer until meatballs are tender and sauce is thick, about 1 hour.

Serve immediately with steamed rice.

Pork and lime patties

Serves 4

8 oz (250 g) ground (minced) pork
2 teaspoons fish sauce
1 teaspoon oyster sauce
2 teaspoons sambal oelek (see page 230)
1 egg white, lightly beaten
2 cloves garlic, crushed
2 tablespoons cornstarch (cornflour)
2 teaspoon grated lime zest (rind)
4 kaffir lime leaves, shredded
1/4 cup (1 oz/30 g) chopped scallions
(shallots/spring onions)
1/2 cup (4 fl oz/125 ml) vegetable oil, for frying
sweet chili sauce, for serving

In a bowl, combine pork, fish sauce, oyster sauce, sambal oelek and egg white. Mix well. Add garlic, cornstarch, lime zest, lime leaves and scallions. Using moistened hands, mix until well combined. Divide mixture into 16 pieces and shape into patties.

In a wok over medium heat, warm vegetable oil. Working in batches, add pork patties and fry, turning once, until tender and golden on both sides, 6–8 minutes. Drain on paper towels.

Serve hot with sweet chili sauce.

Pork and nectarine stir-fry

Serves 4–6

2 tablespoons vegetable oil
3 cloves garlic, crushed
1 small red chili, seeded and chopped
1 lb (500 g) pork fillet, thinly sliced
1 bunch choy sum or spinach, trimmed and cut into 1¼-inch (3-cm) lengths
3 kaffir lime leaves, shredded
2½ tablespoons light soy sauce
2 teaspoons lime juice
2 firm nectarines, pitted and sliced
steamed white rice, for serving

In a wok over medium–high heat, warm vegetable oil. Add garlic and chili and stir-fry until aromatic, about 1 minute. Add pork, choy sum or spinach and lime leaves and stir-fry until pork changes color, 3–4 minutes. Add soy sauce, lime juice and nectarines and stir-fry until heated through, 1–2 minutes.

Serve hot, accompanied with steamed white rice.

Pumpkin with pork

Serves 4–6

⅓ cup (3 fl oz/90 ml) vegetable oil
9 cloves garlic, crushed
1 lb (500 g) pumpkin or squash, peeled, seeded, and thinly sliced
½ cup (4 fl oz/125 ml) chicken stock (see page 220) or water
12 oz (375 g) boneless pork loin, cut into thin strips
¼ cup (2 fl oz/60 ml) fish sauce
2 eggs, lightly beaten
fresh sweet Thai basil leaves, for garnish

In a wok or large, heavy frying pan, heat oil over medium–high heat. Add garlic, pumpkin or squash, and chicken stock or water. Bring to a boil.

Add pork, reduce heat, and simmer until meat is opaque throughout and pumpkin or squash is tender, about 5 minutes. Add fish sauce, then stir in eggs to just bind sauce.

Transfer to a serving dish, garnish with basil leaves and serve.

Tip

For a spectacular presentation, serve this dish in a hollowed-out pumpkin.

Red curry beef

Serves 4

8 oz (250 g) sirloin (rump) or round (topside) steak
1 tablespoon vegetable oil
1 tablespoon red curry paste (see page 231)
1 cup (8 fl oz/250 ml) coconut milk
2 teaspoons fish sauce
1 teaspoon palm sugar or brown sugar
1 cup (6 oz/180 g) drained canned baby corn
⅓ cup (2 oz/60 g) drained canned straw mushrooms
½ cup (½ oz/15 g) small fresh basil leaves
steamed white rice, for serving

Enclose steak in freezer wrap and freeze until slightly firm, about 30 minutes. Remove from freezer and thinly slice. In a wok, heat oil over medium–high heat. Working in batches, add beef and stir-fry until brown, 1–2 minutes. Remove from wok and drain on paper towels. Add curry paste to wok and cook until paste bubbles, 10–15 seconds. Stir in coconut milk, fish sauce, sugar, corn and mushrooms. Bring to a boil, reduce heat and simmer, uncovered, for 5 minutes. Add beef and stir-fry until heated through, about 1 minute.

Spoon into bowls and sprinkle each serving with basil leaves. Serve hot, accompanied with steamed white rice.

Salt bulgogi

Serves 4

½ cup (4 fl oz/125 ml) pear juice
 or ½ cup (4 oz/125 g) grated pear (preferably nashi)
3 tablespoons rice wine
2 lb (1 kg) beef tenderloin (fillet) or scotch fillet
2 tablespoons table salt
3 tablespoons sugar
3 tablespoons finely chopped scallions
 (shallots/spring onions)
2 tablespoons crushed garlic
1 tablespoon pan-toasted, ground sesame seeds
freshly ground black pepper to taste
3 tablespoons sesame oil
1 scallion (shallot/spring onion)
1 fresh red chili
1 tablespoon sesame oil
shiso leaves or lettuce leaves, for serving

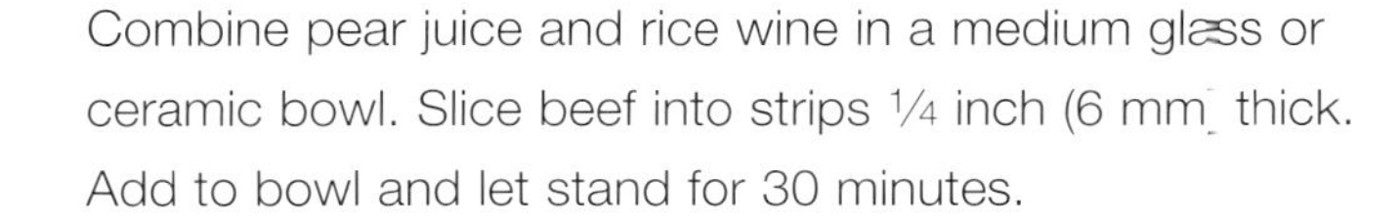

Combine pear juice and rice wine in a medium glass or ceramic bowl. Slice beef into strips ¼ inch (6 mm) thick. Add to bowl and let stand for 30 minutes.

Combine salt, sugar, scallions, garlic, sesame seeds, pepper and 3 tablespoons sesame oil in a large glass or ceramic bowl.

Drain beef, add to marinade and mix well. Cover and refrigerate to marinate for 2–3 hours.

Cut scallion into 1½-inch (4-cm) sections, then slice lengthwise into very thin strips. Place in a bowl of cold water for a few seconds, then drain. Slice chili in half lengthwise, remove seeds and membrane and slice into thin strips. In a wok, heat 1 tablespoon sesame oil over medium heat. Remove beef strips from marinade and stir-fry to the desired tenderness.

Arrange shiso leaves or lettuce on a plate. Place beef on leaves, sprinkle with scallion and chili strips, and serve with steamed rice.

Tip

As salt bulgogi does not have any sauce, drizzle with a little sesame oil to give it a sheen.

Shredded pork and beansprouts

Serves 4

½ lb (250 g) lean pork
1 tablespoon cornstarch (cornflour)
1 tablespoon light soy sauce
⅓ teaspoon white pepper
3 thin slices fresh ginger
2 scallions (spring onions)
6 oz (180 g) fresh beansprouts
3 tablespoons vegetable oil
1 teaspoon sesame oil
½ cup (3 fl oz/90 ml) chicken stock (see page 220)
1½ teaspoons extra cornstarch (cornflour)

Slice the pork, stack slices together and cut into narrow shreds, place in a dish with cornstarch, soy and pepper, mix well and marinate for 30 minutes.

Cut ginger into fine shreds. Trim scallions, cut into 1½-inch (4-cm) pieces and shred lengthwise. Break roots and seed pods from beansprouts and rinse. Drain well.

In a wok, heat the oils together until very hot. Add pork and stir-fry quickly until it changes appearance. Add the ginger, scallions and beansprouts and stir-fry for 2 minutes on high heat. Add chicken stock and cornstarch, stir on high heat until sauce coats the ingredients.

Sliced beef, mushrooms and vegetables in oyster sauce

Serves 4

1 lb (500 g) rump steak
1½ tablespoons cornstarch (cornflour)
2 tablespoons fish sauce
3 teaspoons sugar
¾ lb (375 g) Chinese green vegetables
3 tablespoons vegetable oil
4 scallions (spring onions), cut into 1-inch (2.5-cm) lengths
4 oz (125 g) can baby champignons, drained
¾ cup (6 fl oz/185 ml) beef stock (see page 220)
cracked black pepper to taste
2 tablespoons oyster sauce

Enclose steak in freezer wrap and freeze until slightly firm, about 30 minutes. Remove from freezer and thinly slice. Place in a dish and sprinkle on 1 tablespoon cornstarch, the fish sauce and sugar. Mix well and marinate for 10 minutes.

Cut the vegetables into 3-inch (8-cm) pieces and blanch in boiling water for 3 minutes. Drain.

In a wok, heat the oil and stir-fry the beef until it changes appearance. Add the onion and champignons and the beef stock mixed with remaining cornstarch. Stir over high heat until the sauce thickens. Add the vegetables and heat through in the sauce. Stir in pepper, transfer to a serving dish and evenly pour over the oyster sauce.

Steamed pork ribs

Makes 8 small servings

1 lb (500 g) pork spareribs, trimmed and cut into 3¼-inch (8-cm) lengths (ask your butcher to prepare these for you)
1 tablespoon rice wine
1 teaspoon salt
2 teaspoons superfine (caster) sugar
1 teaspoon Asian sesame oil
4 cloves garlic, finely chopped
2 tablespoons fermented black beans, washed and chopped
½ teaspoon dry chili flakes
2 teaspoons cornstarch (cornflour)
½ red bell pepper (capsicum), seeded and finely shredded

Place ribs in a shallow dish. Combine rice wine, salt, sugar, sesame oil, garlic, black beans, chili flakes and cornstarch and mix well. Pour over ribs, cover and refrigerate for 2 hours.

Half fill a medium wok with water (steamer should not touch water) and bring to a boil. Working in batches, place ribs on a heatproof plate and put it into a bamboo steamer. Cover and place steamer over boiling water. Steam until ribs are tender, about 25 minutes, adding more boiling water to wok when necessary. Lift steamer off wok and carefully remove ribs. Garnish with shredded red bell pepper.

Stir-fried beef with eggs

Serves 4

8 oz (250 g) egg noodles
4 tablespoons vegetable oil
3 cloves garlic, crushed
¼ cup (1 oz/30 g) chopped scallions (shallots/spring onions)
8 oz (250 g) lean ground (minced) beef
3 tablespoons water
1 tablespoon soy sauce
1 tablespoon oyster sauce
1 teaspoon cornstarch (cornflour) mixed with 1 tablespoon water
4 butter lettuce leaves, trimmed
4 eggs, soft-boiled, peeled and halved
¼ cup (⅓ oz/10 g) fresh mint leaves, for garnish

Cook noodles as directed on package or on page 29. Drain and pat dry with paper towels.

In a wok or frying pan over medium–high heat, warm 3 tablespoons of oil. Add garlic and cook until aromatic, about 1 minute. Add noodles and stir-fry for 2 minutes. Remove from wok or pan. Add remaining 1 tablespoon oil to wok or pan over medium–high heat. Add scallions and ground beef and stir-fry until meat changes color, 3–4 minutes. Add water, soy and oyster sauces and noodles and stir-fry for 3 minutes. Stir in cornstarch and water and cook, stirring, until sauce thickens, about 2 minutes.

To serve, arrange lettuce leaves on individual plates. Spoon beef and noodles on top. Garnish with egg halves and mint leaves. Serve immediately.

Stir-fried beef with red curry paste

Serves 4

1¼ cups (10 fl oz/300 ml) vegetable oil
¼ cup (2 fl oz/60 ml) commercial or fresh red curry paste (see page 231)
1 cup (8 fl oz/250 ml) coconut cream, plus 2 tablespoons, for serving
12 oz (375 g) beef round, blade, or sirloin, trimmed and cut into very thin strips
1 cup (3½ oz/100 g) chopped eggplant (aubergine) or 3 round Thai eggplants, quartered then sliced
1 cup (4 oz/125 g) pea eggplants (optional)
¼ cup fresh green peppercorns on stems, or 2 tablespoons canned peppercorns, drained
6 kaffir lime leaves, stemmed
2 tablespoons fish sauce
1 tablespoon soy sauce
1 teaspoon granulated (white) sugar
¼ cup (2 fl oz/60 ml) chicken stock (see page 220) or water
1 fresh long red chili, coarsely chopped
1 cup (1 oz/30 g) loosely packed fresh sweet Thai basil leaves

Heat ¼ cup (2 fl oz/60 ml) oil in a wok or large, heavy frying pan over medium–high heat. Add curry paste and fry, stirring constantly, until fragrant, 1–2 minutes. Add ½ cup (4 fl oz/125 ml) coconut cream, and beef. Stir until gently boiling. Cook 2 minutes for sirloin, or up to 30 minutes for tougher cuts like blade.

Add eggplants and peppercorns. Add kaffir lime leaves and cook, stirring, for 1 minute. Add fish sauce, soy sauce, sugar, and stock or water. Boil for 1 minute. Stir in the remaining ½ cup (4 fl oz/125 ml) coconut cream and chili. Remove from heat. Wash and pat the basil leaves completely dry with paper towels.

Heat remaining 1 cup (8 fl oz/250 ml) oil in a wok until surface shimmers. Add basil leaves all at once and fry for a few seconds, or until lightly crisp. To serve, transfer beef mixture to a platter, and top with fried basil. Drizzle with reserved 2 tablespoons coconut cream.

fish and seafood

Braised octopus and onions

Serves 6

1 octopus, about 2 lb (1 kg)
¼ cup (2 fl oz/60 ml) corn oil
1 medium yellow (brown) onion, chopped
2 cloves garlic, finely chopped
1 cup (8 fl oz/250 ml) tomato purée
¼ cup (2 fl oz/60 ml) dry red wine
¼ cup (2 fl oz/60 ml) red wine vinegar
salt
freshly ground black pepper
2 whole cloves
1 cinnamon stick, about 3 inches (8 cm) long
1½ lb (750 g) small boiling (pickling) onions

Pull tentacles from octopus and set aside. Remove intestines, ink sac, eyes and beak and discard. Wash head and tentacles and pull skin from head. Place head and tentacles in a saucepan, cover and cook over medium heat until octopus releases its juice, about 10 minutes. Drain, let cool, and cut into bite-sized pieces.

In a heavy wok, heat oil over medium heat and gently fry chopped onion until translucent, about 7 minutes. Add garlic and octopus and fry for 5 minutes. Add tomato purée, wine, vinegar, salt and pepper to taste, cloves and cinnamon stick. Cover and simmer over low heat for 30 minutes.

Peel boiling (pickling) onions and cut an X in the root end of each. Add to pan; cover and cook until octopus is tender, about 1 hour.

Remove cloves and cinnamon stick, adjust seasonings and serve octopus with steamed rice.

Braised shrimp in ginger-coconut sauce

Serves 4

2 tablespoons peeled and grated fresh ginger
4 cloves garlic, crushed
1 tablespoon ground turmeric
1 small red chili, seeded and chopped
2 tablespoons white vinegar
2 tablespoons peanut oil
2 onions, chopped
1 lb (500 g) jumbo shrimp (king prawns), peeled and deveined, tails intact
2 tomatoes, chopped
¾ cup (6 fl oz/180 ml) coconut milk
2 teaspoons cracked black pepper
2 tablespoons chopped fresh cilantro (coriander)
¼ cup (¼ oz/7 g) small whole cilantro (coriander) leaves, for garnish

In a food processor or blender, combine ginger, garlic, turmeric, chili and vinegar. Process to form paste.

In a wok over medium-high heat, warm peanut oil. Add onions and spice paste and stir-fry until onions soften, 2 to 3 minutes. Add shrimp and stir-fry until shrimp change color, 3 to 4 minutes. Stir in tomatoes and cook until soft, about 2 minutes. Add coconut milk, reduce heat to low, cover and simmer until sauce thickens slightly and shrimp are tender, 6 to 8 minutes. Stir in pepper and chopped cilantro.

Serve hot, garnished with cilantro leaves.

Cha ca fish with turmeric

Serves 4

3 tablespoons ground turmeric, or a 3-inch (7.5-cm) knob fresh turmeric, peeled and chopped
1-inch (2.5-cm) knob fresh galangal or ginger, peeled
1–2 fresh long red chilies, seeded
2 tablespoons fish sauce
¼ cup (2 fl oz/60 ml) water
1 tablespoon rice vinegar or distilled white vinegar
1 tablespoon sugar, or more to taste
1 lb (500 g) skinless catfish fillets (see Tips), cut into bite-sized pieces
5-oz (150-g) packet dried rice vermicelli (bun), softened and cut into manageable lengths for serving
¼ cup (2 fl oz/60 ml) vegetable oil
1 bunch dill, stemmed and cut into 1½-inch (4-cm) lengths
4 scallions (shallots/spring onions), including green parts, coarsely chopped
½ cup (2 oz/60 g) thinly sliced brown or pink shallots (French shallots)
2 cloves garlic, thinly sliced
⅓ cup (2 oz/60 g) chopped peanuts, lightly toasted

In a mortar, using a pestle, pound turmeric, galangal and chili to a paste. Alternatively, process in a blender or food processor. Add fish sauce, water, vinegar and sugar and stir until dissolved. Pour into a bowl. Add fish, toss to coat, and refrigerate for 3 hours.

Transfer fish to a plate, scrape off marinade and reserve, and pat fish dry with paper towels. In a wok, heat oil over medium–high heat until surface shimmers. Add fish, a few pieces at a time, to hot oil, stirring carefully so as not to break up pieces. Cook until flaky to the touch but not crisp, 1–3 minutes. Using a skimmer, transfer to a platter. Repeat with remaining fish. Reduce heat to medium, add dill and scallions to pan, and stir-fry just until wilted. Place these on top of cooked fish. Quickly stir-fry shallots and garlic in same pan, with any reserved marinade, and spoon on top. Finally, top with crushed peanuts.

Tips

- Ca bong lau and ca lang, varieties of catfish, are used for this dish in Vietnam. Trout substitutes well, as do pike and salmon. Asian alternatives include deep-sea mullet and Taiwanese milk fish.
- To give fish a distinct smoky flavor, it may be grilled then fried, but the grilling is optional. If grilling, cook until opaque throughout, 3–4 minutes, then follow instructions above.

Crab in black bean sauce

Serves 4–6

1 tablespoon peanut oil
3 tablespoons chopped scallions (spring onions/shallots)
2 cloves garlic, chopped
1 teaspoon chopped fresh ginger
⅓ cup (3 fl oz/90 ml) black bean sauce
½ cup (4 fl oz/125 ml) fish stock (see page 221)
1 tablespoon sherry (optional)
3 lb (1.5 kg) uncooked crab, segmented and claws cracked
steamed rice, for serving

In a wok or frying pan, heat oil over medium heat. Add scallions, garlic, and ginger and sauté until fragrant, about 1 minute. Pour in sauce, stock, and sherry and bring to a boil. Simmer until slightly thickened, about 4 minutes. Add crab and stir well. Cover and cook 10–15 minutes or until crab is cooked through—to test, crack a shell and see if flesh is tender.

Serve immediately with steamed rice.

Tip

When serving crabs in the shell, it's important to have the claws cracked to allow your guests easy eating. Claws are easily cracked using a nutcracker or meat mallet. Be sure to have lots of finger bowls and hand towels available.

Crab with yellow curry powder

Serves 4–6

1½ lb (750 g) cooked or raw crab in the shell
1 cup (8 fl oz/250 ml) evaporated milk
1 egg, beaten
2 tablespoons soy sauce
½ teaspoon granulated (white) sugar
½ cup (4 fl oz/125 ml) strained chili oil (see page 223) or ¼ cup chili oil with ¼ cup vegetable oil
1 teaspoon curry powder
¼ cup (2 fl oz/60 ml) vegetable oil
1 fresh long red chili, cut into strips
4 scallions (shallots/spring onions), coarsely chopped
¼ cup (1 oz/30 g) coarsely chopped Chinese or regular celery

Clean crab by pulling off the apron flap on the bottom of the shell. Pry off top shell, remove gills, intestines, and mouth parts. Cut small crabs in half, or large crabs into eight pieces. Twist off claws. Refrigerate until ready to use.

In a medium bowl, combine milk, egg, soy sauce, sugar, chili oil, and curry powder; whisk to blend well.

In a wok or large, heavy frying pan over high heat, heat vegetable oil. Add milk mixture and bring to a boil, stirring constantly. Add crab and cook for 2 minutes, then turn off heat and add chili, scallions, and celery. Spoon into a deep serving dish and serve.

Tip

For a less piquant dish, substitute half the chili oil with vegetable oil and use a mild curry powder.

Crispy fried fish

Serves 4

- ½ onion, grated
- 3 cloves garlic, finely chopped
- 2 teaspoons ground coriander
- ½ teaspoon chili powder
- 1 teaspoon ground black pepper
- 1 tablespoon fresh lemon juice
- 1 teaspoon sea salt
- 1 tablespoon vegetable oil
- 4 white fish fillets (6 oz/185 g each)
- 1 cup all-purpose (plain) flour
- 3 cups (24 fl oz/750 ml) vegetable oil, for deep-frying

In a food processor, combine onion, garlic, coriander, chili powder, black pepper, lemon juice, salt, and oil. Process to a paste. Place fish fillets in a baking dish and spread onion paste over fish. Cover and refrigerate for 1 hour.

Place flour in a shallow bowl. Coat fish in flour, shaking off excess. In a large wok, heat oil to 375°F (190°C), or until a small bread cube dropped in the oil sizzles and turns golden in 1 minute. Fry the fish in batches until golden, 1–2 minutes. Using a slotted spoon, transfer to paper towels to drain. Serve immediately, with lime and tomato wedges.

Fish curry

Serves 6

1½ lb (750 g) fish steaks or fillets
salt
2 tablespoons ghee or oil
2 medium-sized yellow (brown) onions, chopped
1 teaspoon peeled and grated fresh ginger
2 cloves garlic, crushed
½ teaspoon ground red chili
1 teaspoon baharat (see Tip below)
1 teaspoon ground turmeric
1 cinnamon stick, about 1½ inches (4 cm) long
1 cup (6 oz/180 g) chopped, peeled tomatoes
2 dried limes or zest (rind) of ½ lemon
½ cup (4 fl oz/125 ml) water
steamed rice, for serving

Rinse fish and pat dry with paper towels. Cut into serving sizes and sprinkle lightly with salt. Place on a plate, cover and set aside.

In a wok over medium–low heat, heat ghee or oil. Add onion and cook until translucent, about 10 minutes. Add ginger, garlic, chili, baharat, turmeric and cinnamon stick and cook, stirring, for 2 minutes.

Add tomatoes, dried limes (pierced twice with a skewer) or lemon zest, and water. Add salt to taste, cover and simmer for 15 minutes.

Place fish pieces in sauce, cover and simmer until fish is cooked through, 15–20 minutes. Lift fish onto a platter with prepared rice. Remove dried lime or lemon zest and cinnamon stick from sauce and spoon sauce over fish. Serve hot.

Tip

Baharat is a blend of spices used in the Persian Gulf States and Iraq. It can be found in Middle Eastern markets, or you can mix your own by combining the following spices:
4 tablespoons each black pepper and mild paprika;
2 tablespoons each coriander seed, cassia cinnamon and cloves; 3 tablespoons cumin; and 1 teaspoon each cardamom and nutmeg. Store baharat in a tightly covered jar in a dark place for up to 6 months.

Fish fillets with coconut rice parcels and cilantro-tomato relish

Serves 4

2 tomatoes, chopped
1/4 cup (1/3 oz/10 g) chopped cilantro (fresh coriander)
3 tablespoons lime juice
1 kaffir lime leaf, finely shredded
2 teaspoons peeled and grated ginger
1/4 teaspoon ground coriander
pinch of ground turmeric
1 small white onion, finely chopped
1 green chili, seeded and chopped
2 tablespoons unsweetened dried (desiccated) shredded coconut
1 clove garlic, crushed
4 whole cloves
3–4 teaspoons lime juice
4 fish fillets such as perch or monk fish, 4–6 oz (125–180 g) each
3/4 cup (5 oz/150 g) glutinous rice
1 tablespoon peanut oil
1 white onion, chopped
1 teaspoon ground cardamom
1 cup (8 fl oz/250 ml) water
1/2 cup (4 fl oz/125 ml) coconut milk
1/3 cup (3 fl oz/90 ml) warm water
4–6 fresh young banana leaves, rinsed and cut into 7-inch (18-cm) squares

In a bowl, combine tomatoes, cilantro, lime juice and kaffir lime leaves. Mix well and set aside.

In a small bowl, combine ginger, coriander, turmeric, onion, chili, coconut, garlic and cloves. Gradually add enough lime juice to form thick paste. If fish fillets have skin, slash skin side several times with sharp knife. Spread spice paste on flesh side of each fillet. Place on glass or ceramic plate, cover and refrigerate until ready to serve.

Place rice in fine-mesh sieve, rinse with cold running water and drain well.

In a wok over medium heat, warm peanut oil for 1 minute. Add onion and stir-fry until softened, about 2 minutes. Add rice, cardamom and water. Bring slowly to a boil, reduce heat to very low, cover tightly and cook until rice is tender, 12–14 minutes. Stir in coconut milk and warm water. Turn out on plate, leaving soft rice on bottom of wok. Allow to cool.

Working with one banana leaf square at a time, lay on work surface and spoon 2–3 tablespoons coconut rice in middle. Fold leaf over rice to form parcel. Secure with kitchen string.

Half fill large wok with water (steamer should not touch water) and bring to a boil. Working in batches if necessary, arrange parcels in bamboo steamer. Place each fish fillet on square of parchment (baking) paper and arrange fish in steamer. Cover, place steamer in a wok and steam until fish flakes when tested with fork, 6–8 minutes, depending on thickness of fillets. Remove fish and rice parcels from steamer and arrange on individual plates. Top each fish fillet with relish. Coconut rice parcels can be cut in half before serving, or guests can open parcels at table.

Fish with green curry paste

Serves 4

1/4 cup (2 fl oz/60 ml) vegetable oil
1/4 cup (2 fl oz/60 ml) green curry paste (see page 231)
12 oz (375 g) white fish fillets such as snapper, sole, or cod, thinly sliced
4 kaffir lime leaves, stemmed
1 cup (4 oz/125 g) chopped eggplant (aubergine) or 3 round Thai eggplants, chopped
1/2 cup (2 oz/60 g) pea eggplants (optional)
1/4 cup (2 fl oz/60 ml) fish stock (see page 221) or water
1 fresh long red chili, coarsely chopped
1 cup (1 oz/30 g) loosely packed fresh sweet Thai basil leaves
1/3 cup (3 fl oz/90 ml) coconut cream plus 2 tablespoons, for garnish
1 tablespoon fish sauce
1 tablespoon soy sauce
1 tablespoon granulated (white) sugar
1 tablespoon palm sugar

In a wok or large, heavy frying pan, heat oil over medium–high heat. Add curry paste and fry, stirring constantly, until fragrant, 1–2 minutes. Add fish and gently stir until coated on all sides. Add kaffir lime leaves and eggplants. Cook for 1 minute, then add stock or water.

Bring just to a boil, stirring, then add chili, basil, 1/3 cup (3 fl oz/90 ml) coconut cream, fish sauce, soy sauce and sugars. Cook for 1–2 minutes to heat through. Transfer to a serving bowl, drizzle over the remaining 2 tablespoons coconut cream, and serve.

Tips

- This is delicious chilled as well as hot but when serving chilled, delete the coconut cream garnish.
- For pork with green curry paste, substitute an equal quantity pork shoulder, loin, or tenderloin for the fish. Slice thinly, and proceed as above. Lamb leg or loin also makes a delicious substitute.

Ginger fish in nori wrapper

Serves 4

¼ cup (2 fl oz/60 ml) shaoxing wine or dry sherry
¼ cup (2 fl oz/60 ml) light soy sauce
1 tablespoon fish sauce
1 teaspoon Asian sesame oil
4 fish fillets (snapper, bream, perch, salmon), about 6 oz (185 g) each, and 5–6 inches (12–15 cm) long
8 scallions (shallots/spring onions)
4 sheets toasted nori (yaki-nori or toasted seaweed)
½ red bell pepper (capsicum), seeded and thinly sliced
3 tablespoons Japanese pickled ginger

Mix wine, soy sauce, fish sauce and sesame oil in a bowl, and pour over fish fillets in a flat dish. Leave for 20–30 minutes, turning once. Drain, discarding marinade.

Cut scallions into same length as fish fillets, leaving some green top on. Lay each fillet diagonally across a sheet of nori. If nori is too big for fillets, trim to smaller square shape. Place 2 or 3 strips of bell pepper and slices of pickled ginger down center of fish fillet. Add 2 scallions, with one green tip and one white tip at each end. Lightly brush each side flap of nori with water and fold over fish towards center, pressing gently to seal. Fish and vegetable strips will still be visible at either end. Place 2 fish on each level of steamer, and cover.

Partially fill a large wok or pot with water (steamer should not touch water) and bring to a rapid simmer. Place steamer over water and steam until fish flakes when tested with fork and flesh is opaque, 5–8 minutes, depending on thickness of fillets. Switch steamer levels halfway through for even cooking. Remove fish from steamer and serve with remaining pickled ginger and steamed rice.

Lobster salad

Serves 6–8

1 cucumber
4 carrots
2 celery stalks, chopped into fine julienne
6 oz (180 g) pearl onions or small boiling (pickling) onions
1 tablespoon rice vinegar or distilled white vinegar
1 teaspoon sugar
1 tablespoon fish sauce
2 teaspoons salt
1 fresh long red chili, seeded and chopped
1½ cups (3 oz/90 g) fresh bean sprouts, rinsed and drained
1 lb (500 g) shelled meat from lobster tails or langoustines (scampi/saltwater crayfish)
1 tablespoon fish sauce
¼ teaspoon ground pepper
½ teaspoon chili powder or to taste
2 teaspoons finely chopped brown or pink shallots (French shallots)
½-inch (12 mm) piece fresh ginger, peeled and finely grated

For lime and chili dressing
1 teaspoon Asian sesame oil
2 teaspoons water
1 tablespoon fresh lime juice
½ teaspoon grated fresh ginger or ginger juice
¼ fresh long red chili, seeded and finely chopped
½ teaspoon salt
¼ teaspoon ground pepper
2 tablespoons coarsely chopped cilantro (fresh coriander) sprigs, for garnish

Cut cucumber lengthwise in half, then use a spoon to scoop out and discard seeds. Cut carrots and cucumber into strips the size of French fries. Plunge pearl onions into boiling water, then drain and slip off skins. If using small boiling onions, peel and quarter. In a medium bowl, combine vinegar, sugar, fish sauce, salt and chili. Add vegetables and sprouts and toss to coat. Let stand for 15–20 minutes.

Cut lobster meat into medallions about ½ inch (12 mm) thick. In a medium bowl, combine fish sauce, pepper, chili powder, shallots and ginger. Add lobster and toss to coat. Let stand for 10 minutes. In a large nonstick wok over medium–high heat, sauté lobster until opaque, about 2 minutes.

For lime and chili dressing: In a small bowl, combine sesame oil, water, lime juice, ginger, chili, salt and pepper. Add to lobster and toss to coat. To serve, drain marinated vegetables and arrange on a serving plate. Layer lobster medallions on top and sprinkle with cilantro.

Mussels with garlic and lime butter

Serves 4

2 lb (1 kg) mussels
½ cup (4 oz/125 g) butter, softened
2 cloves garlic, crushed
2 tablespoons chopped fresh parsley
2 tablespoons chopped fresh chives
1 teaspoon grated lime zest (rind)
freshly cracked black pepper to taste

Scrub mussels under cold running water with a nylon pad or stiff brush and pull off hair-like "beards", discarding any mussels that are cracked or do not close when tapped. Place in a large bamboo steamer or steamer basket. In a small bowl, mix butter, garlic, parsley, chives, lime zest and pepper.

Partially fill a large wok or pot with water (steamer should not touch water) and bring to a rapid simmer. Place steamer over water, cover, and steam until mussels open, 4–6 minutes. Remove from steamer, spoon butter mixture into each shell, and serve immediately with a tossed green salad and crusty bread.

Tips

- Substitute basil pesto for garlic and lime butter.
- Remove mussels from shells and place one or two on an endive (chicory/witloof) leaf, and serve topped with lime butter.
- Substitute shelled and deveined shrimp (prawns) for mussels.

Pad thai with shrimp

Serves 4

5 oz (150 g) thick rice stick noodles
5 tablespoons vegetable oil
4 oz (125 g) firm tofu, cut into 1-inch (2.5-cm) cubes
2 cloves garlic, crushed
1 lb (500 g) jumbo shrimp (king prawns), peeled and deveined, tails intact
3 tablespoons lemon juice
2 tablespoons fish sauce
3 tablespoons palm sugar or brown sugar
2 eggs, beaten
2 tablespoons chopped chives
2 tablespoons chopped cilantro (fresh coriander)
2 tablespoons chopped fresh basil
2 tablespoons fried onion
lemon wedges for serving

Cook noodles, then drain and set aside. In a wok or frying pan, heat oil over medium–high heat. Add tofu and cook, stirring constantly, until golden, 1–2 minutes. Drain on paper towels. Drain all but 2 tablespoons oil from pan and return to medium–high heat. Add garlic and shrimp and cook, stirring occasionally, until shrimp change color, 4–5 minutes. Add lemon juice, fish sauce and sugar, stirring until sugar dissolves. Mix in noodles.

Push noodle mixture to one side of wok or pan. Add eggs and cook, without stirring, until partially set. Then stir gently until scrambled. Stir egg through noodle mixture. Add tofu, chives, cilantro and basil. Cook until heated through, about 1 minute.

To serve, divide among individual plates and sprinkle with fried onion. Accompany with lemon wedges.

Sautéed squid with leeks

Serves 6

1 lb (500 g) cleaned squid (calamari) (see Tips below)
3 tablespoons fish sauce
½ teaspoon ground pepper
2 large leeks or 6 baby leeks, white part only, well rinsed
4 scallions (shallots/spring onions), including green parts, chopped
3 tablespoons vegetable oil
3 small tomatoes, quartered or sectioned
1 onion, coarsely chopped
⅓-inch (1-cm) knob fresh ginger, peeled and cut into fine julienne
1 tablespoon cornstarch (cornflour) or arrowroot dissolved in 1 tablespoon water
steamed rice, for serving

Marinate squid (calamari) in 2 tablespoons fish sauce and pepper.

Cut leeks and scallions into fine julienne.

In a wok, heat oil over high heat and sauté squid for 1 minute. Add leeks, tomatoes, onion, ginger and scallions. Stir-fry for 2 minutes, then add cornstarch and water mixture. Stir well, then reduce heat to low, cover, and simmer for 3 minutes. Stir in remaining 1 tablespoon fish sauce. Serve hot with steamed rice.

Tips

- Do not overcook squid as it becomes tough and rubbery.
- If using uncleaned squid, increase proportion accordingly. To clean, pull tentacles and head from the tubelike body. Cut directly behind eyes to free tentacles from eyes. Use two fingers to pull out plastic-like cartilage and innards, and discard. Rinse and reserve tentacles and tubes. If small, cut squid bodies in half or quarters, and larger squid into 1-x-2-inch (2.5-x-5-cm) pieces.
- To tenderize and beautify larger squid, lightly score inside of flesh with a sharp knife, making a lattice pattern. This works best with larger bodies, as small squid are thin.

Scallops with arugula pesto and sweet potato purée

Serves 4

1 bunch arugula (rocket)
¼ cup (1 oz/30 g) pine nuts, toasted
¼ cup (1 oz/30 g) grated parmesan cheese
ground pepper to taste
2 cloves garlic, crushed
¼ cup (2 fl oz/60 ml) extra virgin olive oil
1 lb (500 g) sweet potatoes, peeled and cut
into 2-inch (5-cm) pieces
2 tablespoons olive oil
3 cloves garlic, crushed
2 tablespoons vegetable oil
1 small red chili, seeded and chopped
1 lb (500 g) scallops, halved if large
1 tablespoon lime juice
lime wedges for serving

Place arugula, pine nuts, parmesan cheese, pepper and garlic in food processor. Process until finely chopped. With motor running, gradually pour in olive oil and process until well combined. Set aside.

Half fill saucepan with water. Bring to a boil, add sweet potatoes, reduce heat to medium and cook until tender, 10–12 minutes. Drain, transfer to bowl and mash with fork or potato masher. Stir in olive oil and 2 garlic cloves. Set aside and keep warm.

In a wok over medium heat, warm vegetable oil. Add chili and remaining garlic clove and stir-fry until aromatic, about 1 minute. Add scallops and stir-fry until tender (do not overcook or scallops will toughen), 2–3 minutes. Remove from heat and stir in lime juice.

To serve, spoon sweet potato purée on individual plates. Top with pesto, then place scallops over pesto. Serve hot, accompanied with lime wedges. Store any leftover pesto in screw-top jar in refrigerator.

Seafood, basil and almond stir-fried with mixed greens

Serves 4

1 lb (500 g) medium uncooked shrimp (prawns)
¼ cup (2 fl oz/60 ml) vegetable oil
2 cloves garlic, minced
1 large hot red chili, finely chopped
4 oz (125 g) slivered almonds, toasted
2 tablespoons oyster sauce
2 tablespoons soy sauce
8 scallions (shallots/spring onions), chopped
3 bunches (about 1½ lb/650 g) baby bok choy, chopped
4 oz (125 g) snow peas (mange tout), sliced diagonally
1 handful shredded basil leaves
cooked rice or noodles, to serve

Remove head and shells from shrimp, leaving tails intact. Heat oil in wok or large frying pan until just smoking.

Add shrimp and stir-fry 2 minutes or until they start to change color.

Add garlic, chili, almonds, sauces and scallions and stir-fry 2–3 minutes or until fragrant and onions are tender.

Stir in bok choy and snow peas and cook, stirring, 2 minutes or until just tender. Stir in basil and serve with rice or noodles.

Semolina-crusted shrimp

Serves 4–5

¼ cup coriander seeds
1–2 tablespoons vegetable oil
4 teaspoons finely grated fresh ginger
4 teaspoons crushed garlic
4 teaspoons tamarind concentrate
2–4 teaspoons chili powder
2 teaspoons fennel seeds
1 teaspoon ground turmeric
18 fresh curry leaves, finely chopped
salt to taste
2 lb (1 kg) medium shrimp (prawns), peeled and deveined
vegetable oil for deep-frying
1 cup (6 oz/180 g) coarse semolina
juice of 1 lemon

In a spice grinder, grind coriander seeds to a powder. Place in a bowl and combine with 1–2 tablespoons oil, ginger, garlic, tamarind, chili powder, fennel seeds, turmeric, curry leaves and salt to form a paste.

Add shrimp to spice paste and mix well until coated. Set aside to marinate for 5 minutes.

Fill a karhai or wok with vegetable oil to a depth of 2 inches (5 cm) and heat over medium heat to 375°F (190°C) on a deep-frying thermometer. While oil is heating, dip shrimp, one at a time, in semolina to coat. Fry shrimp in batches until light golden, 1–2 minutes. Use a slotted spoon to remove shrimp to paper towels to drain.

Drizzle shrimp with lemon juice and serve hot.

Spiced shrimp and rice

Serves 4–5

2–3 tablespoons ghee or vegetable oil
2 cloves garlic, chopped
2 lb (1 kg) raw shrimp (prawns), shelled and deveined
1 large yellow (brown) onion, chopped
2 teaspoons baharat (page 120)
2 teaspoons turmeric
1½ cups (9 oz/280 g) chopped, peeled tomatoes
2 teaspoons salt
freshly ground black pepper
1 tablespoon chopped fresh flat-leaf (Italian) parsley
1 teaspoon chopped cilantro (fresh coriander)
2½ cups (20 fl oz/625 ml) water
2 cups (14 oz/440 g) basmati rice

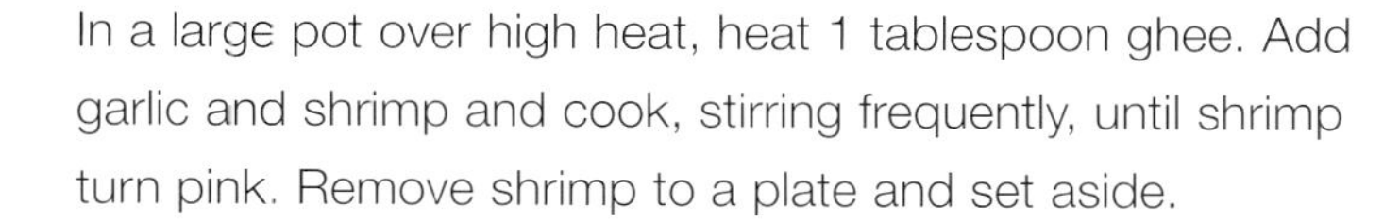

In a large pot over high heat, heat 1 tablespoon ghee. Add garlic and shrimp and cook, stirring frequently, until shrimp turn pink. Remove shrimp to a plate and set aside.

Add remaining ghee to the pot and heat over medium–low heat. Add onion and cook until translucent and lightly browned, about 8 minutes. Stir in Baharat and turmeric and cook for 1 minute.

Add tomatoes, salt, pepper to taste, parsley and cilantro. Bring to a boil and add water. Cover and cook over medium heat for 5 minutes.

Place rice in a fine-mesh sieve and rinse under cold running water until water runs clear. Stir into sauce and bring to a boil. Reduce heat to low, cover and cook for 18 minutes.

Stir rice, then put shrimp on top of rice and gently stir through rice. Cover pot and simmer over low heat for 3 minutes.

Stir rice again then leave covered, off the heat, for 5 minutes. Serve with pita bread, pickles and salad.

Spicy snapper with parsnip chips

Serves 4

2 teaspoon ground cumin
1 green chili, seeded and sliced
½ cup (⅔ oz/20 g) cilantro (fresh coriander) leaves
3 cloves garlic
1 piece peeled fresh ginger, about 1¼ in (3 cm)
2 teaspoons garam marsala (see page 225)
4 small snapper, 6–8 oz (180–250 g) each, cleaned
6 cups (48 fl oz/1.5 L) vegetable oil for deep-frying
2 parsnips, peeled
lime wedges for serving

Place cumin, chili, cilantro, garlic, ginger and garam marsala in food processor and process until smooth. Using sharp knife, cut 3 shallow slits in each side of fish. Rub spice mixture into each side. Place on glass or ceramic plate, cover and refrigerate for 1 hour.

Heat vegetable oil in a wok until it reaches 375°F (190°C) on a deep-frying thermometer or until a small bread cube dropped in oil sizzles and turns golden. Add fish, one at a time, and cook, turning once, until golden and crisp on both sides, about 4 minutes. Using tongs and spatula, carefully remove fish from wok and drain on paper towels. Repeat with remaining fish. Keep warm.

Thinly slice parsnips lengthwise, using vegetable peeler. Add slices to wok and cook until golden and crisp, about 1 minute. Using slotted spoon, remove from wok and drain on paper towels.

Arrange fish and parsnip chips on individual plates. Garnish with lime wedge and serve.

Squid bulgogi

Serves 4

3 medium squid tubes (bodies), about 6½ oz (200 g) total, cut open and cleaned
4 fresh shiitake mushrooms or dried Chinese mushrooms soaked for 30 minutes in several changes of water
2 small green bell peppers (capsicums), cut into bite-sized pieces
2 tablespoons vegetable or sunflower oil
lettuce leaves, for serving
1 teaspoon pan-toasted sesame seeds
1 teaspoon freshly ground black pepper
1 teaspoon thin hot red chili strips

For marinade
3 tablespoons light soy sauce
2 tablespoons sugar
2 tablespoons crushed garlic
2 scallions (shallots/spring onions), finely chopped
1 teaspoon ginger juice (obtained by grating fresh ginger)
1 teaspoon sesame oil
steamed rice, for serving

Using the tip of a knife, score surface of squid in a crisscross pattern to prevent it over-curling during cooking. Cut squid into bite-sized pieces.

If using fresh shiitake mushrooms, dip in rapidly boiling water for a few seconds. Remove and drain on paper towels, then chop roughly. If using dried mushrooms, squeeze out excess water. Remove and discard stems and roughly chop caps.

To make marinade: In a small bowl, combine marinade ingredients and mix well.

In a large glass or ceramic bowl, combine squid, mushrooms and bell peppers with marinade and marinate for 20–30 minutes.

In a wok or frying pan, heat oil until very hot. Drain squid, mushroom and bell pepper pieces and cook over high heat until liquid has evaporated and marinade has caramelized, about 5 minutes.

Arrange lettuce leaves on individual plates and place squid bulgogi in center. Sprinkle with sesame seeds, black pepper and chili strips, and serve with steamed rice.

Steamed fish in banana leaves

Makes 8–10

- 1 tablespoon sticky (glutinous) rice
- 1/4 cup (2 fl oz/60 ml) vegetable oil
- 1/4 cup (2 fl oz/60 ml) red curry paste (see page 231)
- 1/2 cup (2 oz/60 g) chopped eggplant (aubergine)
- 1/4 cup (1 oz/30 g) pea eggplants (optional)
- 4 long beans or 12 green beans, cut into 1/2-inch (12-mm) pieces
- 1/4 cup (2 fl oz/60 ml) chicken stock (see page 220) or water
- 2 tablespoons fish sauce
- 8 fresh eryngo (sawtooth coriander) leaves, finely shredded, or 7 sprigs cilantro (fresh coriander), coarsely chopped
- 12 oz (375 g) firm white-fleshed fish fillets such as cod, skinned and very thinly sliced
- 4 kaffir lime leaves, stemmed
- 1–2 large banana leaves (optional)
- about 10 fresh piper (beetle) leaves, or 2–3 cabbage leaves, each cut into 4 squares

In a wok or small frying pan over low heat, stir rice until golden brown, 3–5 minutes. Transfer to a mortar and pulverize with a pestle; set aside.

In a wok or large, heavy frying pan, warm oil over medium–high heat and fry curry paste, stirring constantly, until fragrant, 1–2 minutes. Add eggplants and beans and stir well to coat. Add chicken stock or water, fish sauce, and eryngo leaves or cilantro, and bring to a boil. Add fish, stirring to coat well, then add ground rice and cook until mixture is very thick and fish is just opaque throughout, about 1 minute. Remove from heat.

Roll kaffir lime leaves together into a tight cylinder and cut into fine shreds. If using, wipe banana leaf with a clean cloth. Spread out each banana leaf and cut each into 8–10 pieces, 8 x 6 inches (20 x 15 cm) in size, removing hard center stem. Center a piper leaf on each piece of banana leaf (or alternatively, cut each cabbage leaf into 8–10 small squares and place 1 square on each banana leaf) and spoon about 1/4 cup fish mixture on top. Sprinkle strands of shredded lime leaf over. Gently roll over sides of banana leaf, overlapping them to make a shape resembling a flat sausage. Fold or pull over 2 opposite ends to center, and secure with a toothpick. Cook parcels in covered steamer over rapidly simmering water for about 15 minutes. Let cool slightly, then open parcels and serve on banana leaves.

Tips

- This dish is ideal for picnics or at a buffet, as it is delicious eaten at room temperature.
- Lay banana leaves in the sun for a couple of hours to soften slightly so they are easier to fold. Or, run them briefly over a gas flame until they become waxy and pliable. Very fresh leaves, especially young tender ones, are best. Alternatively, use aluminum foil.
- If available, you can also add 1 teaspoon prickly ash (kamchatton), coarsely ground, to the ground rice.

Stir-fried chili-lime shrimp

Serves 4

1 lb (500 g) jumbo shrimp (king prawns), peeled and deveined, tails intact
pinch of ground chili
¼ teaspoon ground turmeric
3 tablespoons vegetable oil
3 cloves garlic, crushed
1 small red chili, seeded and chopped
1 teaspoon black mustard seeds
1 tablespoon lime juice
lime wedges for serving

Place shrimp in bowl. Combine ground chili and turmeric and sprinkle over shrimp. Using hands, rub spices into shrimp.

In a wok over medium–high heat, warm vegetable oil. Add garlic, chili and mustard seeds and stir-fry until seeds begin to pop, 1–2 minutes. Raise heat to high, add shrimp and stir-fry until shrimp change color and are tender, 3–4 minutes. Remove from heat and stir in lime juice.

Serve hot, accompanied with lime wedges.

Stir-fried octopus with long beans and snow peas

Serves 4

- 1 lb (500 g) baby octopus
- 1 tablespoon light soy sauce
- 3 tablespoons vegetable oil
- 1 tablespoon dry sherry
- 2 cloves garlic, crushed
- 2 teaspoons grated lime zest (rind)
- 2 tablespoons lime juice
- 3 small red chilies, seeded and halved lengthwise
- 5 oz (150 g) long beans, cut into 4-inch (10-cm) lengths
- 4 kaffir lime leaves, shredded, or 1 teaspoon grated lime zest (rind)
- 5 oz (150 g) snow peas (mange-tout), trimmed and sliced crosswise

Working with one octopus at a time, slit open head and remove intestines. Rinse and place in glass or ceramic bowl. In small bowl, combine soy sauce, 1 tablespoon vegetable oil, sherry, garlic, 2 teaspoons lime zest and lime juice. Pour over octopus, cover and refrigerate for 1 hour.

Drain octopus and reserve marinade. In a wok over medium heat, warm remaining 2 tablespoons vegetable oil. Add chilies and stir-fry until aromatic, 1–2 minutes. Add octopus and stir-fry for 2 minutes. Add beans, lime leaves or lime zest, snow peas and reserved marinade. Stir-fry until vegetables are tender-crisp and octopus is cooked through (do not overcook or octopus will toughen), 1–2 minutes.

Serve hot.

Tip

You may like to substitute octopus with six 1-lb (500-g) squid bodies. Cut squid tubes in half lengthwise. Cut shallow slashes in a criss-cross pattern on outside of squid and cut squid into 3⁄4-inch (2-cm) strips. Marinate and cook as for octopus.

Stir-fried seafood with noodles

Serves 4

8 oz (250 g) soft Asian noodles
1 tablespoon peanut oil
2 teaspoons sesame oil
1 tablespoon chopped lemongrass
3 cloves garlic, chopped
1 red chili, seeded and chopped
8 oz (250 g) uncooked shrimp (prawns), peeled and deveined
8 oz (250 g) fish fillets, skinned and cut into small pieces
8 oz (250 g) scallops, deveined if necessary
2 tablespoons fish sauce
2 tablespoons chopped cilantro (fresh coriander) leaves
1 tablespoon sweet chili sauce

Cook noodles in boiling salted water for 5 minutes. Drain.

In a wok over medium heat, warm peanut and sesame oils. Add lemongrass, garlic and chili and cook until fragrant, about 1 minute. Add shrimp and fish and cook until tender and opaque, 3–5 minutes. Stir in noodles, scallops, fish sauce, cilantro and chili sauce and cook, stirring well, until noodles are heated through and scallops are tender, about 3–4 minutes. Serve immediately.

Stir-fried squid with chili

Makes 4 small servings

4 cleaned squid tubes, about 12 oz (375 g) total
2 tablespoons vegetable oil
1 teaspoon Asian sesame oil
3 cloves garlic, finely chopped
1–2 small red chilies, seeded and finely chopped

Cut squid in half lengthwise, then cut into strips ¾-inch (2-cm) wide. In a wok or frying pan, warm oils over medium heat. Fry garlic and chili until aromatic, about 1 minute. Add squid and stir-fry for 1 minute. Do not overcook or squid will become tough. Remove from heat and serve hot.

Thai curry fish in banana leaf cups

Serves 6

2–3 large banana leaves, cut into six 6-inch (15-cm) rounds
1 lb (500 g) white fish fillets, finely diced
2 tablespoons red curry paste (see page 231)
1 tablespoon chopped roasted peanuts
1 cup (8 oz/250 ml) thick coconut cream
2 eggs, lightly beaten
1 tablespoon fish sauce
salt and pepper to taste
1 cup (3 oz/90 g) Chinese cabbage leaves, finely shredded
2 tablespoons thick coconut cream, for garnish (optional)
1 fresh long red chili, seeded and thinly sliced, for garnish (optional)

Drop each banana leaf round into hot water to soften, 30–60 seconds. Drain and pat dry with paper towels. Fold each round and staple into a round or square custard cup, or use rounds to line oiled rice bowls or ramekins.

Partially fill a wok or pot with water (steamer should not touch water) and bring to a rapid simmer. In a bowl, combine fish, curry paste, peanuts, coconut cream, eggs, fish sauce, salt and pepper. Fill each banana cup with ⅙ fish mixture, then ⅙ shredded cabbage, and place in a bamboo steamer or steamer basket. Cover with double layer of greased plastic wrap or parchment (baking) paper, or place a cloth under lid to stop any condensation dripping onto cups. Place steamer over water, cover, and steam until set, 10–15 minutes. Garnish with a dollop of coconut cream and sliced chili if desired. Serve hot.

Thai red curry shrimp

Serves 4

1½ lb (750 g) jumbo shrimp (king prawns), with heads
1 tablespoon vegetable oil
2 tablespoons red curry paste (see page 231)
2 cups (16 fl oz/500 ml) coconut milk
1 tablespoon fish sauce
1 fresh red Thai or Anaheim chili, seeded and cut into shreds 2 inches (5 cm) long, for garnish

Shell and devein shrimp, leaving tails intact and reserving shrimp heads. Wash shrimp heads. In a wok or large skillet, heat oil over medium heat and fry shrimp heads until they turn pink, about 1 minute. Add curry paste and fry until fragrant, about 30 seconds. Add coconut milk and fish sauce. Reduce heat to low and simmer for 10 minutes. Using a slotted spoon, remove and discard shrimp heads. Add shrimp to curry and stir over low heat until shrimp turn pink, 4–5 minutes. Spoon into serving bowls. Garnish each serving with shredded red chili. Serve with steamed jasmine rice.

Whole fried fish with chili and basil

Serves 4

1–2 whole fish, about 9½ inches (24 cm) long, such as snapper, bream, flounder or trout, scaled and gutted
vegetable oil, for deep-frying, plus 2 tablespoons
6 cloves garlic, coarsely chopped
1 onion, finely chopped
5 fresh medium-sized red chilies, thinly sliced
1 fresh long red chili, cut into large pieces
1 fresh long green chili, cut into large pieces
1 tablespoon fish sauce
1 tablespoon soy sauce
¼ cup (2 fl oz/60 ml) chicken stock (see page 220) or water
¾ cup (¾ oz/20 g) loosely packed sweet Thai basil leaves, coarsely chopped
½ cup (¾ oz/20 g) chopped cilantro (fresh coriander) leaves

With a very sharp knife, score each side of fish with three deep slashes to the bone.

In a large wok or deep-fryer, heat 4 inches (10 cm) oil to 350°F (180°C). Add fish and cook until crispy and brown on both sides and opaque throughout, 7–10 minutes, depending on thickness. Using a skimmer, transfer fish to paper towels to drain.

Meanwhile, in a wok or medium-sized heavy frying pan over medium–high heat, heat 2 tablespoons oil and fry garlic, onion, and all chilies until garlic just begins to brown. Add fish sauce, soy sauce and chicken stock or water, stir to combine, then cook for 1 minute. Add basil leaves, stir well and pour over fish. Transfer to a large serving platter, sprinkle with chopped cilantro, and serve.

Tips

- For a less piquant dish, remove seeds from chilies.
- This dish can also be garnished with fried basil leaves. In a large wok, heat 1 cup (8 fl oz/250 ml) oil. Working in batches, fry about 20 fresh basil leaves. Using a slotted spoon, remove from oil and drain on paper towels.

vegetables and salads

Asian greens stir-fry with shiitake mushroom

Serves 4

1 lb (500 g) Asian greens, such as bok choy, choy sum or Chinese cabbage
2 tablespoons vegetable oil
1 red bell pepper (capsicum), seeded and sliced into strips
1 small red chili, seeded and sliced
10 scallions (shallots/spring onions), trimmed and sliced
2 celery stalks, sliced
1 lemongrass stalk, trimmed and chopped
2 cloves garlic, crushed
1 inch (2.5 cm) piece fresh ginger, peeled and chopped
6 oz (180 g) shiitake mushrooms, sliced
3 tablespoons soy sauce
cooked egg noodles or jasmine rice, for serving

Wash Asian greens well and pat dry with paper towels. Trim off root ends and slice greens into 2½-inch (6-cm) lengths.

In a wok or large frying pan, heat oil over medium heat, until oil is hot but not smoking. Add bell pepper, chili, scallions, celery, lemongrass, garlic and ginger. Raise heat to medium-high and stir-fry for 2 minutes. Add greens and mushrooms and stir-fry for 2 minutes. Reduce heat to low, cover and allow mixture to cook slowly until greens are tender–crisp, about 2 minutes. Remove from heat and stir in soy sauce.

Serve immediately with egg noodles or jasmine rice.

Asian greens with lemon and ginger oil

Serves 4

⅓ cup (3 fl oz/90 ml) sunflower oil
finely grated zest (rind) of 2 lemons
1 lemongrass stalk, bottom 3 inches (7.5 cm) only, inner stalks roughly chopped
3 teaspoons peeled and grated fresh ginger
1 lb (500 g) mixed Asian greens, such as bok choy, choy sum and Chinese cabbage
pinch sea salt
pinch sugar
juice of 1 lemon
lemon wedges, for serving

Place oil, lemon zest, lemongrass and ginger in a screw-top jar and shake until well combined. Set aside in a warm place for 5 days so flavors infuse oil. After 5 days, strain oil and discard solids. Seal and store lemon and ginger oil in a cool, dark place.

Wash greens well. Pat dry with paper towels. Trim roots from greens and cut into 2-inch (5-cm) lengths. If using bok choy, remove dark outer leaves, separate younger leaves and trim ends.

Warm 2 tablespoons lemon and ginger oil in a wok or frying pan over medium heat. Add greens and stir-fry until tender-crisp, 3 to 4 minutes. Remove from heat and stir in salt, sugar and lemon juice.

Serve immediately, accompanied with lemon wedges.

Asian greens with tempeh and oyster sauce

Serves 2–4

1 bunch bok choy or choy sum, trimmed and cut into 4-inch (10-cm) lengths
3 oz (90 g) tempeh or tofu (bean curd), cut into ½-inch (12-mm) pieces
3 oz (90 g) enoki mushrooms, trimmed
3½ oz (100 g) bottled baby corn, halved
¼ cup (2 fl oz/60 ml) oyster sauce
1 clove garlic, crushed
1 teaspoon Asian sesame oil
½ teaspoon peeled and grated fresh ginger
2 scallions (shallots/spring onions), finely chopped
1 tablespoon sesame seeds, toasted

Put bok choy, tempeh, enoki and baby corn in a large bamboo steamer or steamer basket. Partially fill a wok or pot with water (steamer should not touch water) and bring to a rapid simmer. Put steamer over water, cover and steam until vegetables are softened, 3–4 minutes.

Meanwhile, put oyster sauce, garlic, sesame oil, and ginger in a small saucepan and mix well. Place saucepan over medium heat to warm sauce, 3–4 minutes.

Remove vegetables from steamer and arrange on serving plates with enoki in the center. Drizzle warm sauce over vegetables. Sprinkle with scallions and sesame seeds. Serve as a side dish or light vegetarian dish.

Beans foogarth

Serves 4

2 lb (1 kg) green beans, trimmed and cut into ½-inch (12-mm) pieces
1½ teaspoons ground turmeric
2½ tablespoons vegetable oil
1 teaspoon brown or black mustard seeds
5 dried red chilies
18 fresh curry leaves
1 tablespoon finely grated fresh ginger
2 yellow (brown) onions, chopped
½ teaspoon salt
4 fresh green chilies, chopped
½ cup (2 oz/60 g) finely grated fresh coconut
juice of ½ lemon

Fill a saucepan with water and bring to a boil. Add beans and ½ teaspoon turmeric and boil for 1–2 minutes. Drain and rinse beans under cold running water. Drain well.

In a karhai or wok, heat oil over medium–low heat. Add mustard seeds and cook until they crackle, about 30 seconds. Add dried chilies, curry leaves and ginger, and cook, stirring, for 30 seconds. Add onions, remaining 1 teaspoon turmeric and salt. Cook, uncovered, stirring often, until onions are translucent, about 5 minutes.

Stir in beans and fresh chilies, and toss over medium– low heat until well combined and heated through. Sprinkle with coconut and drizzle with lemon juice. Serve hot.

Tip

The addition of turmeric when cooking beans helps to intensify the green color of the beans.

Black-eyed pea and sugar snaps stir-fry

Serves 4

1 cup ($6\frac{1}{2}$ oz/200 g) dried black-eyed peas (beans)
2 red onions, sliced
juice from 2 lemons
1 tablespoon vegetable oil
2 teaspoons Asian sesame oil
5 oz (150 g) sugar snap peas or snow peas (mange-tout), trimmed
½ cup (2 oz/60 g) chopped scallions (shallots/spring onions)
1 cup (1 oz/30 g) mint leaves
½ cup (¾ oz/20 g) snipped chives
1 teaspoon fish sauce
1 teaspoon light soy sauce

Place black-eyed peas in large bowl, add cold water to cover, cover and allow to stand overnight. Drain and rinse peas and place in saucepan with plenty of water to cover. Bring to a boil, reduce heat to low and simmer, uncovered, until tender, about 1 hour. Drain and allow to cool completely.

In bowl, combine onions and lemon juice, cover and allow to stand for 1 hour.

In wok over medium-high heat, warm vegetable and sesame oils. Add sugar snap peas or snow peas and stir-fry until tender-crisp, about 2 minutes. Remove from heat and allow to cool completely. Add black-eyed peas and sugar snap peas or snow peas to bowl with onions. Add scallions, mint, chives, fish sauce and soy sauce. Mix well, cover and refrigerate for 30 minutes. Serve chilled.

Butternut squash and lentil salad

Serves 4

1/3 cup (3 fl oz/90 ml) olive oil
2 teaspoons grated lime zest (rind)
1/3 cup (3 fl oz/90 ml) lime juice
2 tablespoons chopped cilantro (fresh coriander)
1/2 teaspoon superfine (caster) sugar
ground pepper to taste
1 butternut squash (pumpkin), about 1 lb (500 g), peeled and cut into 1 1/2-in (4-cm) cubes
1/2 cup (3 1/2 oz/100 g) dried red lentils
1 tablespoon vegetable oil
1 small red chili, seeded and chopped
1 teaspoon cumin seeds
2 teaspoons coriander seeds, cracked

Place olive oil, lime zest and juice, cilantro, sugar and pepper in screw-top jar. Shake well to combine. Set aside

Line large steamer with parchment (baking) paper. Half fill wok with water (steamer should not touch water) and bring to a boil. Place squash cubes in steamer, cover and place steamer over boiling water. Steam until squash cubes are tender but retain their shape, 10–12 minutes. Add more water to wok when necessary. Remove steamer from wok and let squash cool.

Place lentils in saucepan with water to cover. Bring to a boil and cook until tender (do not overcook), about 5 minutes. Drain and cool.

In wok over medium–high heat, warm vegetable oil. Add chili, cumin and coriander and cook until aromatic, 1–2 minutes. Add squash and lentils and stir-fry until flavors are blended, about 1 minute. Remove from heat and stir in dressing. Mix well.

Serve warm or refrigerate for 30 minutes and serve chilled.

Chickpeas with spinach

Serves 6

1½ cups (10 oz/300 g) dried chickpeas (garbanzo beans)
4 cups (32 fl oz/1 L) cold water
⅓ cup (3 fl oz/90 ml) olive oil
1 large yellow (brown) onion, chopped
2 cloves garlic, chopped
¼ cup (2 oz/60 g) tomato paste
2 tablespoons chopped fresh flat-leaf (Italian) parsley
1 tablespoon chopped fresh mint
1 teaspoon ground cumin
1 teaspoon sugar
salt
freshly ground black pepper
1½ lb (750 g) spinach
extra-virgin olive oil, for serving

Put chickpeas in a bowl, add water and let soak in a cool place for 8–10 hours or overnight.

Drain chickpeas and rinse well. Place in a large saucepan with fresh water to cover. Bring to a boil, cover and cook over low heat until tender, 1–1½ hours.

Heat oil in a wok over medium–low heat. Add onion and cook until translucent, about 7 minutes. Add garlic and cook for a few seconds. Stir in tomato paste, parsley, mint, cumin, sugar and salt and black pepper to taste. Add to chickpeas, cover and simmer for 10 minutes.

Remove any attached roots and damaged leaves from spinach and discard. Wash spinach leaves and stems well in several changes of water. Drain, then coarsely chop leaves and stems. Add to chickpeas, stir well and simmer, uncovered, until spinach is cooked, about 10 minutes. Mixture should be moist, but not too liquid.

Serve hot or at room temperature. Add extra-virgin olive oil to taste.

Deep-fried tofu with vegetables

Serves 4

13 oz (400 g) firm tofu, drained and pressed
canola oil for deep-frying
3 tablespoons vegetable or chicken stock
3 tablespoons mirin or sweet white wine
2 tablespoons Japanese soy sauce
¼ teaspoon sugar
½ teaspoon Asian sesame oil
½ teaspoon grated fresh ginger
1 large carrot, julienned
½ small green bell pepper (capsicum), seeded and julienned
½ small red bell pepper (capsicum), seeded and julienned
1 medium red (Spanish) onion, cut into thin wedges
watercress sprigs for garnish

Cut tofu into 1½-inch (3-cm) cubes and pat dry with paper towels. Fill a large wok one-third full with oil and heat to 365°F (185°C). Deep-fry tofu until golden, 3–4 minutes, turning occasionally. Drain on paper towels. In a medium saucepan, combine stock, mirin, soy sauce, sugar, sesame oil and ginger. Bring to a boil, add vegetables and simmer 1 minute. Combine tofu with vegetables and sauce. Garnish with watercress and serve immediately.

Fried tofu salad

Serves 4

8 oz (250 g) egg noodles
1 English (hothouse) cucumber, thinly sliced
1 red bell pepper (capsicum), seeded and sliced
1 cup (4 oz/125 g) fresh bean sprouts, rinsed
3 tablespoons sliced scallions (shallots/spring onions)
2 tablespoons sesame seeds, toasted
3 tablespoons vegetable oil
6½ oz (200 g) firm tofu, cut into 1-inch (2.5-cm) cubes
2 cloves garlic
1-inch (2.5-cm) piece fresh ginger, peeled
6 tablespoons crunchy peanut butter
1 tablespoon Asian sesame oil
3 tablespoons rice wine
1 tablespoon Worcestershire sauce
3 teaspoons palm sugar or brown sugar
5 tablespoons chicken stock (see page 220)

Cook noodles, then drain and let cool.

In large bowl, combine cucumber, bell pepper, bean sprouts, scallions and sesame seeds. Cover and chill.

In wok or frying pan, heat oil over medium–high heat. Add tofu and cook, stirring constantly, until golden, 3–4 minutes. Drain on paper towels and let cool.

Add tofu and noodles to bowl. Add dressing and toss until well combined.

Place garlic, ginger, peanut butter, sesame oil, rice wine, Worcestershire sauce, sugar and stock in food processor. Process 10 seconds to make dressing.

Cover salad and refrigerate for 30 minutes.

To serve, divide chilled salad among individual plates and pour over dressing.

Green beans in oil

Serves 6

1 lb (500 g) green beans
1/4 cup (2 fl oz/60 ml) olive oil
1 medium yellow (brown) onion, chopped
2 cloves garlic, chopped
1 cup (6 oz/185 g) chopped, peeled tomatoes
1 tablespoon tomato paste
1/2 cup (4 fl oz/125 ml) water
1/2 teaspoon sugar
salt
freshly ground black pepper
2 tablespoons chopped fresh flat-leaf (Italian) parsley

Trim beans and remove strings if necessary. Cut into 2-inch (5-cm) lengths or slit lengthwise.

Heat olive oil in a wok over medium–low heat. Add onion and fry until translucent, about 8 minutes. Add garlic and cook for a few seconds longer.

Add tomatoes, tomato paste, water, sugar and salt and pepper to taste. Cover and simmer until tomatoes are soft, about 15 minutes.

Add beans and parsley; cover and simmer until beans are tender, 15–20 minutes. Serve hot, or at room temperature as is traditional.

Homemade cottage cheese with spinach

Serves 4

2 bunches spinach, trimmed and rinsed well
1½ teaspoons ground turmeric
2 tablespoons water
3 tablespoons vegetable oil and melted unsalted butter combined
4 teaspoons cumin seeds
3 yellow (brown) onions, chopped
½ teaspoon salt
2 tablespoons coriander seeds, crushed
1½ tablespoons grated fresh ginger
2 fresh green chilies, finely chopped
1 teaspoon chili powder
3 tomatoes, unpeeled, finely chopped
1 recipe paneer (see page 229), cut into 1-inch (2.5-cm) pieces
1 teaspoon dried fenugreek leaves

Place spinach in a large saucepan. In a small bowl, combine ½ teaspoon turmeric with water and add to pan. Cook over medium–high heat, covered, turning spinach occasionally, until spinach is wilted, 3–5 minutes. Remove from heat, drain excess water and let spinach cool. Place spinach in a food processor or blender and purée. Set aside.

In a wok, heat oil and butter mixture over medium–low heat. Add cumin seeds and cook until fragrant, about 30 seconds. Add onions and salt, and cook uncovered, stirring often, until onions are translucent, about 5 minutes.

Add coriander seeds, ginger, chilies, chili powder and remaining 1 teaspoon turmeric, and cook, stirring, until fragrant, 2–3 minutes.

Stir in tomatoes and cook, stirring occasionally, until tomatoes are soft, about 5 minutes. Stir in puréed spinach and mix well. Add paneer and stir gently to coat with sauce. Cook over medium–low heat until paneer is warmed through, 2–3 minutes. Sprinkle with fenugreek leaves and serve hot.

Tip

Adding ground turmeric to spinach before cooking helps spinach to retain a bright green color.

Japanese seaweed salad

Serves 4

1½ oz (40 g) hijiki
4 sheets usuage
boiling water
3 tablespoons vegetable oil
½ carrot, peeled and cut into thin matchstick strips
1 teaspoon instant dashi dissolved in
 1 cup (8 fl oz/250 ml) water
½ cup (4 oz/125 g) sugar
½ cup (4 fl oz/125 ml) soy sauce

Wash hijiki well in a large bowl of water. Any dust and sand will settle to bottom of bowl. Scoop hijiki from bowl and then soak in clean water for 20 minutes. Drain well. Place usuage in a bowl. Add boiling water to cover and soak for 3–4 minutes to remove some of oil. Remove from water, draining well. Cut usuage into strips ¼ inch (6 mm) wide. Heat oil in a saucepan over high heat. Add carrot strips and stir-fry until softened, about 2 minutes. Add hijki and stir-fry for 2 minutes. Add usuage and stir-fry for 2 minutes. Add dashi and sugar, bring to a boil then reduce heat to medium-low and simmer for 4–5 minutes. Add soy sauce and cover pan with a slightly smaller lid. Cook for 20–30 minutes over medium-low heat, stirring occasionally. Liquid should reduce by two-thirds. Serve warm or cold.

Korean mung bean pancakes

Makes 15 pancakes

2 cups (14 oz/440 g) mung beans
water, for soaking
3 cups (24 fl oz/750 ml) extra water
1/3 cup (1 1/2 oz/45 g) sticky rice powder
1 1/2 oz (45 g) yellow (brown) onion
1 oz (30 g) Chinese cabbage kimchi
1 teaspoon table salt
5 daepa or scallions (shallots/spring onions), white parts only
2 oz (60 g) ground (minced) pork fillet
1 tablespoon finely chopped scallions (shallots/spring onions)
1 tablespoon crushed garlic
vegetable or sunflower oil, for frying

For dipping sauce
2 teaspoons light soy sauce
1 teaspoon white vinegar

Soak mung beans in water overnight to soften. Using your hands, rub soaked beans together to remove skins. Remove skins when they float to surface of water

Transfer beans to a food processor and blend to a paste with extra water. Add sticky rice powder and mix with a spoon.

Finely slice onion and kimchi. Sprinkle with salt and let stand for about 15 minutes to sweat (do not rinse off salt).

Cut white parts of 5 daepa or scallions into fine strips.

Mix pork with onion, kimchi, finely chopped scallion and garlic.

Add mung bean paste and mix to combine. Add salt to taste.

Heat 1 tablespoon oil in a wok. Ladle enough bean mixture into pan to make an 8-inch (20-cm) pancake. Cook until golden brown, about 3 minutes on each side.

To make dipping sauce: Combine soy sauce and white vinegar in a bowl.

Transfer pancakes to a plate and serve whole or sliced, accompanied by dipping sauce. Serve immediately. If pancake cools, reheat in heated wok for about 1 minute on each side.

Mango and yogurt curry

Serves 2

1 tablespoon vegetable oil
1 teaspoon brown mustard seeds
1 onion, cut into 8 wedges
1 teaspoon peeled and grated fresh ginger
1 large green Thai or Anaheim chili, seeded and sliced
¼ teaspoon chili flakes
1 teaspoon ground turmeric
12 curry leaves
1½ cups (12 oz/375 g) plain (natural) yogurt
3 mangoes, peeled, cut from pit, and sliced
sea salt to taste
1 tablespoon chopped fresh mint

In a large, heavy saucepan or wok, heat oil over medium heat and fry mustard seeds, onion, ginger, and chili for 2 minutes, or until onion is soft. Add chili flakes, turmeric, and curry leaves, and cook for 2 minutes. Remove from heat and stir in yogurt. Return to stove and cook over very low heat for 1 minute. Remove from heat, and add mangoes, salt, and mint. Stir until well combined. Serve warm immediately.

Mixed vegetable curry

Serves 4–6

1 tablespoon sticky (glutinous) rice
1/4 cup (2 fl oz/60 ml) vegetable oil
1/4 cup (2 fl oz/60 ml) red curry paste (see page 231)
1 1/4 cups (5 oz/150 g) chopped eggplant (aubergine)
1/4 cup (1 oz/30 g) pea eggplants (optional)
4 long beans or 12 green beans, cut into 1-inch (2.5-cm) pieces
1/2 cup (2 oz/60 g) canned or 1 cup (4 oz/125 g) fresh straw mushrooms, rinsed, drained and halved
1/2 cup (2 oz/60 g) coarsely chopped cauliflower florets
2 cups (16 fl oz/500 ml) vegetable stock (see page 221) or water
2 tablespoons soy sauce or fish sauce
4 fresh piper (beetle) leaves, or 2 cabbage leaves, coarsely chopped
7 fresh eryngo (sawtooth coriander) leaves or 6 sprigs cilantro (fresh coriander), coarsely chopped or torn
1 fresh long red chili, coarsely chopped
1/4 teaspoon salt

In a wok or small frying pan over low heat, stir rice until golden brown, 3–5 minutes. Transfer to a mortar and pulverize with a pestle; set aside.

In a wok or large, heavy frying pan, heat oil over medium–high heat and fry curry paste, stirring constantly, until fragrant, 1–2 minutes. Add eggplants, beans, mushrooms and cauliflower, and stir together well. Add 1 cup (8 fl oz/250 ml) stock or water, and simmer for 2 minutes. Add remaining stock or water and soy or fish sauce. Bring to a boil.

Add remaining ingredients and ground rice. Bring to a boil, then reduce heat and simmer for 2 minutes. Transfer to a serving bowl and serve.

Tips

- If available, you can also add 1 cup dried cotton buds or kapok flowers (ngiu) at the same time as the eggplant, and/or 1 cup chopped acacia leaves at the end.
- You can add 1/4 teaspoon prickly ash (kamchatton) with the chicken stock.

Mushroom and sesame stir-fry

Serves 4

2 tablespoons sesame oil
1 bunch scallions (shallots/spring onions), trimmed and sliced
8 oz (250 g) carrots, peeled and diced
1 red bell pepper (capsicum), seeded and sliced
1 green bell pepper (capsicum), seeded and sliced
1 yellow or orange bell pepper (capsicum), seeded and sliced
8 oz (250 g) button mushrooms, trimmed and halved or quartered
8 oz (250 g) zucchini (courgettes), trimmed and cut into sticks
1 tablespoon light soy sauce
1 tablespoon lemon juice
1 tablespoon clear honey
salt and pepper
1½ cups (6 oz/180 g) bean sprouts
1–2 tablespoons sesame seeds

In a wok or frying pan, heat oil and stir-fry scallions for about 1 minute. Add carrots and bell peppers and cook for 2–3 minutes, stirring frequently.

If mushrooms are tiny they may be left whole, otherwise halve or quarter them then add to wok or pan with zucchini and cook for a further 2–3 minutes.

Combine soy sauce, lemon juice and honey and add to wok or pan. Season well with salt and pepper then add bean sprouts. Cook for a further 2–3 minutes. Serve generously sprinkled with sesame seeds.

Pumpkin dumplings in malai sauce

Serves 4–5

1 lb (500 g) pumpkin or butternut squash, peeled and grated
2 large desiree or pontiac potatoes, 10 oz (300g) total, boiled, peeled and mashed
¼ cup (⅓ oz/10 g) chopped cilantro (fresh coriander)
1 tablespoon finely grated fresh ginger
3 teaspoons finely chopped fresh green chilies
salt to taste
¼ cup (2 fl oz/60 ml) vegetable oil
1-inch (2.5-cm) cinnamon stick
4 green cardamom pods
4 whole cloves
1 small yellow (brown) onion, halved and thinly sliced
½ teaspoon salt, plus extra salt to taste
1 tablespoon finely grated fresh ginger
1 tablespoon crushed garlic
3 teaspoons ground turmeric
2 teaspoons chili powder
2 tomatoes, unpeeled, chopped
1 teaspoon honey
1 teaspoon ground mace
cornstarch (cornflour) for dusting
vegetable oil for deep-frying
3–4 tablespoons heavy (double) cream
½ teaspoon garam masala (see page 225)

Place grated pumpkin or squash in a colander and squeeze well to extract any excess water. Place in a bowl with potatoes, cilantro, ginger and chilies. Season with salt and mix well. Set aside.

To make sauce: In a wok, heat oil over medium–low heat. Add cinnamon, cardamom and cloves, and cook until fragrant, about 30 seconds. Add onion and ½ teaspoon salt, and cook uncovered, stirring often, until onion is dark golden brown, 10–15 minutes. Stir in ginger and garlic, and cook for 30 seconds. Add turmeric and chili powder, and cook, stirring, for 30 seconds. Stir in tomatoes and cook, stirring, until tomatoes soften, 3–4 minutes. Stir in honey and mace. Cover to keep warm.

Meanwhile, shape pumpkin mixture into walnut-sized balls, dust with cornstarch and place on a baking sheet dusted with cornstarch. Fill a medium saucepan with oil to a depth of 3 inches (7.5 cm). Heat oil over medium–high heat to 375°F (190°C) on a deep-frying thermometer. Carefully add dumplings in batches of five and cook until golden brown, 2–3 minutes. Remove with a slotted spoon and drain on paper towels.

Place dumplings on a serving dish. Stir cream into sauce and pour over dumplings. Sprinkle with garam masala, season with extra salt to taste, and serve hot.

Tip

Dumplings are best shaped and cooked close to serving time. The mixture can be made 2 hours ahead and kept at room temperature.

Stir-fried Asian greens with tempeh

Serves 4

canola oil for deep-frying
3 garlic cloves, thinly sliced
8 dried shiitake mushrooms
3 tablespoons soybean oil
5 oz (150 g) tempeh, cut into thin strips
8 oz (250 g) firm tofu, drained and diced
1 medium yellow (brown) onion, cut into thin wedges
1 clove garlic, finely chopped
8 water chestnuts, thinly sliced, or 6 slices lotus root
14 ears fresh baby corn, halved lengthwise
3 small bunches baby bok choy, chopped
1 cup (2 oz/60 g) soybean sprouts, tails trimmed
⅓ cup (3 oz/90 g) ketjap manis with
  1 tablespoon light soy
1 small red chili, seeded and finely chopped
fried shallots (French shallots), for garnish, optional
steamed jasmine rice, for serving

Fill a small wok or saucepan one-third full of oil and heat to 350°F (180°C). Cook garlic slices until golden, about 1 minute. Drain on paper towels.

Soak mushrooms in warm water until soft, about 20 minutes. Squeeze out excess water, discard stems and thinly slice tops. In a wok or frying pan, heat 2 tablespoons oil over medium-high heat and stir-fry tempeh and tofu slices until lightly browned, 3–4 minutes. Remove and drain on paper towels. Add remaining oil to pan and stir-fry onion and garlic until onion is soft. Add tempeh, tofu, water chestnuts, baby corn, bok choy and soybean sprouts and stir-fry until bok choy is wilted, about 3 minutes. Stir in ketjap manis and chili and cook for 2 more minutes to blend flavors. Garnish with garlic flakes and shallots and serve with steamed jasmine rice.

Stir-fried choy sum with ginger

Serves 4

3 tablespoons fish sauce
3 tablespoons water
2 teaspoons peeled and grated fresh ginger
2 tablespoons vegetable oil
1 bunch choy sum, about 16 oz (500 g), trimmed and cut into 3-inch (7.5-cm) lengths

In a small bowl, combine fish sauce, water and ginger. Warm vegetable oil in a wok over medium heat. Add choy sum and stir-fry until slightly softened and color intensifies, about 3 minutes. Stir in fish sauce mixture and toss until choy sum is well coated. Cover and cook for 2 minutes. Serve hot.

Stir-fried fennel, celery, snow peas and bean sprouts

Serves 4

2 cloves garlic, roughly chopped
½ cup (½ oz/15 g) cilantro (fresh coriander) leaves
1 stalk lemongrass, bottom 3 inches (7.5 cm) only, inner stalks roughly chopped
juice of 1 lime
2 tablespoons soy sauce
2 tablespoons superfine (caster) sugar
sea salt and freshly ground black pepper to taste
2 tablespoons vegetable oil
1-inch (2.5-cm) piece fresh ginger, peeled and finely chopped
1 green chili, seeded and thinly sliced
12 scallions (shallots/spring onions), roots trimmed, sliced
2 bulbs fennel, roots and leaves trimmed and thinly sliced
2 celery stalks, sliced
3½ oz (105 g) snow peas (mange-tout)
⅔ cup (5 fl oz/150 ml) thick coconut cream
3½ oz (105 g) bean sprouts, rinsed
¼ cup (1½ oz/45 g) unsalted roasted peanuts
steamed jasmine rice, for serving

Place garlic, cilantro, lemongrass and lime juice in a mortar and using a pestle, pound into a smooth paste. Alternatively, place in a small food processor and process to form a smooth paste, about 20 seconds. Transfer to a bowl and add soy sauce, sugar, and salt and pepper to taste.

In a wok or large frying pan, heat oil over medium heat. Add ginger, chili and scallions, and stir-fry until aromatic, about 2 minutes. Add fennel, celery and snow peas, and stir-fry for 3 minutes. Add spice paste and coconut cream and cook, continuing to stir, until sauce thickens slightly, about 2 minutes. Stir in bean sprouts. Remove from heat.

Sprinkle with peanuts and serve immediately with steamed jasmine rice.

Stir-fried vegetables

Serves 4

1 tablespoon vegetable oil
1 small carrot, cut into matchstick strips
½ yellow (brown) onion, thinly sliced
¼ green bell pepper (capsicum), thinly sliced
10 snow peas (mange-tout), halved if large
6 leaves Chinese napa cabbage, shredded
1 cup (4 oz/125 g) bean shoots
1 teaspoon salt
1 teaspoon sugar
1 teaspoon instant dashi
1 tablespoon mirin

Preheat a wok or large frying pan over high heat until very hot, then add oil. Add carrot and onion and stir-fry until softened, about 2 minutes. Add bell pepper and snow peas, then cabbage and bean shoots. Stir-fry until carrot and on on are soft and snow peas and cabbage are wilted. Add salt, sugar, dashi and mirin. Continue to stir-fry until flavors are blended and vegetables are cooked to your liking, about 3 minutes. Serve hot.

Stir-fried vegetables with soy and ginger

Serves 4

1 yellow (brown) onion, cut into thin wedges
3 baby white bok choy, washed and coarsely chopped
3 baby green (shaughai) bok choy, washed and coarsely chopped
1 medium fresh jkama (yam bean), peeled and thinly sliced, or 1 can (7 oz/220 g) water chestnuts, drained
2 tablespoons Japanese soy sauce
1 teaspoon grated fresh ginger
1 cup (2 oz/60 g) fresh soybean sprouts, tails trimmed

In a large wok, combine all ingredients, cover and cook over medium-low heat until vegetables are just tender but still crisp, 3–4 minutes, tossing occasionally. Do not overcook. Serve immediately.

Tip

Substitute other Asian greens such as Chinese broccoli (gai lan), Chinese flowering cabbage (choy sum) and/or tat soi for the bok choy. Also, substitute soy sauce with rinsed fermented black soybeans.

Stuffed eggplants

Serves 4–8

8 medium-sized Japanese (long) eggplants (aubergines)
3 medium-sized yellow (brown) onions
6 tablespoons olive oil
4 cloves garlic, chopped
3 medium tomatoes, peeled and chopped
3 tablespoons chopped fresh flat-leaf (Italian) parsley
salt
freshly ground black pepper
2 tablespoons lemon juice
pinch sugar
½ cup (4 fl oz/125 ml) water

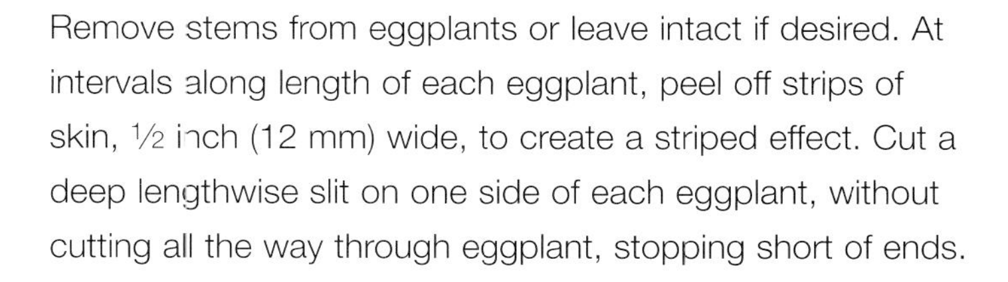
Remove stems from eggplants or leave intact if desired. At intervals along length of each eggplant, peel off strips of skin, ½ inch (12 mm) wide, to create a striped effect. Cut a deep lengthwise slit on one side of each eggplant, without cutting all the way through eggplant, stopping short of ends.

Slice each onion lengthwise, then cut into slender wedges. In a large wok or frying pan over medium–low heat, heat 3 tablespoons oil. Add onion and fry until translucent, about 8 minutes. Add garlic and cook for 1 minute. Place onions and garlic in a bowl and combine with chopped tomatoes, parsley and salt and pepper to taste.

Heat remaining 3 tablespoons oil in same wok over high heat. Add eggplants and fry until lightly browned on all sides but still rather firm, about 10 minutes. Remove wok or pan from heat and turn eggplants slit-side up.

Spoon vegetable mixture into slits, forcing in as much filling as possible. Spread remaining filling on top. Add lemon juice, sugar and water to wok or pan and cover tightly. Cook over low heat until eggplants are tender, about 45 minutes. Add more water only if liquid in pan evaporates.

Let cool to room temperature and serve as an appetizer or a light meal with bread, or as an accompaniment.

Sweet-and-sour potatoes

Serves 4

1 lb (500 g) uniformly sized desiree or pontiac potatoes, (about 3–4 medium)
salt as needed
3 tablespoons vegetable oil
½ teaspoon brown or black mustard seeds
36 fresh curry leaves
½ teaspoon ground turmeric
½ cup (4 fl oz/125 ml) coconut milk
¼ cup (⅓ oz/10 g) chopped cilantro (fresh coriander)
4 teaspoons finely chopped fresh green chilies
1 teaspoon sugar
juice of 1 lemon

Place potatoes and large pinch salt in a saucepan with enough cold water to cover. Bring to a boil over medium–high heat. Reduce heat to medium–low and cook, partially covered, until potatoes are tender, about 20 minutes. Drain potatoes and let cool for 15 minutes. Peel potatoes and cut into 1½-inch (4-cm) cubes. Set aside.

In a wok, heat oil over medium–low heat. Add mustard seeds and cook until they crackle, about 30 seconds. Add curry leaves and turmeric, and cook, stirring, for 15 seconds. Add potatoes and season with salt. Toss gently to combine. Add coconut milk, cilantro, chilies and sugar, and simmer, gently stirring occasionally, for 2 minutes. Drizzle with lemon juice and serve hot.

Tofu and vegetable stir-fry

Serves 4

1⁄3 cup (3 fl oz/90 ml) vegetable oil
6½ oz (200 g) firm tofu, cut into 1-in (2.5-cm) cubes
3 cloves garlic, crushed
2 teaspoons peeled and grated fresh ginger
2 onions, cut into eighths
1 bunch Chinese broccoli, trimmed and cut into 1½-in (4-cm) lengths
3½ oz (105 g) snow peas (mange-tout), trimmed and sliced crosswise
1 red bell pepper (capsicum), seeded and sliced
1 cup (6 oz/180 g) drained canned baby corn
1 bunch bok choy, trimmed and cut into 1½-in (4-cm) lengths, or 1 bunch spinach, trimmed
2 tablespoons oyster sauce
1 tablespoon light soy sauce
steamed white rice, for serving

In a wok over medium heat, warm vegetable oil. Working in batches, add tofu and stir-fry until golden on all sides, 2–3 minutes. Using slotted spoon, remove from wok and drain on paper towels. Pour off all but 2 tablespoons oil from wok and return to medium heat. Add garlic, ginger and onions and stir-fry until softened, 2–3 minutes. Add broccoli, snow peas, bell pepper, corn and bok choy or spinach. Stir-fry until vegetables are tender-crisp, 3–4 minutes. Add tofu and oyster and soy sauces and gently stir-fry until heated through, 1–2 minutes.

Serve hot, accompanied with steamed white rice.

Vegetarian green curry

Serves 4

5 oz (150 g) firm tofu, drained then cut into ¾-inch (2-cm) cubes
1 cup (8 fl oz/250 ml) vegetable oil
2 cups (16 fl oz/500 ml) coconut milk
1–2 tablespoons vegetable oil (optional)
¼ cup (2 fl oz/60 ml) fresh or commercial green curry paste (page 231)
½ cup (2 oz/60 g) chopped eggplant (aubergine) or 3 round Thai eggplants, chopped
½ cup (2 oz/60 g) pea eggplants (optional)
1 cup (4 oz/125 g) coarsely chopped fresh or canned bamboo shoots, rinsed and drained
6 ears fresh or canned baby corn, rinsed and drained, cut into bite-sized pieces
2 tablespoons palm sugar
2 kaffir lime leaves, stemmed
1 cup (1 oz/30 g) loosely packed fresh sweet Thai basil leaves
2 tablespoons soy sauce
1 fresh long green chili, cut into large pieces, for garnish
1 fresh long red chili, cut into large pieces, for garnish

Pat tofu dry with a paper towel. In a large wok, heat oil and, working in batches, fry tofu cubes until golden. Remove using a slotted spoon and drain on paper towels; reserve.

Let coconut milk stand, allowing the thick coconut milk to rise to the top. Spoon thick coconut milk into a small bowl, reserving 2 tablespoons for garnish.

In a wok or large, heavy frying pan, heat thick coconut milk over medium-high heat for 3–5 minutes, stirring constantly, until it separates. If it does not separate, add optional oil. Add green curry paste and fry, stirring constantly, until fragrant, 1–2 minutes. Add vegetables and fried tofu and stir until well coated. Add remaining thin coconut milk and bring to a boil. Reduce heat and simmer until vegetables are slightly soft, about 4 minutes.

Add palm sugar—if using a wok, add it along the edge of the wok so that it melts before stirring into the curry; if using a standard frying pan, add directly to the curry. Tear kaffir lime leaves and basil into pieces. Stir in soy sauce, kaffir lime leaves and half the basil.

Remove from heat and transfer to a serving bowl. Drizzle over reserved 2 tablespoons thick coconut milk. Garnish with green and red chilies, and remaining basil leaves and serve.

Vegetarian stir-fry

Serves 4

2 tablespoons sesame or walnut oil
1 large onion, peeled and thinly sliced
4 celery stalks, thinly sliced
8 oz (250 g) carrots, peeled and cut into strips
2–4 oz (50–100 g) pecan or walnut halves
1 red bell pepper (capsicum), seeded and cut into strips
8–12 oz (250–375 g) zucchini (courgettes), trimmed and thinly sliced
1–1½ lb (500–750 g) white cabbage, finely shredded
4 oz (125 g) pitted dates, halved
salt and pepper
1 tablespoon lemon juice
freshly chopped parsley

In a wok, heat oil and fry onion briskly until beginning to color. Add celery and carrots and continue cooking for 3–4 minutes, stirring occasionally.

Stir in pecans or walnuts, bell pepper and zucchini and stir-fry, for 3–4 minutes. Add cabbage and dates and continue to stir-fry for 3–4 minutes.

Season well with salt and pepper and add lemon juice. Stir to heat through thoroughly and serve in a warmed dish liberally sprinkled with parsley.

rice and noodles

Bell peppers and mushrooms with noodles

Serves 4

5 oz (150 g) fresh egg noodles
6 Chinese dried mushrooms
1 tablespoon vegetable oil
1 teaspoon Asian sesame oil
1 red bell pepper (capsicum), seeded and sliced
1 yellow bell pepper (capsicum), seeded and sliced
1 cup (4 oz/125 g) fresh bean sprouts, rinsed
4 oz (125 g) fresh shiitake mushrooms, sliced
4 oz (125 g) fresh oyster mushrooms, sliced if large
1/4 cup (2 fl oz/60 ml) sweet chili sauce
1 tablespoon light soy sauce
1/4 cup (1/4 oz/7 g) cilantro (fresh coriander) leaves, for garnish

Bring saucepan of water to a boil. Add noodles and cook until tender, about 3 minutes. Drain and set aside

Place dried mushrooms in small bowl, add boiling water to cover and allow to stand until softened, 10–15 minutes. Drain and squeeze out excess liquid. Thinly slice mushrooms, discarding thick stems.

In a wok, heat vegetable and sesame oils over medium heat. Add bell peppers, bean sprouts and fresh mushrooms and stir-fry until slightly softened, 1–2 minutes. Add noodles, reconstituted mushrooms and chili and soy sauces and stir-fry until heated through, 2–3 minutes.

Serve hot, garnished with cilantro leaves.

Chili broccoli with noodles

Serves 4

12 oz (375 g) egg noodles
1½ lb (750 g) broccoli, cut into florets
3 tablespoons olive oil
1 medium red (Spanish) onion, chopped
2 cloves garlic, crushed
1 small red chili pepper, seeded and thinly sliced
sea salt and freshly ground black pepper to taste
balsamic vinegar, for drizzling
⅓ cup (1½ oz/45 g) parmesan shavings, for serving

Cook noodles as directed on package or on page 29, then drain and rinse. Meanwhile, bring a saucepan of water to a boil. Add broccoli florets and cook for 2 minutes. Drain and refresh in cold water. Drain again and set aside.

In a wok or large frying pan, heat oil. Add onion, garlic and chili pepper and stir-fry until onion softens, about 2 minutes. Stir in broccoli and cooked noodles. Stir-fry until heated through, about 3 minutes. Season with salt and pepper to taste.

Serve hot, drizzled with balsamic vinegar and topped with parmesan shavings.

Chili fried rice

Serves 4

3 tablespoons vegetable oil
1 onion, chopped
1 small red chili, seeded and chopped
1 tablespoon red curry paste (see page 231)
5 oz (150 g) pork fillet, thinly sliced
12 jumbo shrimp (king prawns), peeled and deveined, tails intact
4 cups (20 oz/625 g) cooked white rice, chilled
2 eggs, beaten
1 tablespoon fish sauce
1/2 cup (1 1/2 oz/45 g) chopped scallions (shallots/spring onions)
1/3 cup (1/2 oz/15 g) chopped cilantro (fresh coriander)
3 small red chili flowers (see page 25) (optional)

In a wok, heat oil over medium–high heat. Add onion and chili and stir-fry until onion is softened, about 2 minutes. Stir in curry paste and cook for 1 minute. Add pork and stir-fry until pork changes color, 3–4 minutes. Add shrimp and stir-fry until shrimp change color, about 3 minutes. Add rice and stir-fry until rice is coated with oil.

Push rice to one side of wok. Add beaten eggs and allow to partially set without stirring, then mix with rice. Stir in fish sauce, scallions and cilantro.

Serve hot as main course or as accompaniment to stir-fried dishes. Garnish with chili flowers, if desired.

Chinese fried rice

Serves 4

2 eggs
pinch of salt
4 scallions (spring onions/shallots) with some green tops
½ red or green bell pepper (capsicum)
½ stick celery
4 oz (125 g) roasted or barbecued pork, chicken, or leg ham
3 tablespoon peanut or vegetable oil
7 oz (220 g) can shrimp (prawns), drained
3 cups cooked white or brown rice
½ cup (2 oz/60 g) cooked green peas
2 tablespoon chicken stock (see page 220)
1½ tablespoon Chinese rice wine or dry sherry
2 teaspoon soy sauce

Whisk together eggs and salt until blended. Cut scallions, bell pepper, celery and meat into thin slivers.

In a wok or large, heavy-based frying pan, heat 1 tablespoon oil over medium heat. Add eggs and cook stirring, until scrambled but not dry. Remove from pan and set aside.

Heat remaining oil in pan until hot. Add scallions, vegetables, meat and shrimp and stir-fry 45–60 seconds.

Add rice to pan and stir-fry until rice is heated through, 2–3 minutes. Stir in reserved egg and peas.

Stir together sauce ingredients and drizzle over rice. Toss lightly to mix well. Serve immediately.

Fried cellophane noodles

Serves 4–6

6 oz (180 g) cellophane (bean thread) noodles
1/4 cup (2 fl oz/60 ml) vegetable oil
3 eggs, beaten
1 onion, cut into wedges
3 firm tomatoes, cut into 4 or 8 wedges
3 cloves pickled garlic, coarsely chopped
2 tablespoons fish sauce
3 tablespoons oyster sauce
1 teaspoon granulated (white) sugar
1/2 teaspoon ground white pepper
2 scallions (shallots/spring onions), finely chopped

Soak noodles in cold water for at least 15 minutes, to soften. Drain and coarsely cut with scissors into 6-inch (15-cm) lengths.

In a wok or large, heavy frying pan, heat half oil (2 tablespoons) over medium–high heat. Add eggs and stir-fry until cooked and dry, 1–2 minutes. Remove with a slotted spoon and reserve. Add remaining 2 tablespoons oil to wok. Add noodles and stir-fry while adding onion, tomatoes and pickled garlic. Stir-fry for 1 minute to heat through, then add fish sauce, oyster sauce, sugar and pepper and stir until well combined. Add three-quarters scallions and eggs, stir to combine and remove from heat. Transfer to a serving dish, sprinkle with remaining scallion and serve.

Fried glass noodles with fish or eel

Serves 4

1 lb (500 g) skinless fish or eel fillets (see Tip below), finely diced
2 tablespoons fish sauce
½ teaspoon ground pepper
12 dried black mushrooms
leaves from 2 large sprigs Vietnamese mint or spearmint
1 bunch Chinese (flat/garlic) chives
6½-oz (200-g) packet cellophane (bean thread) noodles
about 1 cup (8 fl oz/250 ml) vegetable oil, for frying
2 onions, thinly sliced
6 cloves garlic, crushed
2 cups (4 oz/125 g) bean sprouts, rinsed and drained
2 fresh long red chilies, seeded and cut into thin strips
2 lemons, cut into wedges
Asian chili sauce, for serving (optional)

In a medium bowl, combine fish or eel, fish sauce and pepper. Stir well and refrigerate until ready to use, at least 20 minutes.

Soak mushrooms in hot water for 20 minutes, then drain, squeezing to remove all liquid. Use scissors or a small knife to cut tough stems; discard. Cut mushroom caps into small dice and set aside.

Stack a few Vietnamese mint leaves together and roll tightly into a cylinder. Use a sharp knife to cut crosswise into thin shreds. Repeat with remaining leaves. Cut chives into 1½-inch (4-cm) pieces.

Prepare noodles as described on page 29. Using scissors, cut noodles in manageable lengths for serving.

Transfer fish to a plate, reserving marinade in bowl, and pat fish dry with paper towels. In a wok or large frying pan, heat oil over medium–high heat until it shimmers. Add one-third of fish and stir-fry until almost crisp, 3–5 minutes. Transfer to paper towels to drain.

Reduce heat to medium, draining all but ¼ cup (2 fl oz/60 ml) of the oil. Add remaining fish plus marinade and mushrooms, and stir-fry for 3 minutes. Then add noodles and stir-fry for 2 minutes. Finally, add chives, onion, garlic, bean sprouts, reserved fried fish and remaining marinade. Stir-fry for 1 minute and sprinkle with Vietnamese mint. Transfer to a serving plate, and garnish with the reserved crispy-fried fish and chilies. Serve with lemon wedges, and chili sauce if desired.

Tip

This is a very old Hanoi recipe, and popular restaurants there specialize in eel dishes. Sturgeon is probably the closest in texture to eel, although tender catfish fillets, as well as oily garfish and smelt, can also be substituted.

Fried noodles with pork

Serves 4

8 oz (250 g) fresh or dried egg noodles
1 tablespoon vegetable oil
1 bunch Chinese broccoli, cut into 3-in (7.5-cm) lengths
8 oz (250 g) Chinese barbecue pork, sliced
½ cup (5 oz/150 g) chunky peanut butter
2 teaspoon Asian sesame oil
2 tablespoons light soy sauce
2 teaspoons garam masala (see page 225)
3 cloves garlic, crushed
1 small red chili, seeded and chopped

Bring saucepan of water to boil. Add noodles and cook until tender, about 3 minutes for fresh noodles, about 5 minutes for dried noodles. (If using precooked noodles, soak in boiling water for 8–10 minutes.) Drain and keep warm.

In a wok, heat vegetable oil over medium–high heat. Add broccoli and pork and stir-fry for 4 minutes. In small bowl, combine peanut butter, sesame oil, soy sauce, garam masala, garlic and chili. Mix until well combined. Add peanut butter mixture and noodles to wok. Raise heat to high and stir-fry until heated through, about 1 minute. Do not overcook.

Serve hot.

Fried rice with pineapple

Serves 4–6

¼ cup (2 fl oz/60 ml) vegetable oil
2 Chinese sausages, cut in small rounds
2 tablespoons butter
½ teaspoon curry powder
3 cups (15 oz/470 g) cooked long-grain jasmine rice
1 small onion, coarsely chopped
3 scallions (shallots/spring onions), chopped
1 firm tomato, coarsely chopped
½ cup (3 oz/90 g) raisins (sultanas)
½ cup (3 oz/90 g) coarsely chopped fresh pineapple pieces, or canned in water, and drained
1 teaspoon granulated (white) sugar
2 tablespoons soy sauce

In a wok or large, heavy frying pan, heat oil over medium–high heat and fry sausages for 1 minute. Using a slotted spoon, transfer to paper towels to drain.

Add butter and curry powder to wok and stir-fry, stirring constantly, until fragrant, about 1 minute. Stir in cooked rice until well coated. Add sausages, onion, scallions, tomato, raisins and pineapple. Stir-fry for about 4 minutes, then add sugar and soy sauce.

Tip

For an impressive presentation, place a pineapple on its side on a cutting board and slice in half or slice off the top third lengthwise. Scoop flesh from bottom half or two-thirds to make a cavity. Set aside ½ cup (3 oz/90 g) pineapple for recipe, and save rest for another use. Spoon fried rice into hollowed-out pineapple, cover with "lid," and serve.

Garlic and cumin lentils

Serves 4

1 cup (7 oz/220 g) masoor dhal (dried red lentils)
2/3 cup (5 fl oz/150 ml) chicken stock (see page 220) or water
1/2 teaspoon peeled and finely chopped fresh ginger
1/2 teaspoon ground coriander
1 tablespoon ghee or vegetable oil
2 teaspoons toasted cumin seeds
1 medium onion (5 oz/150 g), sliced
2 cloves garlic, crushed
1 fresh long green chili, seeded and thinly sliced (optional)
1 tablespoon finely chopped fresh mint

Place lentils in a sieve and wash under cold running water. Pick over, and remove any foreign matter. Soak in water for a minimum of 1 hour. Drain well and place in a dish that will fit a bamboo steamer or steamer basket. Add stock, ginger and coriander, stir well, and place bowl in steamer.

Partially fill a wok or pot with water (steamer should not touch water) and bring to a rapid simmer. Place steamer over water, cover, and steam until lentils are soft, about 30 minutes.

In a medium pan, heat ghee and cook cumin seeds, onion, garlic and chili until onion browns, 8–10 minutes, stirring occasionally. Stir mint and half of onion mixture into lentils. Spread remaining onion mixture on top for garnish. Serve as a dip or side dish with crispy fried pappadums.

Tip

Lentils can be cooked for less time to retain shape (if not being mashed), and used in salads or as a vegetable.

Ginger-coconut rice

Serves 4

2 tablespoons vegetable oil
1 teaspoon chili oil
1 onion, chopped
1 red bell pepper (capsicum), seeded and chopped
3 cloves garlic, crushed
3 teaspoons peeled and grated fresh ginger
1½ cups (10½ oz/330 g) short-grain white rice
1½ cups (12 fl oz/375 ml) chicken stock (see page 220)
1 cup (8 fl oz/250 ml) water
½ cup (4 fl oz/125 ml) coconut milk
3 scallions (shallots/spring onions)
3 tablespoons chopped cilantro (fresh coriander)
2 tablespoons unsweetened shredded coconut, toasted
3 tablespoons lemon juice
¼ cup (1 oz/30 g) unsweetened shredded coconut, for serving

In a wok, heat vegetable and chili oils over medium–high heat. Add onion, bell pepper, garlic and ginger and stir-fry until softened, about 3 minutes. Add rice and stir until well coated with oil, about 2 minutes.

Add stock, water and coconut milk and bring to a boil. Reduce heat to low, cover and simmer until all liquid is absorbed and rice is tender, 15–20 minutes. Remove from heat and stir in scallions, cilantro, toasted coconut and lemon juice.

Serve hot, topped with shredded coconut.

Herb and lemon noodle salad with ponzu dressing

Serves 4

For dressing

¼ cup (2 fl oz/60 ml) fresh lemon juice
1 tablespoon soybean oil
1 tablespoon soy sauce
2 teaspoons grated lemon zest (rind)
2 scallions (shallots/spring onions), green parts, finely sliced
1 medium red chili, seeded and finely chopped (optional)

1 tablespoon soybean oil
4 oz (125 g) firm tofu, cut into strips ¾ x 1 inch (2 x 2.5 cm)
1 cup (2 oz/60 g) soybean sprouts
4 oz (125 g) dried soba noodles
1 cup (2 oz/60 g) shredded spinach leaves
1 cup (1½ oz/40 g) finely chopped mixed fresh herbs such as parsley, chives, oregano, basil
1 cup (6 oz/185 g) finely chopped celery
1 English (hothouse) cucumber, seeded and finely diced, unpeeled

To make dressing: In a small bowl, combine all dressing ingredients and whisk until blended. Set aside.

In a large wok, heat oil over medium heat and stir-fry tofu until golden, about 2 minutes each side. Cook soybean sprouts in boiling water for 2 minutes. Using a skimmer, remove sprouts. Rinse under cold water, then drain. Return water to a boil, gradually add noodles and return to a boil. Add ¼ cup (2 fl oz/60 ml) cold water and bring back to a boil. Add another ¼ cup cold water, return to a boil and cook noodles until tender, 8–10 minutes total cooking time. Drain noodles, add remaining ingredients and dressing, toss well to combine, and serve.

Indian noodle stir-fry

Serves 2–4

2 tablespoons peanut oil
1 onion, chopped
1 tomato, chopped
2 tablespoons chives or scallions (shallots/spring onions), chopped
2 teaspoons curry paste
1–2 tablespoons tomato ketchup (sauce)
1 tablespoon chili sauce or minced chili, or to taste
2 teaspoons soy sauce, preferably light
1 lb (500 g) hokkein egg noodles
2–4 tablespoons cooked stock (see page 220) or water
2 eggs, lightly beaten (optional)

In wok or large frying pan, heat oil. Add onion and fry over medium heat until soft. Add tomato and chives and cook for a few minutes. Add curry paste, sauces and stock and simmer gently for a few minutes. Add noodles and toss through to heat. Pour over beaten egg and leave to set for about 45 seconds on hot noodles. Mix through and serve.

Tips

- Yellow hokkein noodles can be bought fresh in sealed plastic bags from the refrigerated section of supermarkets, delicatessens, and Chinese food stores. They'l keep refrigerated for over a week, even longer if frozen.
- Add whatever takes your fancy. Some suggestions are: blanched Chinese long (snake) beans cut into pieces, squares of tofu, 4 oz (125 g) raw peeled shrimp (prawns), cubes of boiled potato, green peas, bean sprouts, shredded lettuce or cabbage, sliced zucchini (courgette) and mushrooms, and strips of green pepper (capsicum). Raw vegetables or meat should be sautéed after, or with, the onion.

Indian pilaf

Serves 4

1¼ cups (9 oz/280 g) basmati rice
1 tablespoon vegetable oil
1 onion, chopped
2 cloves garlic, finely chopped
1 teaspoon fennel seeds
1 tablespoon sesame seeds
½ teaspoon ground turmeric
1 teaspoon ground cumin
½ teaspoon sea salt
2 whole cloves
3 cardamom pods, lightly crushed
6 black peppercorns
1¾ cups (14 fl oz/440 ml) chicken stock (see page 220)
fresh curry leaves, for garnish

Rinse rice in several changes of cold water until water runs clear. Put rice in a bowl and add cold water to cover. Let stand for 30 minutes. Drain.

In a medium, heavy saucepan, heat oil over medium heat and fry onion and garlic until onion is soft, 1–2 minutes. Stir in fennel, sesame seeds, turmeric, cumin, salt, cloves, cardamom pods, and peppercorns. Fry until fragrant, 1–2 minutes. Add drained rice, and fry, stirring constantly, for 2 minutes, or until rice is opaque. Pour in stock and bring to a boil. Cover, reduce heat to low, and simmer until rice is tender and all liquid has been absorbed, 15–20 minutes. Remove from heat and let stand, covered, for 5 minutes. Spoon into serving bowls and garnish with curry leaves.

Metropole fried rice

Serves 6

For omelet
4–6 eggs
4 tablespoons water
pinch sugar
pinch salt (optional)
vegetable oil, for cooking

vegetable oil, for cooking
2 large onions, coarsely chopped
4 oz (125 g) shelled shrimp (prawns), coarsely chopped
1½ cups (9 oz/280 g) diced cooked chicken meat, firmly packed
½ cup (4 fl oz/125 ml) fish sauce or to taste
¼ green bell pepper (capsicum), seeded and finely diced
¼ red bell pepper (capsicum), seeded and finely diced
4 cups (18 oz/ 550g) cold steamed rice
2 teaspoons ground pepper
1 tablespoon Asian chili sauce or more to taste
cilantro (fresh coriander) sprigs, for garnish
shrimp crackers, for serving (optional)

To make a single omelet: Using a fork, beat egg(s)—you can use one egg or two to make a single omelet—until blended. Add 1 tablespoon water and sugar, and salt if using. Heat an 8-inch (20-cm) frying pan over medium heat. Add enough oil to coat bottom. It should sizzle if hit with a drop of water. Pour beaten egg into pan, lifting pan to tilt it quickly to allow egg to spread out evenly. Reduce heat to low and cook just until set, about 30 seconds. Carefully flip over omelet and cook a few seconds on second side. It shoud be firm and not runny. Transfer to a plate to cool, then roll, cut into strips and set aside. Prepare 4 omelets this way.

In a large frying pan or wok, heat 2 tablespoons oil over high heat and stir-fry onions until barely wilted, about 1 minute. Add shrimp and chicken, and stir-fry for 2 minutes. Season with half of fish sauce, add bell peppers, and stir-fry for 1 minute. Add rice, pepper, chili sauce and remaining fish sauce to taste. Reduce heat to medium–high and stir-fry for 5 minutes.

Moisten six individual rice bowls or small ramekins and pack with fried rice. Alternatively, press all rice into a lightly oiled 6-cup (48-fl oz/ 1.5-L) bowl. Press firmly, then unmold into center of a plate. Sprinkle with omelet strips and cilantro. If desired, accompany with shrimp crackers.

Mushroom and noodle stir fry

Serves 4

6 Chinese dried mushrooms
6½ oz (200 g) rice stick noodles, wheat flour noodles or egg noodles
1 tablespoon vegetable oil
3 cloves garlic, crushed
8 oz (250 g) fresh shiitake mushrooms, brushed clean and sliced
8 oz (250 g) fresh oyster mushrooms, brushed clean and sliced
1 cup (3 oz/90 g) chopped scallions (shallots/spring onions)
3 tablespoons rice wine
2 tablespoons soy sauce
⅓ cup (½ oz/15 g) cilantro (fresh coriander) leaves

Place dried mushrooms in small bowl, add boiling water to cover and let stand for 10 minutes. Drain and squeeze out excess liquid. Slice mushrooms, discarding tough stems.

Cook noodles as directed on package or on page 29. Drain and set aside.

In wok or frying pan, heat oil over medium–high heat. Add garlic, fresh mushrooms and scallions and stir-fry until slightly softened, about 3 minutes. Stir in rice wine, soy sauce and noodles. Cook until heated through, about 2 minutes. Remove from heat and stir in cilantro. Serve immediately.

Nasi goreng

Serves 4–6

3 teaspoons peeled and grated fresh ginger
1 teaspoon ground turmeric
1 teaspoon shrimp paste
2 teaspoons chili sauce
3 tablespoons peanut oil
1 onion, chopped
3 cloves garlic, crushed
½ red bell pepper (capsicum), seeded and chopped
1 celery stalk, chopped
1 carrot, peeled and chopped
½ cup (2½ oz/75 g) thawed frozen peas
4 oz (125 g) Chinese barbecue pork, chopped
1 cup (4 oz/125 g) fresh bean sprouts, rinsed
1 cup (3 oz/90 g) shredded bok choy
4 cups (20 oz/625 g) cold cooked jasmine rice
4 oz (125 g) cooked shrimp (prawns), peeled and deveined, tails intact
¼ cup (2 fl oz/60 ml) coconut milk
2 tablespoons light soy sauce

In a small bowl, combine ginger, turmeric, shrimp paste and chili sauce. Mix to form paste. Set aside.

In wok, heat peanut oil over medium–high heat. Add onion and garlic and stir-fry until onion softens, about 1 minute. Stir in spice paste, bell pepper, celery, carrot, peas, pork, bean sprouts and bok choy. Raise heat to high and stir-fry until vegetables soften slightly, 3–4 minutes. Add rice and shrimp and stir-fry until rice is heated through, about 3 minutes. Combine coconut milk and soy sauce, add to wok and stir until evenly combined and mixture is hot.

Spoon into individual bowls. Serve hot as a main course or as an accompaniment to other stir-fried dishes.

Noodles with baked vegetables

Serves 4

8 oz (250 g) fresh or dried egg noodles or udon noodles
1 lb (500 g) butternut squash (pumpkin), cut into 1-inch (2.5-cm) pieces
2 carrots, peeled and cut into 1-inch (2.5-cm) pieces
3 tablespoons vegetable oil
5 cloves garlic, crushed
6½ oz (200 g) zucchini (courgettes), cut into 1-inch (2.5-cm) pieces
2 onions, chopped
1 cup (8 fl oz/250 ml) coconut milk
¼ cup (⅓ oz/10 g) chopped cilantro (fresh coriander)
1 small red chili, seeded and chopped
salt and ground pepper to taste

Preheat oven to 400°F (200°C/Gas 6). Bring saucepan of water to boil. Add noodles and cook until tender, about 2½ minutes for fresh udon noodles, about 3 minutes for fresh egg noodles, about 5 minutes for dried egg noodles, 10–12 minutes for dried udon noodles. Drain and set aside.

In baking dish, combine squash, carrots, 2 tablespoons vegetable oil and 3 cloves garlic. Toss to coat vegetables in oil. Bake, uncovered, for 15 minutes. Remove from oven, add zucchini, stir vegetables, return to oven and bake until vegetables are tender, about 15 minutes longer.

In wok over medium–high heat, warm remaining 1 tablespoon vegetable oil. Add onions and remaining 2 cloves garlic and stir-fry until onions soften, 2–3 minutes. Add coconut milk, cilantro and chili. Stir until heated through, 3–4 minutes. Add baked vegetables and noodles. Cook until heated through, 1–2 minutes. Taste and season with salt and pepper.

Divide among individual bowls and serve immediately.

Noodles with squash and green papaya

Serves 4

250 g (8 oz) rice stick noodles
2 tablespoons vegetable oil
2 cloves garlic, crushed
1 lb (500 g) butternut squash (pumpkin), peeled and cut into 1-inch (2.5-cm) cubes
13 oz (400 g) green papaya, grated
¾ cup (6 fl oz/180 ml) chicken stock (see page 220)
2 eggs, beaten
2 tablespoons fish sauce

Cook noodles as directed on package or on page 29. Drain and set aside. In wok or frying pan, heat oil over medium–high heat. Add garlic and squash and cook until garlic is golden, about 2 minutes. Add papaya and stock. Reduce heat to low and simmer, covered, until squash is tender and stock is absorbed, about 15 minutes.

Push squash mixture to one side of wok or pan and raise heat to medium. Add eggs and cook, without stirring, until partially set. Stir gently until eggs are scrambled. Stir eggs into squash mixture. Stir in noodles and fish sauce. Cook until heated through, about 1 minute.

Divide among individual plates and serve immediately.

Pad Thai noodles

Serves 4–6

6 oz (180 g) dried rice noodles
3 tablespoons vegetable oil
3 oz (90 g) firm tofu, rinsed and patted dry, cut into small cubes
2 large cloves garlic, finely chopped
1 tablespoon dried shrimp
⅓ cup (3 fl oz/90 ml) chicken stock (see page 220) or water
3 tablespoons fish sauce
1 tablespoon soy sauce
1–2 tablespoons tamarind purée, to taste
2–3 tablespoons granulated (white) sugar, to taste
2 eggs, beaten
3 tablespoons chopped roasted peanuts
1 small bunch Chinese (garlic or flat) chives, or regular chives, cut into 1-inch (2.5-cm) pieces
1 cup (2 oz/60 g) bean sprouts
2 limes, cut into wedges

Soak noodles in cold water for about 10 minutes to soften; drain and set aside.

In a wok or large, heavy frying pan, heat oil over high heat. Add tofu, garlic and dried shrimp and stir-fry until garlic begins to brown, about 1 minute. Add noodles and stir-fry carefully, so as not to break them. Add stock or water and continue cooking until noodles are tender, 2–3 minutes. Reduce heat to medium and add fish sauce, soy sauce, tamarind and sugar. Cook until mixture sputters, then add eggs, and stir-fry constantly until eggs are cooked and dry, about 1–2 minutes. Add peanuts, chives and bean sprouts, and stir to mix.

Transfer to a serving dish and serve, garnished with lime wedges.

Tips

- Pad Thai is a popular Thai dish found in all parts of the kingdom. The noodles used here are about the thickness of a bean sprout. You can substitute 14 oz (400 g) fresh rice noodles, but do not pre-soak.
- For a striking presentation, fry a thin, flat omelet in a nonstick pan (see page 187), and fold this over the fried noodle mixture. Make a small incision at the top to expose the contents, and serve.

Salmon laksa

Serves 4

6½ oz (200 g) cellophane (bean thread) noodles
3 small red chilies, seeded and chopped
3 cloves garlic
1 piece peeled fresh ginger, about 2½ in (6 cm) long
½ cup (2/3 oz/20 g) cilantro (fresh coriander) leaves
3 teaspoons vegetable oil
1 teaspoon Asian sesame oil
4 cups (32 fl oz/1 L) coconut milk
3 cups (24 fl oz/750 ml) fish stock (see page 221)
8 oz (250 g) salmon fillet, skin and errant bones removed, sliced into 12 thin slices
2 tablespoons lemon juice
1 tablespoon fish sauce
4 scallions (shallots/spring onions), sliced, for garnish
¼ cup (¼ oz/7 g) fresh mint leaves, for garnish

Place noodles in bowl and soak in boiling water for 10 minutes. Drain and set aside.

Place chilies, garlic, ginger and cilantro in food processor. Process to form smooth paste.

In a wok, heat vegetable and sesame oils over medium–high heat. Add spice paste and cook until aromatic, about 1 minute. Add coconut milk and stock and bring to a boil. Reduce heat to low and simmer, uncovered, for 10 minutes. Add salmon, lemon juice and fish sauce and simmer until salmon is opaque, 2–3 minutes.

To serve, divide noodles among individual bowls. Ladle soup over noodles. Sprinkle each serving with scallions and mint leaves.

Soba noodles with bell peppers

Serves 4

6½ oz (200 g) soba noodles
1 tablespoon vegetable oil
2 teaspoons Asian sesame oil
3 cloves garlic, crushed
2 teaspoons peeled and grated fresh ginger
½ teaspoon red pepper flakes
1 onion, chopped
1 red bell pepper (capsicum), seeded and sliced
1 yellow bell pepper (capsicum), seeded and sliced
2 small zucchini (courgettes), julienned
5 oz (150 g) green beans, trimmed
3 tablespoons soy sauce
2 tablespoons rice wine
3 teaspoons palm sugar or brown sugar
1½ tablespoons Worcestershire sauce
⅓ cup (1½ oz/45 g) unsalted roasted peanuts, chopped

In a wok or frying pan, heat vegetable and sesame oils over medium–high heat. Add garlic, ginger, red pepper flakes and onion and cook until aromatic, about 1 minute. Add bell peppers, zucchini and beans and stir-fry until slightly softened, about 3 minutes. Combine soy sauce, rice wine, sugar, Worcestershire sauce and noodles. Add to wok or pan and stir-fry until heated through, about 2 minutes.

To serve, divide among individual plates and top with peanuts. Serve immediately.

Spicy cellophane noodle salad

Serves 4–6

4 oz (125 g) cellophane (bean thread) noodles
2 cups (16 fl oz/500 ml) coconut milk or water
4 oz (125 g) ground (minced) pork
12 jumbo shrimp (king prawns), shelled and deveined
2–3 tablespoons fish sauce, to taste
2 tablespoons fresh lime juice
5 cloves pickled garlic
1 tablespoon thinly sliced shallots (French shallots), preferably pink
10–20 fresh small red chilies, thinly sliced, to taste
½ cup (2 oz/60 g) coarsely chopped celery, preferably Chinese celery
1 firm tomato, halved and thinly sliced
1 oz (30 g) fresh or dried cloud or tree ear mushrooms (black or white fungus), trimmed and rinsed, soaked if dried (optional)
½ cup (¾ oz/20 g) coarsely chopped cilantro (fresh coriander)

Soak noodles in cold water for 10 minutes to soften. (If required, noodles can be prepared several hours in advance, left in the water until ready to use.) Drain and coarsely cut with scissors into 6-inch (15-cm) lengths.

In a wok or large saucepan over high heat, bring 1 cup (8 fl oz/250 ml) coconut milk or water to a boil. Add pork, stirring vigorously to break meat apart, and cook for 2 minutes. Drain, reserving ¼ cup (2 fl oz/60 ml) of the liquid. Set meat aside. In the same wok or saucepan, bring remaining coconut milk or water to a boil over high heat. Add shrimp and cook, stirring constantly, until evenly pink, about 1 minute. Drain and set shrimp aside. (If desired, reserve this cooking liquid for another dish. Do not use it to flavor salad.)

In a large pot bring water to a boil, then pour boiling water into a heatproof bowl. Plunge noodles in and soak for 1 minute; drain, then soak in cold water for 1 minute. (Be precise with these timings, as you do not want the noodles to become water-logged.)

In a large bowl, combine reserved cooking liquid, fish sauce, and lime juice. Add garlic, shallots, chilies to taste, celery, tomato, and mushrooms if using. Toss together, then add noodles. Transfer to a serving plate, sprinkle cooked pork and shrimp over, garnish with cilantro, and serve immediately.

Tips

- Purchase individual small packets of cellophane noodles, or a packet of small bunches, as they are difficult to pry apart in large bunches.
- For a less spicy salad, simply bruise the whole chilies; do not cut them.

Steamed rice in lotus parcels

Serves 6

4 cups (18 oz/540 g) cold steamed rice
25 dried black mushrooms
¼ cup (1½ oz/45 g) dried lotus seeds (optional)
3 tablespoons vegetable oil
2 cups (10 oz/300 g) diced cooked chicken meat, firmly packed
2 teaspoons salt
1 teaspoon ground pepper
2–3 scallions (shallots/spring onions), including green parts, coarsely chopped
2 tablespoons fish sauce
1–2 large fresh or dried lotus leaves (see Tips below)

Soak mushrooms in hot water for 20 minutes, then drain, squeezing to remove all liquid. Use scissors or a small knife to cut tough stems; discard. Cut mushroom caps into small dice and set aside. If using dried lotus seed, soak in warm water for 20 minutes, then use a toothpick inserted from end to end to remove any bitter green sprouts. Cook lotus seed in gently boiling water until tender, about 20 minutes; drain and set aside.

In a wok, heat 2 tablespoons of the oil over medium–high heat. Add mushroom, chicken and lotus seed, if using, and stir-fry for 5 minutes. Season with salt and pepper and transfer to bowl.

In same wok, heat remaining 1 tablespoon of oil over medium–high heat and stir-fry rice and scallions for 5 minutes. Season with fish sauce. Add chicken and mushrooms and mix well.

If using a dried lotus leaf, cover it with boiling water to soften, then drain. The water will become brown and somewhat murky. Fresh leaves should be wiped to remove any grit or sediment.

Spread out leaf and pile steamed rice mixture in middle. Press lightly to compact the pile into a 10-x-7-inch (25-x-18-cm) mound, 2–3 inches (5–7 cm) high. Leave a 5-inch (13-cm) clearance on all sides. Fold the two sides over each other as if folding an envelope, leaving narrow ends still exposed. Fold one end over, then hold packet upright. Lightly press to compress rice, then fold remaining end over to enclose firmly. Tie packet securely both crosswise and lengthwise with coarse kitchen string. The dish can be prepared to this point up to 1 hour ahead, or 3–4 hours if refrigerated.

Place parcel in a steamer over rapidly boiling water. Cover and steam until heated throughout, about 5 minutes. (Refrigerated parcels will require 15–20 minutes of steaming.) Carefully remove from steamer. To serve, use scissors to cut open parcel, rolling back lotus for a decorative appearance.

Tips

- Large, voluptuous lotus leaves are imbued with a slight taste of chestnut. Fresh lotus is available from May to September in Southeast Asia, but dried leaves are more commonly sold overseas. If unavailable, don't enclose the rice mixture in a parcel but serve hot, directly from wok or pan.
- For individual servings, use 6 lotus leaves and divide filling equally into 6 portions. Place 1 portion onto each leaf. Fold as above.

desserts

Almond cream pudding

Serves 6

3 tablespoons ground rice
3 cups (24 fl oz/750 ml) milk
pinch of salt
¼ cup (2 oz/60 g) sugar
¾ cup (3 oz/90 g) ground blanched almonds
1 tablespoon rosewater
chopped pistachios or almonds, for garnish
pomegranate seeds (optional)

In a small bowl, mix ground rice in ¼ cup (2 fl oz/60 ml) milk. In a large wok, bring remaining milk to a boil. Stir in ground rice mixture, salt and sugar.

Reduce heat to medium and cook, stirring constantly with a wooden spoon, until mixture bubbles gently. Reduce heat to low and simmer for 5 minutes, stirring often so mixture cooks slowly and does not scorch.

Stir in ground almonds until blended smoothly, then add rosewater. Remove from heat and stir occasionally until mixture cools slightly.

Pour into a serving bowl or six individual small bowls.

Chill in refrigerator and serve garnished with chopped nuts, and with pomegranate seeds if desired.

Banana tempura

Serves 4

1 egg
1 cup (8 fl oz/250 ml) ice cold water
1⅓ cups (7 oz/220 g) tempura flour
vegetable oil, for deep-frying
4 bananas, sliced in half lengthwise
½ cup (2½ oz/75 g) all-purpose (plain) flour
2 tablespoons superfine (caster) sugar
4 scoops vanilla ice cream

In a bowl, beat egg lightly. Add water and continue to beat lightly. Mix in tempura flour; do not overmix. Batter should be slightly lumpy.

Pour oil in a deep, heavy-bottomed wok or pan to fill 3 inches (7.5 cm) deep. Heat oil until it reaches 375°F (190°C) on a deep-frying thermometer. Working in batches, dredge banana pieces in flour, shaking off excess, then dip in batter, allowing excess to drain away. Carefully slip bananas into hot oil. When batter is beginning to set, use chopsticks to drip a little extra batter on bananas. Cook until bananas are light golden brown, 3–4 minutes. Using a wire skimmer, remove bananas from oil and drain on paper towels. Arrange 2 pieces banana on each serving plate. Sprinkle lightly with sugar and serve with a scoop of ice cream.

Chinese lemon, date and walnut cake

Makes 9-inch (23-cm) square cake

4 eggs
2/3 cup (5 oz/150 g) white sugar
2 teaspoons grated lemon zest (rind)
1 cup (5 oz/150 g) all-purpose (plain) flour, sifted
2 tablespoons coarsely chopped walnuts
2 tablespoons coarsely chopped dates
1/2 teaspoon ground cinnamon

Put eggs in a bowl and beat until frothy, about 2 minutes. Add half of sugar and beat until light and fluffy, 2–3 minutes. Add remaining sugar and lemon zest and beat for 10 minutes.

Gradually stir flour into egg mixture. Do not add too quickly, or flour will sink to bottom. Grease a 9-inch (23-cm) square cake pan, and spoon in half mixture. Sprinkle with half of nuts and dates and carefully spoon in remaining egg mixture. Sprinkle top with remaining nuts and dates, then cinnamon. Cover pan loosely, to allow for rising, with a double layer of greased plastic wrap or parchment (baking) paper, or place a kitchen towel under steamer lid to keep any condensation from falling on cake. Place in a large steamer and cover.

Partially fill a wok or pot with water (steamer should not touch water) and bring to a rapid simmer. Place over water, cover, and steam until a skewer inserted in cake comes out clean, about 15 minutes. Cut cake into squares or slices and serve warm or cold with fresh fruit or fruit coulis and fresh cream.

Cream and berry stack

Serves 4

vegetable oil, for deep-frying
8 wonton wrappers
8 oz (250 g) ricotta cheese
½ cup (4 fl oz/125 ml) heavy (double) cream
4 tablespoons confectioners' (icing) sugar, sifted
2 teaspoons Grand Marnier
1 teaspoon grated orange zest (rind)
5 oz (155 g) fresh raspberries
5 oz (155 g) fresh strawberries, hulled (stemmed) and sliced
3 oz (90 g) fresh blueberries

In a wok or frying pan, heat oil until it reaches 375°F (190°C) on a deep-frying thermometer or until a small bread cube dropped in oil sizzles and turns golden. Working in batches, add wonton wrappers and fry until golden on both sides, about 1 minute. Using slotted spoon, remove from pan and drain on paper towels. Allow to cool.

In bowl, combine ricotta cheese, cream, 3 tablespoons of sugar, Grand Marnier and zest. Using electric mixer beat until light and fluffy, 2–3 minutes. Cover and chill until ready to serve.

In another bowl, combine raspberries, strawberries and blueberries. Cover and chill.

To serve, place one wonton on each plate. Spread with ricotta filling. Spoon berries over filling. Top with second wonton. Dust with some of the remaining sugar.

Creamy coconut black rice

Serves 4–5

1 cup (7 oz/220 g) black glutinous rice
1 cup (8 fl oz/250 ml) cold water
1½ cups (12 fl oz/375 ml) thin coconut cream or coconut milk
⅓ cup palm or brown sugar
2 teaspoons grated lime or lemon zest (rind)
pinch salt
1 cup (8 fl oz/250 ml) thick coconut cream (optional)
1 medium (12 oz/375 g) mango, peeled and sliced, for serving

Place rice in a bowl and add cold water to cover. Let soak overnight, drain, and rinse well under cold running water. Place rice and water in a bowl that fits in a bamboo steamer or steamer basket.

Partially fill a wok or pot with water (steamer should not touch water) and bring to a rapid simmer. Place steamer over water, cover, and steam until rice is tender, 40–45 minutes, stirring occasionally. Remove from heat and stir in thin coconut cream, sugar, lime zest, and salt. Cover and steam until thickened to consistency of hot cereal, 15–20 minutes. Swirl thick coconut cream through, if desired, and serve with sliced mango. Alternatively, cut a small cantaloupe (rockmelon) in half, scoop out seeds, and fill with rice.

Figs in syrup

Serves 6–8

1 lb (500 g) dried figs
4 cups (32 fl oz/1 L) cold water
⅓ cup (2 oz/60 g) whole blanched almonds
¾ cup (6 oz/185 g) granulated sugar
thin strip lemon zest (rind)
juice of 1 lemon
3 tablespoons honey
chopped almonds, pistachios or walnuts, for garnish
whipped cream or plain (natural) yogurt, for garnish

Rinse figs well, place in a bowl and add cold water. Let stand for 8 hours until plump. Drain off water into a large wok.

Insert an almond into each fig from bottom. Set aside.

Add sugar to water in the wok and cook over medium heat, stirring occasionally, until sugar dissolves. Add lemon zest, juice and honey, and bring to a boil. Add stuffed figs and return to a boil. Reduce heat to low and cook, uncovered, until figs are tender and syrup is thick, about 30 minutes. Remove lemon zest and discard.

Arrange figs upright in a bowl. Pour syrup over figs, let cool, cover, and chill in refrigerator.

Sprinkle with chopped nuts and serve with whipped cream or yogurt.

Ginger and nutmeg sweet potato pudding

Makes 6

10 oz (300 g) sweet potato (kumara), peeled and roughly chopped
1 cup (8 fl oz/250 ml) thick coconut cream
¼ cup (2 oz/60 g) brown sugar
2 eggs, beaten
2 teaspoons peeled and grated fresh ginger
2 teaspoons freshly grated nutmeg or 2 teaspoons ground nutmeg
whipped cream, for garnish (optional)

Preheat oven to 350°F (180°C/Gas 4). Line a bamboo steamer with parchment (baking) paper or use a heatproof plate. Half fill a wok with water (steamer should not touch water) and bring water to a boil. Arrange sweet potato in steamer, cover and place steamer in wok. Cook sweet potato until tender, adding more water to wok when necessary, about 15 minutes. Lift steamer from wok, carefully remove sweet potato from steamer and transfer to a bowl. Mash with a fork or potato masher until smooth. Set aside and allow to cool.

Place sweet potato, coconut cream, brown sugar, eggs, ginger and nutmeg in a food processor and process until smooth. Pour into 6 Chinese teacups or other heatproof molds. Place on a baking sheet (tray) and cook until firm to the touch, about 20 minutes. Remove from oven. Serve warm or chilled, garnished with whipped cream if desired.

Hot mocha and brandied raisin soufflé

Makes 6 small soufflés or 1 large

For brandy-soaked raisins
⅓ cup (2 oz/60 g) raisins (sultanas)
1 cup (8 fl oz/250 ml) brandy

4 oz (125 g) dark chocolate
¼ cup (2 oz/60 g) superfine (caster) sugar
4 eggs, separated, plus 1 extra egg white
1 teaspoon instant coffee granules
⅓ cup (3 fl oz/90 ml) brandy-soaked raisins

Place raisins in an airtight jar and cover with brandy. Cover jar and soak overnight. Drain to use.

Lightly butter six 1-cup (8-fl oz/250-ml) ramekins or a 6-cup (48-fl oz/1.5-L) soufflé dish. Put chocolate in a bowl and place bowl in a bamboo steamer or steamer basket. Place uncovered, over wok or pot of simmering water, to melt chocolate. Remove from heat and add sugar, stirring until dissolved. Lightly beat 4 egg yolks and coffee and stir into chocolate, mixing gently. In a large bowl, beat 5 egg whites until stiff, glossy peaks form. Stir one-third of egg whites into chocolate mixture, then lightly fold in remaining whites. Drain raisins and divide them among prepared ramekins. Spoon chocolate mixture onto raisins. Cover each ramekin with a piece of buttered parchment (baking) paper or buttered plastic wrap.

Partially fill a 12-inch (30-cm) wok or pot with water (steamer should not touch water) and bring to a rapid simmer. Arrange ramekins on both levels of a two-level steamer, or large soufflé dish on one level. Place over water, cover, and steam until set, 12–15 minutes (switch levels halfway through for even cooking), although soufflé will still be slightly sticky inside. Serve immediately, or refrigerate and serve chilled.

Grand Marnier crème caramels

Serves 6

1⁄3 cup (3 oz/90 g) white sugar
3 tablespoons water
4 eggs
2 tablespoons superfine (caster) sugar
2½ cups (20 fl oz/625 ml) milk
1 teaspoon vanilla extract (essence)
1 tablespoon Grand Marnier
1 teaspoon grated orange zest (rind)

In a small saucepan, combine white sugar and 3 tablespoons water and melt sugar over low heat, stirring constantly. Increase heat and boil until mixture caramelizes to a golden brown color, 4–5 minutes. Be careful not to let it burn. Immediately pour into six 1-cup (8- fl oz/250-ml) ramekins, while tipping each ramekin to cover sides with caramel.

Beat eggs and superfine sugar together until well combined. Stir in milk, vanilla, Grand Marnier and zest. Pour custard into ramekins and cover with oiled aluminum foil or a double layer of plastic wrap.

Partially fill a 12-inch (30-cm) wok or pot with water (steamer should not touch water) and bring to a rapid simmer. Put ramekins in 2 stacked bamboo steamers or 2-level steamer basket. Place steamer over water, cover, and steam until custard has set, about 20 minutes (an inserted skewer will come out clean when custard is cooked). Switch baskets halfway through for even cooking. Remove from steamer and cool to room temperature. Cover each ramekin with a fresh sheet of plastic wrap, and refrigerate until required.

To serve, place a plate over each custard and invert. Serve with fresh berries.

PYREX

Lime and coconut pudding with lime-ginger syrup

Serves 6

¾ cup (6 oz/180 g) butter
⅓ cup (3 oz/90 g) superfine (caster) sugar
1 teaspoon grated lime zest (rind)
1 teaspoon vanilla extract (essence)
3 eggs
1 cup (5 oz/150 g) self-rising flour, sifted
1 cup (4 oz/125 g) unsweetened dried shredded (desiccated) coconut
½ cup (4 oz/125 g) decorating (crystal) sugar
3 tablespoons lime juice
1 tablespoon shredded lime zest (rind)
1 tablespoon peeled and shredded fresh ginger
whipped cream, for serving

Butter six ½-cup (4-fl oz/125-ml) ramekins and line bottoms with parchment (baking) paper. Set aside.

In a bowl, combine butter, sugar and lime zest. Using electric mixer, beat until light and creamy, 3–4 minutes. Add vanilla. Add eggs, one at a time, beating well after each addition. If mixture begins to curdle, add 1 tablespoon all-purpose (plain) flour. Fold in flour and coconut and mix well.

Spoon pudding into prepared ramekins. Cover each with piece of buttered parchment paper. Half fill wok with water (steamer should not touch water) and bring water to a boil. Arrange ramekins in steamer, cover and place steamer over boiling water. Steam until puddings are firm to touch, 40–45 minutes. Add more water to wok when necessary.

In a small saucepan over low heat, combine sugar, lime juice and zest, and ginger. Stir until sugar dissolves. Bring to a boil and let boil for 2 minutes. Remove from heat.

Slowly pour warm syrup over warm puddings. Serve garnished with whipped cream.

Panfried pineapple

Serves 4

¾ cup (6 oz/180 g) unsalted butter

1 small pineapple (about 1½ lb/750 g), peeled, cut lengthwise into quarters, cored and thinly sliced

¾ cup (6 oz/180 g) packed brown sugar

¼ cup (2 fl oz/60 ml) dark rum or brandy

Melt butter in large frying pan over medium heat. Add pineapple slices and cook for 1 minute. Sprinkle evenly with brown sugar and cook, turning pineapple occasionally, until sugar is melted and pineapple is translucent, 2–3 minutes. Add rum or brandy, stir to combine and cook 1 minute.

To serve, place pineapple on plates and spoon warm sauce over top.

Polenta pudding with mango sauce

Makes 6

- ½ cup (4 oz/125 g) butter
- ⅔ cup (5 oz/150 g) white sugar
- 2 teaspoons grated lemon zest (rind)
- 2 eggs
- 1 cup (5 oz/150 g) self-rising flour
- ½ teaspoon baking powder
- ¼ teaspoon salt
- ⅔ cup (3½ oz/100 g) polenta
- ½ cup (4 fl oz/125 ml) sour cream
- ⅓ cup (3 fl oz/90 ml) milk
- 2 mangoes, peeled, pitted and sliced
- 2 tablespoons confectioners' (icing) sugar
- 2 tablespoons lime juice
- 1 teaspoon grated lime zest (rind)

Butter six ½-cup (4-fl oz/125-ml) ramekins and line bottoms with parchment (baking) paper. Set aside.

In a bowl, combine butter, sugar and lemon zest. Using electric mixer, beat until light and creamy, 3–4 minutes. Add eggs, one at a time, beating well after each addition. If mixture begins to curdle, add 1 tablespoon all-purpose (plain) flour.

Sift flour, baking powder and salt into bowl. Stir in polenta. Combine sour cream and milk. Fold flour mixture into egg mixture alternately with sour cream mixture. Mix well.

Spoon pudding into prepared ramekins. Cover each with piece of buttered parchment paper. Half fill wok with water (steamer should not touch water) and bring water to a boil. Arrange ramekins in steamer, cover and place steamer over boiling water. Steam until puddings are firm to touch, 45–50 minutes. Add more water to wok when necessary.

In a food processor, combine mangoes, sugar and lime juice and zest. Process until smooth.

Remove steamer from wok and carefully remove ramekins from steamer. Run sharp knife around sides of each ramekin. Invert onto plate and unmold pudding. Serve warm with mango sauce.

Rose water doughnuts

Makes 30 doughnuts

For yogurt sauce
¾ cup (6 fl oz/180 g) plain (natural) yogurt
3 teaspoons rose water
1 tablespoon confectioners' (icing) sugar, sifted

2¼ cups (11 oz/330 g) self-rising flour, sifted
½ cup (2 oz/60 g) ground almonds
⅓ cup (3 oz/90 g) butter or ghee, plus 2 cups (16 fl oz/500 ml) vegetable oil or ghee, for deep-frying
⅓ cup (3 fl oz/90 ml) plain (natural) yogurt
¼ cup (2 fl oz/60 ml) warm water
2 teaspoons rose water
grated zest (rind) of 1 orange
⅓ cup (2½ oz/75 g) superfine (caster) sugar

In a small bowl, combine yogurt, rose water and sugar. Mix well. Cover and refrigerate until ready to serve.

In a bowl, combine flour and almonds. Using fingertips, rub ⅓ cup (3 oz/90 g) butter or ghee into flour. Stir in yogurt, warm water, rose water and orange zest. Mix to form soft dough. Turn out onto floured work surface. Knead until smooth, about 2 minutes. Divide dough into 30 pieces. Roll each into ball.

In a wok, heat 2 cups (16 fl oz/500 ml) vegetable oil or ghee until it reaches 375°F (190°C) on a deep-frying thermometer or until a small bread cube dropped into oil sizzles and turns golden. Working in batches, add doughnuts and deep-fry until golden, 5–6 minutes. Using slotted spoon, remove from wok and drain on paper towels. Place sugar on plate and roll each doughnut in sugar until well coated. Serve warm with yogurt sauce.

Spicy fruit salad

Serves 4

1¼ cups (10 fl oz/300 ml) water
½ cup (4 oz/125 g) decorating (crystal) sugar
juice and zest (rind) of 1 orange
3 star anise
6 whole black peppercorns
6 whole cardamom pods
3 cinnamon sticks
3 peaches, peeled, pitted and sliced
4 fresh figs, quartered
1½ cups (6½ oz/200 g) blueberries
2 oranges, peeled and cut into segments

In a wok, combine water, sugar, orange zest and juice, star anise, peppercorns, cardamom and cinnamon. Place over low heat and stir until sugar dissolves.

Raise heat to medium and bring to a boil. Reduce heat to low and simmer, uncovered, for 10 minutes. Remove from heat.

Add peaches, figs, blueberries and oranges. Allow to cool to room temperature and serve warm or refrigerate for 30 minutes and serve chilled.

Sweet date wontons

Makes 24 wontons

6½ oz (200 g) dates, pitted and chopped
½ cup (2 oz/60 g) walnuts, chopped
6½ oz (200 g) fresh or canned lychees, pitted and chopped
1 tablespoon grated orange zest (rind)
24 wonton wrappers
1 egg, beaten
vegetable oil, for deep-frying
2 tablespoons confectioners' (icing) sugar, sifted

In a bowl, combine dates, walnuts, lychees and orange zest. Mix well. Place wonton wrappers on work surface and cover with damp kitchen towel. Working with one wrapper at a time, lay on work surface and place 1 teaspoon filling in center. Brush edges of wonton with egg, gather edges and twist to seal. Repeat with remaining wonton wrappers.

In a wok or frying pan, heat oil until it reaches 375°F (190°C) on a deep-frying thermometer or until a small bread cube dropped in oil sizzles and turns golden. Working in batches if necessary, add wontons and fry until golden, 1–2 minutes. Using slotted spoon, remove from wok or pan and drain on paper towels. Let cool.

Sprinkle with confectioners' sugar and serve.

sauces, stocks and condiments

Adjat sauce

Makes about 3/4 cup (6 fl oz/180 ml)

- 1/3 cup (3 oz/90 g) granulated (white) sugar
- 1/3 cup (3 fl oz/90 ml) water
- 2 tablespoons rice vinegar
- 1/4 cup (2 oz/60 g) peeled, thinly sliced cucumber
- 1 1/2 tablespoons ground roasted peanuts
- 1 tablespoon thinly sliced shallots (French shallots), preferably pink
- 1 tablespoon coarsely chopped cilantro (fresh coriander) leaves and stems
- 1/4 fresh long red chili, coarsely chopped

In a small saucepan over low heat, combine sugar and water and stir until sugar dissolves. Increase heat, bring syrup to a full boil, and cook without stirring for a few minutes. Remove from heat and let cool. Stir remaining ingredients into syrup and serve.

Tips

This sauce traditionally accompanies both massaman and yellow curries, although it is rarely served in restaurants today. It may also be served with meat satay, but if doing so, omit the peanuts.

Chili jam

Makes about 1¾ cups (14 fl oz/440 ml)

2 whole bulbs garlic
4 oz (125 g) shallots (French shallots), preferably pink
15 dried long red chilies
1 cup (8 fl oz/250 ml) vegetable oil
2 tablespoons palm sugar
1 tablespoon granulated (white) sugar
¼ teaspoon salt

Preheat oven to 400°F (200°C/Gas 6). Lightly break the unpeeled garlic bulb by pressing down on a knife handle with the heel of your hand, so that the cloves sit loosely together, but do not separate cloves from bulb completely. Separately wrap garlic and shallots in aluminum foil. Roast on top shelf of oven until soft to touch, about 30 minutes. Remove from oven and let cool in foil. Peel shallots and garlic.

Roast chilies by tossing them in a wok or large, heavy frying pan over high heat until lightly brown, 2–3 minutes. Remove stems, but retain the seeds. In a large mortar, grind chilies to a powder with a pestle. Add roasted garlic and shallots and pound until smooth. (Or, place chilies in a food processor to grind, then add garlic and shallots and process until smooth.)

Store in a covered jar for up to 6 months in the refrigerator. Do not drain off any oil from the top, as this helps to preserve the jam.

Tip

Chili jam is served in Thailand as a table condiment, much like ketchup and mustard in the West.

Sweet chili relish

Makes about 5 cups (40 fl oz/1.25 L)

2 cups (8 oz/250 g) peeled and finely shredded daikon
2 jars pickled garlic, 1lb (500 g) each, drained and chopped
1½ cups (12 fl oz/375 ml) rice vinegar
¾ cup (1 oz/30 g) chopped cilantro (fresh coriander) roots and stems
7 fresh long red chilies, finely chopped
3½ cups (28 oz/875 g) granulated (white) sugar
¼ teaspoon salt

In a wok or large saucepan, combine all ingredients and slowly bring to a boil. Reduce heat, then simmer for 20 minutes. Remove from heat and let cool completely. Store in a tightly covered jar in the refrigerator for up to 1 month.

Tips

- To save time, prepare ingredients that require chopping in a food processor.
- This sauce originates from Thailand and it is fast becoming a standard table condiment in the West. Traditionally, it accompanies Thai fish cakes, grilled or fried dishes, and squid rings and spring rolls.

Pictured opposite
Front: Adjat sauce
Center: Chili jam
Back: Sweet chili relish

Chicken stock

Makes 8 cups (64 fl oz/2 L)

1 chicken, whole, about 2 lb (1 kg)
1 large onion, roughly sliced
1 large carrot, peeled and chopped
2 celery stalks, chopped
5 cilantro (coriander) stems, including roots
1 teaspoon sea salt
8 black peppercorns
10 cups (80 fl oz/2.5 L) water

Place chicken, onion, carrot, celery, cilantro, salt and peppercorns in a large saucepan and cover with water.

Place over medium–high heat and bring liquid to a boil.

Reduce heat to medium–low and simmer for 1–1½ hours, skimming surface occasionally to remove scum and fat.

Remove saucepan from heat. Remove chicken and strain liquid. Allow stock to cool completely, then remove remaining fat from surface.

Tips

- To enhance the Asian flavor of this stock, add 5 or 6 slices fresh ginger or galangal, or a 2-inch (5-cm) piece of lime zest (rind), or 2 fresh (or 4 dried) kaffir lime leaves.
- Stock can be refrigerated for 5 days, or frozen for up to 3 months.
- Chicken meat may be pulled from bones and reserved for another use.
- To make beef stock, substitute chicken with beef cuts and bones.

Fish stock

Makes 8 cups (64 fl oz/2 L)

- about 2 lb (1 kg) heads and bones of 2 medium-sized white-fleshed fish
- 2 tablespoons light olive oil
- 1 large onion, roughly chopped
- 1 large carrot, peeled and roughly chopped
- 2 celery stalks, with leaves, roughly chopped
- 3 stems fresh flat-leaf (Italian) parsley
- 3 stems cilantro (fresh coriander), preferably including roots
- 3 fresh or 6 dried kaffir lime leaves (optional)
- 8 black peppercorns
- 1 teaspoon sea salt

Wash fish heads and bones well, removing any gills. Chop bones so that they fit into a large pot.

In a large pot, heat oil over high heat for 1 minute. Add fish heads and bones and cook, stirring and turning heads and bones, until any remaining flesh starts to cook and is slightly golden, 4–5 minutes.

Add remaining ingredients and stir to combine. Add enough water to cover bones completely (approximately 8 cups/64 fl oz/2 L) and bring liquid to a steady simmer. Reduce heat to medium and simmer for 25 minutes. Skim any scum from surface as stock simmers.

Strain liquid through a very fine sieve. If you don't have a very fine sieve, line your sieve with a double layer of damp cheesecloth (muslin). Discard solids.

Let cool then cover with plastic wrap and refrigerate if not using immediately.

Tip

Fish stock can be refrigerated for 2 days. If stored in tightly covered containers, it can be frozen for 2 months.

Vegetable stock

Makes 6 cups (48 fl oz/1.5 L)

- 2 tablespoons oil
- 4 large yellow brown onions, unpeeled and chopped
- 2 large parsnips, unpeeled and chopped
- 2 large carrots, unpeeled and chopped
- 5 sticks celery, including leaves, chopped
- 2 bay leaves
- fresh bouquet garni
- 1 teaspoon whole black peppercorns
- 12 cups (96 fl oz/3 L) water

Preheat oven to 400°F (200°C/Gas 6). In a large baking dish, heat the oil. Add the chopped onion, carrot and parsnip and toss to coat in oil. Bake for 30 minutes, until lightly golden.

Transfer vegetables to a large heavy-based pan. Add remaining ingredients and bring to boil slowly. Reduce heat and simmer uncovered, for 1 hour, until reduced by half.

Strain liquid through a very fine sieve. Discard solids. Let cool then cover with plastic wrap and refrigerate if not using immediately.

Tip

Vegetable stock can be refrigerated for 5 days, or frozen for up to 3 months.

Chili and coriander dipping sauce

Makes 2 cups (16 fl oz/500 ml)

4 cloves garlic, chopped
1 lemongrass stalk, chopped, or 2 teaspoons grated lemon zest (rind)
1 tablespoon chili paste
2 tablespoons fish sauce
1 cup (8 fl oz/250 ml) lemon juice
1 cup (8 fl oz/250 ml) rice wine vinegar
⅓ cup (2 oz/60 g) superfine (caster) sugar
1 teaspoon cornstarch (cornflour) mixed with 1 tablespoon water
½ cup (⅔ oz/20 g) chopped cilantro (fresh coriander)

In a saucepan over high heat, combine garlic, lemongrass or lemon zest, chili paste, fish sauce, lemon juice, vinegar and sugar. Bring to a boil, reduce heat to low and simmer, covered, to blend flavors, about 10 minutes.

Stir cornstarch and water into sauce, raise heat to medium and cook, stirring, until sauce is thickened, 2–3 minutes.

Sauce can be stored in airtight container in refrigerator for up to 7 days.

Dashi

4½ cups (36 fl oz/1.1 L) water
1 piece konbu, 4 inches (10 cm) square
2 cups (½ oz/15 g) bonito flakes

Dashi is the base for many Japanese soups. While instant dashi is readily available and has an excellent flavor, the preparation of dashi in the traditional manner offers a superior result. The brand of instant dashi favored most by Japanese is "Aji No Moto hond-ashi."

Wipe surface of konbu with a damp cloth. Place in a saucepan with water and soak for approximately 2 hours. Bring saucepan with soaked konbu to a rapid simmer over high heat. After 5 minutes, check center of konbu and if it is soft, remove from pan. If it is still hard, cook a little longer, then remove. Let return to a boil. Skim any scum from surface. Remove saucepan from heat, and add a little cold water to lower temperature before adding bonito flakes. Do not stir flakes but push them to bottom of pan. Let stand for 3 minutes. Strain through cheesecloth-lined colander, into a bowl.

Fish sauce with chilies

Makes about 1½ cups (12 fl oz/375 ml)

1 cup (8 fl oz/250 ml) fish sauce
1 cup (5 oz/150 g) thinly sliced, fresh medium red or green chilies
cloves from ½ bulb garlic, finely chopped
2–3 tablespoons fresh lime juice to taste

In a small bowl or screw-top jar, combine all ingredients, stir or shake to blend, and serve. Refrigerate, covered, for several days.

Tip

This is the ubiquitous table seasoning of Thailand, used as commonly as salt and pepper. For a less spicy sauce, halve the chilies lengthwise and scrape away some or all of the seeds. Then thinly slice the chilies as above and continue.

Chili oil

Makes about 1 cup (8 fl oz/250 ml)

¾ cup (6 fl oz/180 ml) vegetable oil
½ cup dried chili flakes

In a well-ventilated room, heat oil in a wok or small, heavy saucepan over medium to medium–high heat, just until surface shimmers. Add chili flakes. Stir briefly and immediately remove from heat. Let cool. If tightly covered, chili oil will keep indefinitely at room temperature.

Pictured above
Front: Fish sauce with chillies
Back: Chili oil

Coconut cream, milk and water

Choose a good-quality coconut by shaking it to see if it is full of water. If there is none present, discard coconut. If the coconut flesh has spoiled or dried, it will rattle slightly. Hold coconut in your hand, resting it in a heavy tea towel, and use a large knife or small machete to crack coconut by scoring lightly across its circumference. Strike sharply with knife to crack shell. Insert the blade into the crack to pry apart. Take extra care lest you cut your hand. Alternatively, drop coconut onto a hard concrete surface, or use a hammer.

Use a small hand grater to scrape out coconut meat in shreds. Alternatively, place shells in a moderate oven for 15–20 minutes. The flesh will shrink slightly, facilitating removal of the coconut matter. Grate in a food processor.

Put grated coconut in a tea towel and wring it tightly, or put it in a sieve and press it firmly with the back of a large spoon to extract cream; reserve liquid. A chinois sieve, or China cap, works well here.

Add just enough warm or hot water to cover shredded coconut, and press it again to extract thick coconut milk. Repeat again to extract thin coconut milk.

Canned coconut milk or cream can be substituted for fresh. Be sure not to use sweetened coconut milk or cream.

Generally speaking, the less the can shakes, the richer the coconut milk. However, just before using, take care not to shake can. Open carefully and spoon off richest portion (refrigeration facilitates this step) to separate it from the thinner coconut milk.

The liquid sloshing inside the coconut is coconut water, not to be confused with its milk or cream. A young coconut with immature flesh holds the greatest volume of coconut water, but only a fully mature coconut should be used for extracting cream or milk from grated meat.

Garam masala

Makes about 1/4 cup (2 fl oz/60 ml)

1 tablespoon cardamom seeds (not pods)
2 cinnamon sticks, broken up
1 teaspoon black peppercorns
1 teaspoon cloves
1 teaspoon cumin seeds
1 teaspoon fennel seeds

In a small skillet, combine all ingredients and stir over medium heat for about 1 minute, or until fragrant. Empty into a bowl and let cool. Transfer to a spice or coffee grinder and grind to a fine powder. Store in a tightly sealed jar in a cool, dark place for up to 4 weeks.

Penang curry paste

Makes about 1/2 cup (4 fl oz/125 ml)

8 dried red chilies
1/4 cup (2 fl oz/60 ml) boiling water
4 scallions (shallots/spring onions)
6 cloves garlic, chopped
2 stalks lemongrass (white part only), chopped
3 cilantro (fresh coriander) roots, coarsely chopped
1 tablespoon peeled and grated fresh ginger
1 teaspoon ground coriander
1 teaspoon ground cumin
2 tablespoons roasted peanuts
2 tablespoons vegetable oil

Put chilies in a small bowl and add boiling water to cover. Let soak for 5 minutes. Drain. Chop chilies coarsely. Transfer to a food processor and add all remaining ingredients. Process to a thick paste. Spoon into a sterilized jar and seal. Store in the refrigerator for up to 3 weeks.

Teriyaki sauce

1 cup (8 fl oz/250 ml) soy sauce
1 cup (7 oz/220 g) brown sugar
2 tablespoons chicken stock (see page 220)
1 teaspoon mirin

In a saucepan over high heat, combine all ingredients and bring to a boil. Simmer for 5 minutes, being careful not to let sauce boil over. Serve hot. Keeps well for up to 2 months in refrigerator.

Front: Garam masala
Back: Penang curry paste

Garlic dipping sauce

Makes ½ cup (4 fl oz/125 ml)

3 tablespoons soy sauce
2 tablespoons Worcestershire sauce
1 tablespoon Asian sesame oil
4 cloves garlic, finely chopped
1 tablespoon superfine (caster) sugar

In a bowl, combine soy sauce, Worcestershire sauce, sesame oil, garlic and sugar. Stir until sugar dissolves. Cover and chill before serving.

Hot chili sauce

Makes 1 cup (8 fl oz/250 ml)

2 lb (1 kg) ripe tomatoes, quartered
3 small dried red chilies, split and seeded
4 tablespoons boiling water
1 tablespoon olive oil
1 onion, finely chopped
1 clove garlic, crushed
olive oil (optional)

Place tomatoes in heavy-bottomed saucepan over low heat and cook stirring occasionally, until they break down and form sauce, about 1 hour. Add a little water if mixture begins to stick. Press through a sieve, set over bowl. (Do not use food processor, as skins need to be removed after tomatoes are cooked.) Set aside.

Place chilies in bowl, add boiling water and let stand 10 minutes. Remove from water and chop; reserve 1 tablespoon of water. Place chilies and reserved water in food processor and process until smooth. Set aside.

In a wok or frying pan, warm oil over medium–high heat. Add onion and cook until softened, about 2 minutes. Add garlic and cook until aromatic, about 1 minute. Reduce heat to low and stir in chili purée. Add tomato pulp and cook until thickened, about 5 minutes. Remove from heat and let cool.

Pour into airtight container and refrigerate until ready to serve. To store for up to 3 weeks, drizzle film of olive oil over top of sauce.

Hot chili sauce

Mango, papaya and green chili relish

Serves 4

1 small ripe mango, peeled, pitted and chopped
¼ small papaya, peeled, seeded and chopped
½ long green chili, seeded and finely chopped
6 scallions (shallots/spring onions), sliced
1 kaffir lime leaf, finely shredded or ½ teaspoon grated lime zest (rind)
3 tablespoons fresh lime juice
2 teaspoons Asian sesame oil

In a small bowl, combine mango, papaya, chili, scallions and lime leaf. Stir in lime juice and sesame oil. Mix well. Cover and chill for 30 minutes.

Massaman curry paste

Makes about ¾ cup (6 fl oz/180 ml)

8 dried long red chilies, seeded
¼ cup (20 g) coriander seeds
2 tablespoons cumin seeds
4 star anise pods, crushed
2 cinnamon quills, broken
10 cloves
1 teaspoon salt
⅔ cup (5 fl oz/150 ml) vegetable oil
6 large cloves garlic, crushed
2 tablespoons finely chopped shallots (French shallots), preferably pink
6 thin slices galangal, chopped
1 stalk lemongrass, white part only, peeled and chopped
1 teaspoon chopped kaffir lime zest (rind)

Soak dried chilies in warm water for 10 minutes. Drain and pat dry. In a small frying pan over medium heat, separately toast each spice, stirring constantly, until fragrant. Immediately remove from heat and pour spices into a large mortar or spice grinder. Add salt and grind to a fine powder. Transfer to a small bowl.

In a wok or large, heavy frying pan, heat oil over medium–high heat. Add the garlic, shallots, and drained chilies. Fry until slightly golden, 1–2 minutes. Remove with a slotted spoon, reserve solids and discard oil. Add galangal, lemongrass, and kaffir lime zest to a large mortar, and pound to a paste, 10–20 minutes. Halfway through, add fried garlic, shallots, and chilies and pound until smooth. Add ground spices. Alternatively, grind dried spices then coarsely chop fresh ingredients, and place them in a food processor and process until finely chopped. If necessary, add a small amount of water, 1 teaspoon at a time.

Mint Raita

Serves 8

½ cup (¾ oz/20 g) coarsely chopped fresh mint
½ cup (¾ oz/20 g) coarsely chopped cilantro (fresh coriander)
4 teaspoons finely grated fresh ginger
2 teaspoons finely chopped fresh green chili
1 cup (8 oz/250 g) plain (natural) whole-milk yogurt
salt to taste

In a food processor, combine mint, cilantro, ginger and chili and process until finely chopped.

In a bowl, whisk yogurt. Add chopped mint mixture and mix well. Season with salt.

Note: Raitas are based on yogurt, which is whipped or whisked. You can use either whole-milk (full-fat) or reduced-fat yogurt. This raita can be made 1 day ahead. Store in an airtight container in refrigerator.

Nuoc cham nem sauce

Makes about 2 cups (16 fl oz/500 ml)

3 cloves garlic
1 fresh long red chili, seeded
½ cup (4 fl oz/125 ml) fish sauce
¼ cup (2 fl oz/60 ml) rice vinegar or distilled white vinegar
⅔ cup (5 fl oz/160 ml) water
3–4 tablespoons sugar to taste
1 carrot, peeled and finely shredded or chopped
½ cup (2 oz/60 g) peeled and shredded and chopped green papaya
½ teaspoon ground pepper

In a mortar, pound garlic and chili with a pestle to a paste. Stir in fish sauce, vinegar, water and sugar, and continue stirring until sugar is dissolved. Alternatively, in a blender or food processor, combine garlic, chili, fish sauce, vinegar, water and sugar and purée. Stir in shredded carrot, papaya and pepper.

Tips

- This sauce is best consumed on the day it is made, or the day after.
- If green papaya is unavailable, substitute shredded, peeled daikon (giant white radish) or jicama (yam bean). Shredded daikon smells strongly if not used within a few hours.

Paneer

4 qt (4 L) whole (full cream) milk
1⅔ cups (13 fl oz/400 ml) heavy (double) cream
⅔ cup (5 fl oz/150 ml) white vinegar

Line a large, flat-bottomed sieve with a double layer of cheesecloth (muslin), allowing it to overhang sides of sieve. Place lined sieve inside a large other bowl. Choose a large, heavy, non-aluminum saucepan that fits inside the sieve.

Pour milk into the saucepan and bring slowly to a boil over medium heat. When milk is almost boiling, stir in cream and bring to a boil again. When milk mixture just comes to a boil (it will begin to bubble and froth, and vibrations from boiling mixture can be felt in the handle of a metal spoon held in milk), pour in vinegar and remove from heat. Set aside for 2 minutes; do not stir.

Using a large slotted spoon or spoon-shaped strainer, gently lift curds from whey and place in lined sieve.

Once all curds have been placed in sieve, carefully tie loose ends of cheesecloth together to form curds into a thick, round disk about 10 inches (25 cm) in diameter.

Return whey in bowl back to saucepan holding remainder of whey. Place saucepan on top of paneer to weight it. Set aside at room temperature until paneer is firm, about 25 minutes.

Remove saucepan from paneer. Carefully untie cheesecloth and remove paneer. Prepare as directed in individual recipes. If not using paneer immediately, place flat in an airtight container and add enough whey to cover. Store in refrigerator for up to 1 week.

Sambal oelek

Makes about 1½ cups (12 fl oz/375 ml)

1 lb (500 g) red chilies
2½ cups water (20 fl oz/625 ml)
1 tablespoon white vinegar
1 teaspoon superfine (caster) sugar
2 tablespoons peanut oil
½ cup (4 fl oz/125 ml) boiling water

This mixture of red chilies, vinegar and salt is used throughout Asian cooking as a flavoring and as a spicy hot condiment.

Remove stems from chilies. Remove seeds if you want less fiery sambal oelek. Place chilies and water in a saucepan over medium heat and bring to a boil. Cover, reduce heat to simmer and cook until chilies are soft, about 15 minutes. Drain. Working in batches, place chilies in a food processor and process until smooth. Add vinegar, sugar, peanut oil and boiling water and process to combine. Pour into sterilized jars, seal and refrigerate for up to 1 month.

Tahini Sauce

Makes 1½ cups (12 fl oz/375 ml)

2 cloves garlic
½ teaspoon salt, plus extra salt to taste
¾ cup (6 fl oz/185 ml) tahini
⅓ cup (3 fl oz/90 ml) cold water
⅓ cup (3 fl oz/90 ml) lemon juice

In a small bowl, crush garlic with ½ teaspoon salt and mix to a paste. Gradually add tahini, beating well with a wooden spoon.

Then alternately beat in small amounts of water and lemon juice. The water will thicken the mixture; lemon juice will thin it. Add all the lemon juice, and enough water to give the sauce a thin or thick consistency, depending on use. The flavor should be tart. Add salt to taste if necessary. Use the sauce as a dip with pita bread or as an accompaniment for falafel, fried or poached fish, or boiled cauliflower or potatoes.

Food processor method: Place tahini and garlic in processor bowl and process for a few seconds to crush garlic. Add lemon juice and water alternately, a small amount at a time, until desired consistency is reached. Blend in salt to taste.

Green curry paste

Makes about 1½ cups (12 fl oz/375 ml)

- 1 tablespoon coriander seeds
- 1 tablespoon cumin seeds
- 4 black peppercorns
- 1 cup (1⅓ oz/40 g) coarsely chopped cilantro (fresh coriander)
- 2 fresh kaffir lime leaves, shredded
- 6 cloves garlic, chopped
- 4 scallions (shallots/spring onions), including green parts, coarsely chopped
- 4 fresh green Thai or Anaheim chilies, seeded and coarsely chopped
- 1 tablespoon grated fresh galangal
- 1 teaspoon dried shrimp paste
- 2 stalks lemongrass, white part only, chopped
- 2 teaspoons fish sauce
- 2 tablespoons vegetable oil

In a wok or small frying pan, combine coriander, cumin and peppercorns and stir over medium heat until fragrant, about 1 minute. Empty into a bowl and let cool. Transfer to a spice or coffee grinder and grind to a fine powder. Transfer to a food processor and add remaining ingredients. Process to a smooth paste. Spoon into a sterilized jar and seal. Store in the refrigerator for up to 3 weeks.

Tips

- Green Thai chilies are medium–hot and grow up to 1½ inches (4 cm) long. The green Anaheim chili is somewhat milder, similarly shaped and grows up to 6 inches (15 cm) long.
- Bird's eye chilies are blazing hot, with a clear fiery taste. These small green or red chilies, about ½ inch (12 mm) long, should be used in small quantities.

Red curry paste

Makes about 1 cup (8 fl oz/250 ml)

- 6 red bird's eye or Thai chilies, seeded and coarsely chopped
- 2 teaspoons black peppercorns
- 2 teaspoons cumin seeds
- 1 teaspoon sweet paprika
- 1 teaspoon dried shrimp paste
- 1 red onion, coarsely chopped
- 2 stalks lemongrass, white part only, chopped
- 4 cloves garlic, chopped
- 1 tablespoon grated fresh galangal
- 2 tablespoons coarsely chopped cilantro (fresh coriander)
- 2 tablespoons vegetable oil
- 2 teaspoons fish sauce

In a wok or small frying pan, combine chilies, peppercorns, cumin seeds, paprika and shrimp paste and stir over medium heat until fragrant, 30–60 seconds. Remove from heat and let cool. Transfer to a food processor. Add remaining ingredients and process to a smooth paste. Spoon into a sterilized jar and seal. Store in the refrigerator for up to 3 weeks.

Front: Thai red curry paste
Back: Thai green curry paste

Thai chili dipping sauce

Makes about 1 cup (8 fl oz/250 ml)

15 fresh long green chilies, roasted
1 whole bulb garlic
9 shallots (French shallots), about 3 oz (100 g), preferably pink
¼ teaspoon dried shrimp paste
½ teaspoon salt
1 tablespoon fish sauce

Peel and stem the roasted chilies but retain seeds. (For a less piquant sauce, discard some or all of the seeds.) Preheat oven to 400°F (200°C). Lightly break unpeeled garlic bulb by pressing on a knife handle with the heel of your hand, so that the cloves sit loosely together; do not separate cloves from bulb completely. Separately wrap the garlic and shallots in aluminum foil. Roast on the top shelf of the oven for about 30 minutes, or until soft to touch. Remove from oven and allow to cool to touch in foil. Peel shallots and garlic (you should have about ⅓ cup (1½ oz/45 g) shallots).

In a mortar, pound chilies gently with a pestle to break them up. Add garlic, and pound briefly, then add shallots. Add shrimp paste and salt and pound again to a coarse paste. Or, pulse ingredients in a food processor. Stir in fish sauce. Serve with a selection of vegetable crudités.

Tomato salsa with chili and cilantro

Serves 4–6

2 large vine-ripened tomatoes, chopped
1 small red chili, seeded and chopped
½ small red (Spanish) onion, chopped
⅓ cup (½ oz/10 g) chopped cilantro (fresh coriander)
2 tablespoons balsamic vinegar
1 tablespoon fresh lime juice
sea salt and freshly ground black pepper

In a bowl, combine tomatoes, chili, onion and cilantro. Combine balsamic vinegar and lime juice in a small bowl, mix well and add to tomato mixture. Stir and season with salt and pepper. Cover and allow to stand at room temperature for 15 minutes before serving.

Tips

- The salsa is excellent with hot-and-spicy money bags, poultry, chili-noodle cakes and shrimp. It also makes a delicious accompaniment for fried wontons and grilled fish or chicken.
- Bird's eye or serrano chilies are recommended for this recipe.

Glossary

Acacia: Pungent smelling feathery light-green leaves, with a spiky stalk and sometimes tiny white flowers. Available in Southeast Asian markets.

Asian sesame oil: Rich, dark- or golden-colored oil extracted from sesame seeds. Oil made from toasted seeds has a pronounced nutty flavor.

Bamboo leaves: Long, narrow leaves available dried from Asian food stores. Leaves impart subtle flavor to food, but are not eaten. Soak briefly in boiling water to soften before use.

Bamboo shoots: Young shoots of a tropical plant, which are boiled to retain their sweet flavor. Most commonly found canned, packed in water.

Banana leaves: Large leaves from the banana plant, used to line bamboo steamers or for wrapping foods prior to steaming. Parchment (baking) paper may be substituted. The leaves are available fresh or frozen.

Bean sprouts: Sprouted beans and peas add a fresh flavor and crunchy texture to salads and other Asian dishes. Mung bean sprouts are sold fresh or canned. Snow pea (mange-tout) sprouts are available fresh. Fresh sprouts are preferred for their clean taste and crisp texture; store in refrigerator for up to 3 days.

Besan flour: A pale yellow flour made from chickpeas. Available from health food stores.

Bok choy: Asian variety of cabbage with dark green leaves and thick white stems. Sizes vary from baby bok choy about 6 inches (15 cm) long to bok choy as long as a celery stalk.

Cellophane noodles: Thin translucent dried noodles made from mung bean starch and sold in bundles. Also called bean thread noodles.

Chili oil: Spicy oil produced by steeping red chilies in oil. It is available bottled or you can prepare your own (see page 223).

Chili paste: Fiery condiment made from ground red chilies and sometimes garlic. Use in small quantities.

Chilies: As a general rule, the smaller the chili the hotter it is. For a milder taste, remove the seeds and membrane of chili before adding to dishes. Dried chili flakes and chili powder can be substituted.

Chinese broccoli: Broccoli with white flowers and a bitter taste. Also known as gai laan. Sometimes confused with choy sum. Chinese broccoli and choy sum can be used in place of each other.

Chinese celery: Straggly and sparse in appearance compared to standard celery, Chinese celery is also a darker green and more pronounced in flavor. Use both the stems and leaves.

Chinese dried mushrooms: Intensely flavorful, dark mushrooms that need to be rehydrated before use. The stems are discarded. Flavorful fresh mushrooms make an acceptable substitute.

Chinese five-spice powder: This is made of an equal mixture of ground Szechuan peppercorns, star anise, fennel, cloves and cinnamon. Available at most supermarkets.

Chinese sausages: These dried, long, thin sausages are sold unrefrigerated in Asian markets by their Chinese name, "lop chong." Made of seasoned pork, they are slightly sweet and are added to stir-fries or steamed.

Choy sum: Also known as flowering cabbage, this mild-flavored Chinese green has thin stalks bearing leaves and yellow flowers, all of which are used in cooking.

Cilantro (fresh coriander): The fresh leaf, stem and root of the coriander plant. Both stems and leaves are commonly chopped and added to food, and sprigs are used as garnish and served at the table as an accompaniment or table green. Also known as Chinese parsley.

Coconut milk and cream: These are made from grated coconut flesh (not the liquid inside coconuts). Thicker coconut cream adds more flavor than the thinner coconut milk. Available in cans from supermarkets or you can prepare your own (see page 224).

Coriander seeds: The tiny yellow-tan seeds of the cilantro (coriander) plant. Used whole or ground as a spice.

Cumin: Also known as comino. The small crescent-shaped seeds have an earthy, nutty flavor. Available whole or ground.

Curry paste: Condiment consisting of curry seasonings and red or green chilies. Both red and green curry pastes are available bottled, or you may make your own versions (see page 231).

Dashi: Japanese fish broth made from dried bonito fish flakes (katsuobushi) and konbu/kombu (a seaweed). Available in concentrated liquid, powder or dried granules, or you may make your own (see page 222).

Fenugreek: The seed of an aromatic plant of the pea family, native to the Mediterranean region. Has a bitter-sweet, burnt sugar aftertaste, available whole or ground.

Fish sauce: Also known as nam pla, nuoc nam and patis, this distinctive, salty sauce is made from fermented shrimp or fish and is used similarly to soy sauce to enhance and balance the flavor of dishes. Some are much saltier than others; use sparingly and add to taste.

Five-spice powder: A mixture of five spices of equal parts—cinnamon, cloves, fennel seed, star anise and Szechuan pepper.

Flat-leaf parsley: Parsley with a flat leaf and stronger flavor than curly-leaf parsley. Also known as Italian or Continental parsley. Fresh parsley can be stored for up to 1 week in a plastic bag in the refrigerator.

Flowering cabbage: See Choy sum.

Garam masala: A blend of spices—cardamom, cumin, coriander, cinnamon, cloves and pepper. Store away from sunlight. (See page 225 for recipe.)

Ghee: A form of clarified fat or pure butter fat, originating in India. Has a high smoke point and nutty, caramel-like flavor.

Ginger: Thick rootlike rhizome of the ginger plant with a sharp, pungent flavor. Once the thin tan skin is peeled away from fresh ginger, the flesh is grated and used in sauces, marinades, stir-fries and dressings, or is sliced, bruised and added to stocks and soups. Store fresh ginger in refrigerator for 2–3 days.

Green papaya: Unripe papaya used grated in Asian cooking. Because it is very sticky, oil your hands or wear gloves and oil the grater before preparing.

Hokkien noodles: Fat, round, thick wheat noodles, usually dark yellow and available fresh from Asian stores.

Kaffir lime: The distinctive fragrant double leaves and fruit of this Asian tree are increasingly available fresh from Asian and many Western supermarkets. Frozen and dried leaves and frozen fruit are also available but lack the flavor of the fresh.

Lemongrass: A popular lemon-scented grass used in Asian-style dishes. Use only the white part or the bulb. Trim the root and remove the outer layer. Chop finely or bruise by hitting with a meat mallet or blunt side of a chef's knife to bring out the flavor.

Long bean: Related to the black-eyed pea, this thin, flexible but crisp-textured green bean is cut into short lengths before cooking. Long beans are also called snake beans and yard-long beans, though most found in markets are 24 inches (60 cm) or less in length.

Massaman curry paste: A mild curry paste with a hint of cinnamon, nutmeg and cloves. Not as hot as Thai green or red curry paste.

Mirin: A sweet Japanese rice wine used for cooking. Sweet sherry can be substituted.

Miso: Thick paste of fermented ground soybeans, used in Japanese soups and other dishes. Light-colored varieties of miso are milder in flavor than dark-colored pastes.

Mizuna: A feathery Japanese salad green with a delicate flavor.

Mushrooms, tree ear or cloud (black or white fungus): These add texture, but little taste, to food, but absorb flavors during cooking. The dried mushrooms must be soaked in water to rehydrate, then rinsed thoroughly and drained. Trim the tough stems from the fresh or dried mushrooms before using.

Nam pla: See Fish sauce.

Oyster mushrooms: Creamy white mushrooms with fanshaped caps, named for their resemblance to an oyster. Possessing a very mild, delicate flavor, oyster mushrooms grow in the wild and are cultivated. Available fresh in well stocked supermarkets and produce markets. Substitute button mushrooms if unavailable.

Paprika: A blend of dried red skinned chilies. The flavor can range from slightly sweet and mild to pungent and hot.

Rice wine: Sweet, low-alcohol Chinese wine, also known as shaoxing wine, made from fermented glutinous rice. Sake or dry sherry can be substituted.

Sambal oelek: Indonesian paste consisting of ground chilies combined with salt and occasionally vinegar. This spicy condiment is available bottled, or you can prepare your own (see page 230).

Shaoxing wine: See rice wine.

Shiso: Aromatic green, jagged-edged leaf from the perilla plant, which is part of the mint and basil family. Shiso leaves are used in salads, cooked dishes such as tempura, and as a garnish. Shiso leaves are available fresh from Asian markets.

Shrimp paste: Produced by drying, salting and pounding shrimp into a pungent-flavored paste that is then formed into blocks or cakes.

Soy sauce: Salty sauce made from soybeans and used both as an ingredient and as a table condiment. Dark soy sauce, usually used in cooking, is thicker and often less salty than light soy sauce, which is added to dipping sauces. Low-sodium products are also available.

Star anise: The dried eight-pointed star-shaped seed pod of a tree belonging to the magnolia family. Star anise is one of the ingredients of Chinese five spice powder. It is also used whole, in segments or ground in Asian cooking. It has an intense liquorice flavor.

Sweet chili sauce: Use as a dipping sauce or combine with other sauces, such as soy, plum or ketjap manis. May also contain garlic and/or ginger. Hotter and less-sweet chili sauces may be substituted.

Tahini (sesame paste): A smooth paste made from ground sesame seeds. Some are thicker than others, so add extra water if required. Available from most supermarkets.

Tamarind pulp: Available as powder, paste or pulp, this popular Asian fruit adds a sour flavor. Soak pulp required in hot water for about 15 minutes, then push through a fine-mesh sieve to extract the liquid, discarding the pulp. Dissolve powders and pastes before use, but be aware that some can be quite salty.

Tikka masala curry paste: A mild curry paste. Other curry pastes can be substituted.

Tofu: Produced from soybeans that have been dried, soaked, cooked, puréed and pressed to form cakes or squares that range in texture from soft to firm. Mild in flavor, tofu readily absorbs the seasonings of the preparations in which it is used.

Turmeric: A dried, powdery spice produced from the rhizome of a tropical plant related to ginger. It has a strong, spicy flavor and yellow color. Also known as Indian saffron.

Vermicelli noodles: Very thin noodles made of rice flour. Sometimes referred to as cellophane noodles. Available dried in Asian food stores and supermarkets.

Index

adjat sauce, 218
almond cream pudding, 200
appetizers, 31–55
Asian greens
  lemon and ginger oil, with, 145
  stir-fried, with tempeh, 162
stir-fry with shiitake mushroom, 144
tempeh and oyster sauce, with, 146
asparagus, thick, 25

baby bok choy, 18
bamboo steamer, two-level, 16
banana leaves
  steamed fish in, 134
Thai curry fish in banana leaf cups, 139
banana tempura, 201
basil, 18
bay leaves, 18
bean sprouts, 18
  fennel, celery, snow peas and bean sprouts, stir-fried, 164
  shredded pork with, 107
  stir-fry chicken with, 63
beans foogarth, 147
beef
  bamboo shoots, with, 92
  basil leaves, with, 93
  braised, in rice wine, 86
  Chinese beef and vegetable stir-fry, 95
  chow mein, 88
  dry beef curry with sweet potato, 96
  kabobs, 89
  red curry beef, 105
  sliced, with mushrooms and vegetables in oyster sauce, 108
  stir-fried beef with eggs, 110
  stir-fried beef with red curry paste, 111
  stir-fry on crisp noodles, 90
  stir-fry with Chinese greens, 91
beer-battered prawns with mango salsa, 32
bell peppers
  bell peppers and mushrooms with noodles, 174
  deseeding, 27
  soba noodles with, 194
berry and cream stack, 203

black bean sauce, crab in, 117
black-eyed pea and sugar snaps stir-fry, 148
black rice, creamy coconut, 204
board, hardwood, 16
boiling with wok, 15
bok choy, 18
bowls, 11
braising with wok, 15
broccoli, chili, with noodles, 175
bulgogi
  salt, 106
  squid, 133
buns
  steamed chicken, 76
  step-by-step basic, 77
butternut squash and lentil salad, 149

cake, Chinese lemon, date and walnut, 202
capsicum, deseeding, 27
cardamon, 19
carrot, coconut and ginger soup, 33
cellophane noodles, 22
  cooking, 29
  fried, 178
  spicy salad, 195
cha ca fish, with turmeric, 116
chicken, 57–83
  chicken and cashew stir-fry, 60
  chicken wings, sweet, 80
  chili chicken and vegetables, 66
  chili-chicken dumplings, 36
  chow mein, 61
  dumplings, spinach and ginger, 34
  fried chicken wontons, 42
  ginger, with, 64
  grilled chicken drumsticks, 70
  green chicken curry, 69
  Indonesian-style chicken fried rice, 71
  larb salad with chicken, 72
  lemongrass and chili, with, 65
  orange rice with, 73
  satay salad, 62
  steamed chicken buns, 76
  stir-fried ginger chicken, 79
  stir fried, in roasted curry paste sauce, 78
  stir-fry with bean sprouts, 63
  stock, 220

  sweet and sour chicken and noodles, 81
  sweet chicken wings, 80
  Teriyaki chicken, 82
  Thai curry with chicken, 83
chickpea
  patties, 35
  spinach, with, 150
chili, 18
  broccoli with noodles, 175
  fish sauce with, 223
  flower, 25
  fresh, 19
  fried rice, 176
  jam, 219
  long, 25
  powder, 20
  sweet chili relish, 219
chili and coriander dipping sauce, 222
chili chicken and vegetables, 66
chili-chicken dumplings, 36
chili oil, 19, 223
chili sauce, hot, 226
Chinese barbecued pork stir-fry, 94
Chinese beef and vegetable stir-fry, 95
Chinese broccoli, 18
Chinese cabbage, 18
Chinese fried rice, 177
Chinese lemon, date and walnut cake, 202
Chinese parsley, 19
Chinese-style tableware, 11
chopsticks
  cooking, 17
  eating, 11
chow mein
  beef, 88
  chicken, 61
choy sum, 18, 20
  stir-fried, with ginger, 163
cilantro, 19
cleaver, 16
coconut cream, 224
coriander, 18, 19
corn
  removing from cob, 25
  sweet corn fritters, 54
cottage cheese, homemade, with spinach, 154
crab
  black bean sauce, 117

  yellow curry powder, with, 118
cream and berry stack, 203
creamy coconut black rice, 204
crème caramels, Grand Marnier, 208
crispy fried wontons with chicken filling, 39
curries
  dry beef curry with sweet potato, 96
  fish, 120
  green chicken, 69
  mango and yogurt, 158
  mixed vegetable, 159
  red curry beef, 105
  red, with roasted duck, 75
  Thai curry with chicken, 83
  Thai red curry shrimp 140
curry paste
  green, 231
  Massaman, 227
  Penang, 225
  red, 231

daikon, 20
Dashi, 222
deep-frying with wok, 15
desserts, 199–215
dipping sauce
  chili and coriander, 222
  garlic, 226
  Thai chili, 232
doughnuts, rose water, 213
dry beef curry with sweet potato, 96
duck, 57–83
  braised, with pineapple, 58
  crispy wontons with, 67
  long beans, with, 68
  Peking duck pancakes, 74
  red curry with roasted duck, 75
dumplings
  chicken, spinach and ginger, 34
  chili-chicken, 36
  panfried pork, 49
  pumpkin, in malai sauce, 161

eel, fried glass noodles with, 179
egg noodles, cooking, 29
eggplants, stuffed, 167
eggs, stir-fried beef with, 110
electric rice cookers, 16
electric spice grinders, 17
entrées, 31–55

fennel, celery, snow peas and bean sprouts, stir-fried, 164
figs in syrup, 205
fish, 113–141
cha ca, with turmeric, 116
crispy fried, 119
curry, 120
fillets, with coconut rice parcels and cilantro-tomato relish, 121
fried glass noodles with, 179
ginger, in nori wrapper, 123
green curry paste, with, 122
steamed, in banana leaves, 134
stock, 221
Thai curry, in banana leaf cups, 139
whole fried, with chili and basil, 141
fish balls, 40
fish cakes, cilantro and lime, 38
fish sauce with chilies, 223
fish wraps, 41
flowering cabbage, 20
French shallots, 22
fresh herbs, chopping, 24
fried rice
chili, 176
Chinese, 177
Indonesian-style chicken, 71
Metropole, 187
pineapple, with, 181
fritters
shrimp and coconut, 52
sweet corn, 54
fruit salad, spicy, 214

galangal, 20
garam masala, 225
garlic, 18, 21
garnishes, 26–27
ginger, 18
chicken with, 64
fish in nori wrapper, 123
ginger and nutmeg sweet potato pudding, 206
ginger-coconut rice, 183
pork, 98
glass noodles, fried, with fish or eel, 179
Grand Marnier crème caramels, 208
green beans in oil, 153
green curry
chicken, 69
vegetarian, 170
green curry paste, 231
fish with, 122
green papaya, noodles with squash and, 191
green tea, 11

herbs, chopping, 24
Hokkien noodles, cooking, 29
hot chili sauce, 226
hot mocha and brandied raisin soufflé, 207

Indian noodle stir-fry, 185
Indian pilaf, 186
Indonesian-style chicken fried rice, 71
ingredients, 18

jam, chili, 219
Japanese seaweed salad, 155

kabobs, beef, 89
kaffir lime leaves, 21
Korean mung bean pancakes, 156

laksa, salmon, 193
lamb with dried fruit, 99
larb salad with chicken, 72
leek, 21
lemon and lime zest curls, 26
lemongrass, 18, 22
lentils
butternut squash and lentil salad, 149
garlic and cumin, 182
lime and coconut pudding with lime-ginger syrup, 210
lobster salad, 124
long beans
duck with, 68
pork and red curry paste, with, 100
stir-fried octopus with, and snow peas, 136

mango and yogurt curry, 158
mango, papaya and green chili sauce, 227
Massaman curry paste, 227
meatballs in tomato sauce, 101
Metropole fried rice, 187
mini noodle baskets with crab and avocado, 44
mint raita, 228
miso with scallops and ginger, 45
mortars and pestles, 17
mushrooms
Asian greens stir-fry with shiitake mushroom, 144
bell peppers and mushrooms with noodles, 174
mushroom and noodle stir-fry, 188
mushroom and sesame stir-fry, 160
Shiitake, 23
sliced beef, mushrooms and vegetables in oyster sauce, 108
mussels with garlic and lime butter, 125
Nasi goreng, 189
noodle baskets, mini, with crab and avocado, 44
noodles, 22
baked vegetables, with, 190
bell peppers and mushrooms with, 174
cellophane, 22
chili broccoli with noodles, 175
cooking, 29
dried, 22
fried, with pork, 180
herb and lemon noodle salad with ponzu dressing, 184
mushroom and noodle stir-fry, 188
Pad Thai, 192
squash and green papaya, with, 191
stir-fried seafood with, 137
sweet and sour chicken and noodles, 81
nori wrapper, ginger fish in, 123
nuoc cham nem sauce, 228
nuts, toasting, 27

octopus
braised, and onions, 114
stir-fried, with long beans and snow peas, 136
onions
braised octopus and, 114
chopping, 24
orange rice with chicken, 73
oyster sauce, sliced beef, mushrooms and vegetables in, 108

Pad Thai
noodles, 192
shrimp, with, 126
pakoras, mixed vegetable, 46
pancakes
Korean mung bean, 156
Peking duck, 74
paneer, 229
panfried pineapple, 211
parsnip chips, spicy snapper with, 132
patties
chickpea, 35
pork and lime, 102
peanut and chili bundles, 47
Peking duck pancakes, 74
Penang curry paste, 225
pilaf, Indian, 186
pineapple, panfried, 211
polenta pudding with mango sauce, 212
pork
Chinese barbecued pork stir-fry, 94
fried, in endive, 97
fried noodles with, 180
ginger pork, 98
long beans and red curry paste, with, 100
panfried pork dumplings, 49
pork and lime patties, 102
pork and nectarine stir-fry, 103
pork ribs, steamed, 109
pumpkin with, 104
rolls, ginger-sesame, 43
shredded pork and bean sprouts, 107
steamed pork ribs, 109
Portugese-style shrimp, 48
pot stickers, 49
potatoes, sweet-and-sour, 168
prawns, beer-battered, with mango salsa, 32
pudding
almond cream, 200
ginger and nutmeg sweet potato pudding, 206
lime and coconut, with lime-ginger syrup, 210
polenta, with mango sauce, 212
pumpkin
dumplings in malai sauce, 161
pork, with, 104

Ramen noodles, cooking, 29
red curry
beef, 105
roasted duck, with, 75
Thai red curry shrimp, 140
red curry paste, 231
long beans with pork and, 100
stir-fried beef with, 111
relish
mango, papaya and green chili, 227
sweet chili, 219
rice
electric rice cookers, 16
ginger coconut, 183
orange, with chicken, 73
savory rice bites, 51
spiced shrimp and, 131
steamed, in lotus parcels, 196
steamed white, 11, 28
rice bites, savory, 51
rice flour crisps, 50
rice stick noodles, cooking, 29
roasted duck with red curry, 75
rose water doughnuts, 213

saffron threads, 22
salads, 143–171
butternut squash and lentil, 149
chicken satay, 62
fried tofu salad, 152
herb and lemon noodle salad with ponzu dressing, 184
Japanese seaweed salad, 155
larb, with chicken, 72
lobster, 124

spicy cellophane noodle salad, 195
salmon laksa, 193
salt bulgogi, 106
sambal oelek, 230
sauce
adjat, 218
black bean, 117
chili and coriander dipping sauce, 222
fish sauce with chilies, 223
garlic dipping sauce, 226
ginger-coconut, 115
hot chili, 226
nuoc cham nem, 228
tahini, 230
Teriyaki, 225
Thai chili dipping sauce, 232
scallion brushes and curls, 26
scallops
arugula pesto and sweet potato purée, 128
miso with ginger and, 45
seafood, 113–141
seafood, basil and almond stir-fried with mixed greens, 129
stir-fried seafood with noodles, 137
seaweed salad, Japanese, 155
seeds, toasting, 27
shallots, 22
Shiitake mushrooms, 23
shrimp
braised, in ginger-coconut sauce, 115
Pad Thai with, 126
Portugese-style, 48
semolina-crusted, 130
shrimp and coconut fritters, 52
shrimp and lemongrass sticks, 53
spiced shrimp and rice, 131
stir-fried chili-lime, 135
Thai red curry shrimp, 140
snapper, spicy, with parsnip chips, 132
soba noodles
bell peppers, with, 194
cooking, 29
somen noodles, cooking, 29
soufflé, hot mocha and brandied raisin, 207
soup, carrot, coconut and ginger, 33
soy sauce, 23
spatulas, wooden or metal, 17
spice grinders, electric, 17
spices, toasting, 27
spring rolls, vegetarian, 55
squash and green papaya, noodles with, 191
squid
bulgogi, 133
sautéed, with leeks, 127
stir-fried, with chili, 138
star anise, 18, 23
steamed fish in banana leaves, 134
steamed chicken buns, 76
steamed pork ribs, 109
steamed white rice, 11
lotus parcels, in, 196
preparing, 28
steaming
bamboo steamer, two-level, 16
wok, with, 15
stir-fries
Asian greens, with shiitake mushroom, 144
Asian greens, with tempeh, 162
beef, on crisp noodles, 90
beef, with Chinese greens, 91
beef with eggs, 110
black-eyed pea and sugar snaps, 148
chicken and cashew, 60
chicken with bean spouts, 63
chili-lime shrimp, 135
Chinese barbecue pork, 94
Chinese beef and vegetable, 95
choy sum, with ginger, 163
fennel, celery, snow peas and bean sprouts, 164
Indian noodle, 185
mushroom and noodle, 188
mushroom and sesame, 160
pork and nectarine, 103
seafood, basil and almond, with mixed greens, 129
stir-fried beef with red curry paste, 111
stir-fried chicken in roasted curry paste sauce, 78
stir-fried ginger chicken, 79
stir-fried octopus, with long beans and snow peas, 136
stir-fried seafood with noodles, 137
stir-fried squid with chili, 138
tofu and vegetable, 169
vegetables, 165
vegetables, with soy and ginger, 166
vegetarian, 171
stir-frying
advantages, 11
popularity, 11
stock
chicken, 220
fish, 221
vegetable, 221
stuffed eggplants, 167
sweet and sour chicken and noodles, 81
sweet and sour potatoes, 168
sweet chili relish, 219
sweet corn fritters, 54
sweet date wontons, 215
sweet potato
dry beef curry with, 96
ginger and nutmeg sweet potato pudding, 206
purée, scallops with arugula pesto and, 128

tableware, Chinese style, 11
tahini sauce, 230
tamarind, 23
tea, green, 11
tempura, banana, 201
Teriyaki
chicken, 82
sauce, 225
Thai chili dipping sauce, 232
Thai curry fish in banana leaf cups, 139
Thai curry with chicken, 83
Thai ginger, 20
Thai red curry shrimp, 140
tofu
deep-fried, with vegetables, 151
fried tofu salad, 152
tofu and vegetable stir-fry, 169
tomato salsa with chili and cilantro, 232
tomato sauce, meatballs in, 101
tomatoes
removing seeds from, 27

udon noodles, cooking, 29

vegetables, 143–171
chili chicken and, 66
deep-fried tofu with, 151
mixed vegetable curry, 159
mixed vegetable pakoras, 46
noodles with baked vegetables, 190
sliced beef, mushrooms and vegetables in oyster sauce, 108
stir-fried, 165
stir-fried, with soy and ginger, 166
stock, 221
tofu and vegetable stir-fry, 169
vegetarian green curry, 170
vegetarian spring rolls, 55
vegetarian stir-fry, 171

wheat flour noodles, cooking, 29
whole fried fish with chili and basil, 141
wok
boiling with, 15
braising with, 15
cleaning, 14
cooking with, 11, 14
deep-frying, 15
heating, 14
meaning of, 12
new, preparing, 14
nonstick, 12
seasoning, 14
shovels, 17
sizes, 12
spatulas, 17
steaming with, 15
varieties, 12
versatile cooking methods, 15
wontons
crispy fried, with chicken filling, 39
crispy wontons with duck, 67
fried chicken, 42
sweet date, 215

yogurt and mango curry, 158

zest curls, lemon and lime, 26

guide to weights and measures

The conversions given in the recipes in this book are approximate. Whichever system you use, remember to follow it consistently, thereby ensuring that the proportions are consistent throughout a recipe.

Weights

Imperial	Metric
1/3 oz	10 g
1/2 oz	15 g
3/4 oz	20 g
1 oz	30 g
2 oz	60 g
3 oz	90 g
4 oz (1/4 lb)	125 g
5 oz (1/3 lb)	150 g
6 oz	180 g
7 oz	220 g
8 oz (1/2 lb)	250 g
9 oz	280 g
10 oz	300 g
11 oz	330 g
12 oz (3/4 lb)	375 g
16 oz (1 lb)	500 g
2 lb	1 kg
3 lb	1.5 kg
4 lb	2 kg

Volume

Imperial	Metric	Cup
1 fl oz	30 ml	
2 fl oz	60 ml	1/4
3 fl oz	90 ml	1/3
4 fl oz	125 ml	1/2
5 fl oz	150 ml	2/3
6 fl oz	180 ml	3/4
8 fl oz	250 ml	1
10 fl oz	300 ml	1 1/4
12 fl oz	375 ml	1 1/2
13 fl oz	400 ml	1 2/3
14 fl oz	440 ml	1 3/4
16 fl oz	500 ml	2
24 fl oz	750 ml	3
32 fl oz	1L	4

Oven temperature guide

The Celsius (°C) and Fahrenheit (°F) temperatures in this chart apply to most electric ovens. Decrease by 25°F or 10°C for a gas oven or refer to the manufacturer's temperature guide. For temperatures below 325°F (160°C), do not decrease the given temperature.

Oven description	°C	°F	Gas Mark
Cool	110	225	1/4
	130	250	1/2
Very slow	140	275	1
	150	300	2
Slow	170	325	3
Moderate	180	350	4
	190	375	5
Moderately Hot	200	400	6
Fairly Hot	220	425	7
Hot	230	450	8
Very Hot	240	475	9
Extremely Hot	250	500	10

Useful conversions

1/4 teaspoon	1.25 ml
1/2 teaspoon	2.5 ml
1 teaspoon	5 ml
1 Australian tablespoon	20 ml (4 teaspoons)
1 UK/US tablespoon	15 ml (3 teaspoons)

Butter/Shortening		
1 tablespoon	1/2 oz	15 g
1 1/2 tablespoons	3/4 oz	20 g
2 tablespoons	1 oz	30 g
3 tablespoons	1 1/2 oz	45 g

A LANSDOWNE BOOK

Published by Apple Press in 2005
Sheridan House
4th Floor
112-116 Western Road
Hove
East Sussex BN3 1DD UK

www.apple-press.com

Created and produced by Lansdowne Publishing Pty Ltd
Principal contributor: Vicki Liley
Contributors: Katharine Blakemore, Robert Carmack, Soon Young Choong, Didier Corlou, Shunsuke Fukushima, Bettina Jenkins, Ajoy Joshi, Sompon Nabnian, Jacki Passmore, Jan Purser, Suzie Smith, Brigid Treloar, Nguyen Thanh Van, Rosemary Wadey
Design: Avril Makula
Photography: Quentin Bacon, Alan Benson, Ben Dearnley, Andrew Elton, Chris Jones, Vicky Liley, Louise Lister, Andre Martin
Editor: Joanne Holliman
Production: Sally Stokes and Eleanor Cant
Project Co-ordinator: Kate Merrifield

ISBN 1 84543 067 0

Set in Helvetica on QuarkXPress
Printed in Singapore by Tien Wah Press (Pte) Ltd.